JANICE M. GRAHAM

Call Me Bill

The remarkable true story of one small-town girl's perseverance to create one of the largest financial technology companies in the US

For Karen Mooney —
Thank you for serving
as a beta reader for
"Call me Bill." You
provided wonderful
suggestions to improve
the book. I'm most
grateful!
    Best wishes,
    Janice M. Graham
    8/14/21

For Dana

"The struggles along the way are only meant
to shape you for your purpose."

— CHADWICK BOSEMAN, 1976-2020

Contents

II   Part Two

Preface

I am not a fiction writer. But after hearing the story of how my high school friend — Dana Adkins — came to be the founder and CEO of such a wildly successful company, while I was off in the Navy, I knew someone had to tell the story. It was too good of a tale to remain unknown. Also, I could count on one hand the number of other people who knew the full story, and the possibility of one of them writing it was zero. So seven years ago, I took an online creative writing class, one additional night class, and started writing. If it weren't for the COVID-19 pandemic, I might not have finished this book for another seven years.

Dana, the book's protagonist, probably has not finished reading the book. "It's hard to read about yourself," she said. I feel lucky she let me write the story. As you will see, she's quiet-natured and unpretentious. She agreed to several interviews, as did her husband and iPay co-founder, Mike Bowers. He wanted her story told because "she's just that talented." I interviewed Jim Fugitte several times too, who is integral to her early success. I did not interview Bernard Johnson, the primary antagonist in *Call Me Bill*. It is believed he passed away years ago, and that he probably knew about Dana's success. To my great regret, I did not interview the retired US Marine attorney who assisted Dana in taking control of MSI. He passed away years ago too. I also did not interview Joey Smolenski, Dana's first husband. I hope he feels I portrayed him in the positive light intended.

The story line in *Call Me Bill* is true — all of it. It is labeled "fiction based on a true story" because the specific conversations and settings are contrived. Many conversations occurred decades ago and were forgotten — as were their settings — but the gist of those conversations were relayed to me in interviews. Other than Dana, her children, Mike Bowers, Jim

Fugitte, and Joey Smolenski, I gave fictional names to the remainder of the main characters in the book.

This story is important because it should give hope to the many women in the workplace who struggle with their sense of personal worth and contribution to their chosen field. Dana was fortunate to have several men recognize her value and support her in her work. She was unfortunate to have many more men devalue her worth and stifle her creativity. But she kept working hard, kept learning, and kept trusting her instincts. That combination allowed her to step over the nay-sayers and succeed in a historically male-dominated field. I hope this book inspires many more women — and men — to do the same.

If you enjoy this book, please tell your friends and book club members to purchase it. Not only should people know about this incredible story, 100% of the profits are being donated to national organizations assisting women in the workplace. Most important to me, I hope this story inspires you to dream big, work hard, and to *never* give up.

Acknowledgement

Numerous individuals assisted me during my writing process. I owe the biggest thanks to my daughter, Brianna Sheppard — a talented writer in her own right — and to my husband, LaMar Willis, for their unflinching faith in, and editing assistance with, this book. Members of several book clubs served as early readers for me. Thanks to Sandy Bolcar, Debbie Beldock, and Brianna Sheppard for arranging this. June Mcpartland gave me her invaluable advice and time. ProWritingAid, an editing tool, made me a better writer, and any flaws you find in this book are mine alone. Finally, thanks to Mike Bowers and Jim Fugitte for tolerating my endless questions, and to Dana for being an incredible friend and inspiring human being.

I

Part One

1

February 1986

Dana sat at her desk and stared out the window of her office. She flipped her pencil back and forth between her fingers, tapping it rapidly on the desk. It was a bright and cheery Winter afternoon, but she barely noticed.

Picking up her notes, she read the bullets for the umpteenth time, then her eyes re-centered at the top. 'Non-Traditional Banking Initiative: Allotments.' She tried not to think about the accounting problems that had surfaced a few weeks ago. Maybe the new president wouldn't ask at their first meeting.

She glanced at her stomach, her baby bump stretching the fabric of her new dress almost to its limit. At nearly nine months, her stomach seemed larger at this point than it was with her son. Weren't girls supposed to be smaller? It was as if her stomach remembered what to do.

"How's it going?"

Dana looked up from her notes and toward the voice at the door. Marie stood in the doorway with her perfectly arched eyebrows raised and a knowing smile across her face. As usual, her stylish skirt and blouse looked specifically tailored for her tall, slim frame.

"Are you ready to show Johnson who's the bank's allotment wiz?"

"Yeah, sure," Dana said, rolling her eyes. After all these years, she still delighted in Marie's crisp British accent. "Have you talked to him today?" she asked, in a voice only Marie could hear. "You're the only one who has been around him enough to know if he's in a good mood or not. What do you think?"

Marie shook her head. "No, I've not seen him yet. But stop fretting. You'll be brilliant as usual."

Dana wondered what she would do without Marie. Through her various struggles working for the bank over the past nine years, Marie had been there. "I suspect Johnson is only interested in how much money the allotments have made for the bank."

Marie crossed her long, slender arms and stared at Dana. "Then you should be all set, Luv."

Dana glanced at the clock on the wall. Fifteen minutes to go. "OK then, I'm off to the ladies room. I'll let you know what happens. Wish me luck!"

"You know I do." Marie flashed a reassuring smile, and then turned to cross the bank's small foyer to her office.

Dana watched through the doorway as Marie disappeared from sight, wishing she could take her along to the meeting. Marie would never be nervous about a simple meeting with the boss. Dana picked up her folders and exited her office for the restroom. This meeting was gravely important to her. She really needed that bonus. Two kids were going to be expensive. She stared at her reflection in the mirror. Her brown, shoulder-length hair curled slightly under her chin, as it had for years. But now her face was full and only slightly resembled the narrow one with smallish features that she saw in the mirror when she wasn't pregnant. Babies. They sure took their toll on your appearance. She sat on the nearby bench and thought about her bonus. Maybe Mr. Johnson wasn't aware of her bonus package. It was his predecessor who'd approved it, and incentive initiatives were brand new at the bank. Yet it would be hard to believe they didn't discuss it at their turnover meeting — unless there hadn't been one. After all, the former president had simply walked into the bank last week, turned in his resignation, and walked out. She tried not to think about that day. The hurt was still fresh. No, there simply was no way Mr. Johnson didn't know about her bonus. She glanced at her watch. Time to go.

Picking up her folders from the bench, she left the restroom and walked toward the executive suite where four separate offices were tucked away. After passing the first three, she headed toward the largest office in the corner. In the suite's foyer just outside Johnson's office sat Marion, the amiable but no-nonsense secretary to every president since the bank opened.

Marion glanced up from her typewriter across the top of her reading glasses and smiled. "Are you ready, Hon?" she asked, in her honeyed, southern drawl.

"Yep, I'm ready!" Dana's voice resounded with more confidence than she felt.

"Then walk this way, my dear." Marion held open the president's door and ushered her in with a wave of her hand.

Stepping carefully into the large office, Dana surveyed the room and then set her eyes on the man behind the desk. Although it was well into the afternoon, he still wore his suit jacket. His eyes fixed on a ledger in the middle of his desk and his balding head stared Dana in the face.

Finally, he glanced up. "Sit down," he said, barely looking at her.

Dana sat down stiffly. Her knees pressed together tightly and her feet pushed hard against the floor. She tried to smile at Mr. Johnson but could feel the corners of her mouth quivering. He looked about 45 to 50 years old. His dark, thinning hair lay greased and combed to one side, and he had a slim, pointed nose that appeared too small for his long face. He wore dark-rimmed glasses, and looked at Dana through small brown eyes that narrowed and pierced when he spoke.

"I thought it was time we discussed this incentive initiative and compensation you think you're getting," he said, with an expressionless face.

Dana blinked several times, trying to read his blank stare. She wasn't sure she'd heard him correctly. Her heart quickened and she swallowed hard. She decided to ignore the part about the compensation and instead talk about the tremendous success they were having lining up new clients.

"Mr. Johnson, about a year ago the bank's board of directors expanded our business into several non-traditional banking areas, and the most successful one to date is the allotment initiative. When I first became

5

involved in the initiative, our revenue was around $9,000 per month. Within a few months, we were generating over $90,000 each month and a 95% margin—"

"I know all about the allotment initiative," Mr. Johnson said abruptly. "I'm talking about this so-called compensation package you think you're getting."

Dana hesitated. "The . . . the board approved a revenue sharing plan if I met certain targets. I *have* met those targets and I'm due to receive my first bonus check in a few weeks." She could feel her cheeks burning. Her hands were clammy.

The corners of Mr. Johnson's mouth curled upward, revealing several teeth. He rose halfway out of his chair, glaring at her from across his desk. "I've got some news for you, Missy. No snotty-nosed kid is going to make more money at this bank than I do!"

Dana froze in her chair. Her heart was pounding so hard she was sure he could see it. Unable to move her legs and not sure how to respond, she could only stare at him. Finally, she managed to open her mouth. "Mr. Johnson, I'm fairly sure the board approved the compensation package. I've met my targets and earned the bonus. I guess I'm not sure what you're saying."

He pushed his chair back and stood, leaning forward with both hands on his desk. "What I'm saying is I don't care who approved what before I got here," he shouted, mocking her voice. "I can assure you, there will be *no* compensation package!"

Dana sat motionless, her mouth open. Her vision blurred and she blinked hard. She didn't know if she was supposed to sit there or stand and leave, but her legs seemed paralyzed.

"That's all I want to discuss!" Mr. Johnson sat back down and began shuffling the papers on his desk erratically. "You can go!" he said, spitting out the words as if there were something distasteful in his mouth.

Dana's hands and legs were shaking badly. Grabbing wildly for her folders, she stood up. She wanted to say something to him, but what? What on earth had possessed him to be so nasty to her? She'd done everything requested of her — *more* actually — and had done it well! She'd worked extremely hard and spent many long months earning that bonus. More important, she needed it! That's what she wanted to yell at him. But nothing came out of her mouth. She turned and stumbled toward the door, leaving the office.

Marion looked up at Dana, and then paused. "Is everything all right, Hon?" she asked, her eyebrows knitted together.

"Yes." Dana's voice was barely audible. Her eyes fixed ahead, she hurried to her office. Closing the door behind her, she placed the folders on the edge of her desk and lowered her trembling body into the chair. For several long minutes, she stared out the window. The beautiful Winter afternoon now appeared foreign and inhospitable. Tears welled up and soon flowed down her cheeks. She looked high into the sky, blinking again and again, trying to stop them, but the tears kept coming. Maybe some other time she might have been able to contain her emotions, but not now — not when she was about to have a baby! She sobbed uncontrollably at the thought. Yesterday she'd been so happy, thinking how well things were going. She had a good job with a promising future, one child and a second nearly here, a supportive husband she loved, a comfortable home, and a large bonus on its way that was going to make their lives much easier! What on earth had just happened?

2

April 1986

Dana sat quietly in the rocking chair in her grandmother's living room, staring at her new baby girl. At only five weeks old, she was big. Grandma Adkins was shuffling around in the small kitchen, making potato soup and homemade bread for lunch. The yeasty, familiar smell of baking bread made Dana sigh contently, and she wanted to ignore everything else. What she really wanted was to stay at her grandmother's house, lock the doors, and retreat to the safety and solace of these four gold-colored walls. After all, that's what she did as a child when she had a problem she didn't want to face.

Grandma Adkins peered around the kitchen wall into the living room. "Dana, are you listening to me?" Flour covered her hands, and she held them out in front of her.

Dana rose from the rocking chair and wandered into the kitchen holding the still-sleeping baby. "I'm sorry, Grandma. I was just thinking how much I'm going to hate having to go back to work next week." She looked down at her baby. "It has been so great being home with Liz, and being able to take care of her with no work distractions — not to mention how hard it's going to be to face *him*." During the past two months, she'd tried not to dwell on her last three weeks in the office and the disastrous meeting with Mr. Johnson. After that day, she'd gone out of her way to avoid running into him. It was hard. The bank was fairly small.

"And little Liz is going to hate having a babysitter," Grandma said, in a child-like voice while staring at the sleeping baby. "But Momma needs to go back to work and earn that money so Liz can fritter it away on clothes when she becomes a teenager."

Dana smiled at the thought. Like mother, like daughter. "Or maybe Momma can squirrel it away for Liz's college tuition."

Grandma Adkins turned back to her countertop, picked up the rolling pin and began pushing it back and forth over the second ball of dough. She pinched a small bit of flour between her two fingers and thumb and sprinkled it evenly over the dough. "I still believe you should let your grandfather have a talk with Mr. Johnson. After all, he did help you get that job."

"No, Grandma," Dana said sharply. "I don't want him to help. He doesn't know Mr. Johnson. He only knows Mr. Hayes and Mr. Fugitte, and neither works there now, remember? I still can't believe Mr. Fugitte isn't there anymore. We'd worked together for several years, ate lunch together, traveled together. And then he just comes into work one day and hands in his resignation, along with my old partner. The three of us were supposed to leave *together* to start the new company. I can't get over the fact they left like that and never said a word to me!"

The phone rang, startling Dana out of her rant. Grandma Adkins set down her rolling pin and rubbed her hands together to remove the pieces of dough that had formed in small clumps on her palms.

"It's OK, Grandma; I'll get it." Dana rounded the corner and picked up the ringing phone hanging on the wall near the back door of the house.

"Hello?"

"Dana, is that you?"

"Hey Marie! It's great to hear your voice! Aren't you at work?" Dana was happy to leave the kitchen and escape the uncomfortable discussion with Grandma Adkins.

Marie sighed heavily into the phone. "I hate to be the bearer of bad news, but I thought someone should tell you they're cleaning out your office and putting your things in boxes, including your personal stuff — photos, the

9

nameplate from your door, your M&M jar, and everything in your drawers, including, I'm sure, a half-eaten Moon Pie."

Marie's attempt at humor fell flat on Dana's ears. Instantly, she could feel her heart quicken. Her throat tightened, and she got that now-familiar sick feeling in her stomach. "What? What do you mean? When I left, they were getting ready to paint the lunchroom and foyer. Are they painting the offices now? Maybe they're just boxing up my things to get ready to paint."

"Dana, they're not getting ready to paint," Marie said painstakingly slowly, as if she were talking to a two-year-old. "I know you're supposed to start back to work in a week or so, but I think you should get in here as soon as possible and find out what's going on. That arse Johnson is capable of anything, and I haven't been able to find out a thing from Marion. The old girl is as tight-lipped as ever."

Dana's hands turned cold. She nearly lost her grip on the phone as she pressed it to her ear. "What? Are you serious? Do you really think they're moving me to another office because I'm in trouble? I can't believe Johnson would do that just because of our last meeting! What on earth did I do wrong?"

"I have no idea because the man's a total wanker. But I strongly recommend you get in here soon and find out. I've got to ring off or they'll be packing up my desk as well," Marie added in a low voice, before hanging up the phone.

Dana placed the receiver back on the telephone and sank into the nearby chair, still holding the sleeping Liz. Her legs felt too weak to stand, and the myriad thoughts racing through her head overwhelmed her. Surely Marie was wrong! This couldn't be as bad as she insinuated. How could one meeting with the new president undermine all her recent accomplishments? He simply must not understand what her allotment initiative had done for the bank! Why, every single board member would admit the bank had been teetering toward insolvency, and without that initiative it could easily have tipped over the edge. That was the entire reason they'd brought in her former boss.

"Dana, who was that on the phone?" Grandma Adkins peered around the corner, her hands still covered in white flour and little balls of dough.

"It was just Marie, Grandma. You remember my friend from the bank? She was the one who helped me so much when I started working there." Dana stood up carefully so she wouldn't wake Liz and followed Grandma Adkins into the kitchen. She tried to make her voice sound normal so Grandma Adkins wouldn't be suspicious. The last thing Dana wanted to do today was get Grandma more stirred up than she was already. But the way Grandma looked at her made it obvious she'd overheard at least part of the conversation and was now ready to restart the inquisition with renewed gusto.

Grandma reached out to take Liz, who was stirring. "Dana, I can tell by the look on your face there's something seriously wrong. You're as white as a sheet. Give me Liz, come sit down, and tell me what's going on."

Dana could feel her eyes well up. She tried holding back the tears so Grandma wouldn't see how worried she was about her job when she had a new baby to care for, in addition to her young son and husband. She followed Grandma to the table and sat down next to her in one of the old, painted chairs. Her hands gripped tightly together in her lap, she stared at them for a long time while Grandma sat next to her, quietly cuddling Liz.

What was safe to tell Grandma? Growing up, Grandma was Dana's confidant, her go-to person for emotional release and reassurance. Grandma would listen to her rant or complain — often accompanied by tears — and when she'd finished, Grandma would make a brief comment or provide some small piece of advice, and that was all. She'd say nothing to make Dana feel bad about her behavior, or thoughtlessness, or whatever had caused the day's plight. Grandma's calm manner made Dana believe things would work out and all would be right with the world again.

But this was different. Grandpa had helped her get the job at the bank. In fact, he'd recommended her to the bank president, Philip Hayes. When Dana had left Western Kentucky University after one semester to return home to now-husband Joey, who also was home from National Guard training, of course Grandpa would call his family banker and friend, Mr. Hayes. Grandpa had told her there was an opening for a part-time teller, which became a full-time position by the time Dana had completed training. Grandpa had gotten the ball rolling for her, and she didn't want to mess up things and let him down.

After much pondering, Dana leaned forward and placed her elbows on the table. She stared ahead while rubbing her fingers up and down the center of her forehead. A tear rolled off her face and onto the kitchen table, followed by another, and then another. She squeezed her eyes tight to make the tears stop, but they overflowed to her cheeks and dropped one by one onto the table.

Grandma rocked Liz back and forth and then looked up at Dana. She leaned forward in her chair and with her spare hand reached out and lifted Dana's chin to look straight into her eyes. "Was that call about your job, Dear? Has something happened?"

Dana's eyebrows scrunched together. "I just don't know what to think anymore, Grandma. Marie just told me they're packing up my desk at the bank and I need to get in there right now and find out what's going on."

"What do you mean, Hon?" Grandma frowned. "Who's packing up your things?"

"Marie's not sure who's doing it, but she said they definitely are packing up my belongings — my pictures, my personal things that were on my desk, and all the stuff in my drawers."

Grandma was silent. She held Liz on her knees and rocked her slowly from side to side. "What else did Marie say?"

"Not much. She didn't know anything else. She just said I need to get in there now and talk to Johnson and find out what's going on." Dana's voice quivered. Tears streaked her face.

"Well, I reckon that's good advice and you should pick up the phone and make an appointment to talk to him," Grandma said firmly. "There's no sense speculating about what's going on. Just go into the bank as soon as possible and find out for yourself."

Dana looked up at Grandma and stared into her blue eyes for a good long while. She'd always thought Grandma had the most beautiful clear, blue eyes. But several years ago, she'd noticed Grandma's eyes were losing their luster. Instead of the clear blue she remembered, they were turning a milky blue. Dana sighed and looked down at her lap. "You make everything sound so easy, Grandma. I just can't go in there and talk to him. I've no idea what I'm supposed to say. 'Are you packing up my desk because you're firing me?' Or how about, 'Did I do something wrong, Mr. Johnson?' Or, 'Do you just not like me for some reason, Mr. Johnson?'"

"Yes, that *is* what you say." Grandma nodded her head vigorously. "You go right in there and look him straight in the face and ask him why your office was packed up while you're on maternity leave. If it's true your things are being boxed up, there's nothing else you *can* do, and the sooner you talk to him, the better. Otherwise, you'll just sit here and stew about it until your maternity leave is over, and that'll do no one any good."

Dana pushed her chair away from the table and sat up straight. She stared down at the familiar vinyl-tiled floor. She loved this old house. It made her feel safe. She thought of how many times she'd stood on this old floor, often on a stool, helping Grandma with the cooking and baking. And how many times she'd wiped up the spilled flour or sugar from these Harvest Gold tiles — at least that's what they were called when Grandpa laid them about two dozen years ago. Back then, everyone wanted either Harvest Gold or Avocado Green. No one would be caught dead with either one now. But she couldn't imagine Grandma's kitchen looking any other way.

Dana breathed in the lingering smells of baking bread and slowly let the air escape her lungs. She looked up at Grandma and then reached out to take her new baby from Grandma's lap. Grandma smiled down at Liz as she handed her back to Dana. "OK Grandma, you win. I'm sure you're right, as usual. When I get home this afternoon, I'll call Marion and make an appointment to see Mr. Johnson as soon as possible."

13

3

Two weeks later, end of April 1986

Her reflection in the mirrored closet door stared rudely back at Dana as she sat on the edge of her bed, lost in thought. Her light brown hair, curling neatly under her chin, appeared ready for the day's event. But her large, hazel eyes were glassy and unfocused. She'd spent a restless night rehashing the chain of events that had resulted in that disastrous first meeting with the new president. After that terrible day, Dana expected to get up the next morning feeling somewhat better about the situation. Often she'd found after sleeping on a painful experience, a new day would bring with it a palliative effect, and she'd feel a little more hopeful about the situation. But not this time. The start of a new day did little to assuage her anguish, or to provide clarity to what had occurred between her and Mr. Johnson. Now, nearly two months later, she sat on the edge of her bed, the painful memory still churning in her mind, and still making little sense.

She had nine years invested in this job — too many years to start over at another bank. And anyway, she hadn't thought about an alternative. In this small town, everyone would know if things turned out badly at her meeting today, and no one would want her as their employee either. She hadn't exactly turned in a stellar performance as a bank teller, anyway. 'A good employee, but a terrible teller' was what her boss, Mr. Hayes, had said during her last performance review as a teller. In all honesty, he was being kind. She was all too aware of her cash drawer rarely balancing each evening at closing time. She loved talking to the bank's clients, and they clearly enjoyed conversing with her — especially the older ones, who Dana liked best. They had the most interesting stories and the most patience. They also seemed the most appreciative of the time she took to inquire about their daily travails.

So when her branch manager, Jim Aldridge, removed Dana from her position as a teller and made her his secretary and assistant, she remembered him taking great pains to assure her she was an excellent employee worth keeping, just 'a little A.D.D. and a bit too much of a social butterfly.' She didn't believe she had attention deficit disorder, but she knew she was going to miss seeing all her regular customers.

As it turned out, she didn't miss being a teller at all. As Mr. Aldridge's assistant, she learned much more about the bank's operations. She opened new accounts, sold Certificates of Deposit, prepared loan documents, oversaw new projects, and ran interference for most of the bank's problems du jour. Jim Aldridge said as a problem solver, Dana was as effective as anyone he'd seen, and her status at the bank — and her paycheck — soon reflected this. But most important, she was happy. She enjoyed her new position, and the extra money was nice too. Sitting on her bed, staring at herself in the mirrored doors, she remembered this time at the bank as one of simplicity and contentment. She understood what the bank required of her each day, and she understood her boss. In fact, for the first time in her working life, she'd felt truly appreciated and respected.

Dana remembered well the day the allotment initiative gained significant traction. She remembered the dark brown suit and plaid tie Mr. Cunningham wore as he dashed into the bank and straight toward Marion's desk. Mr. Cunningham turned in a complete circle as he scrutinized the bank and its employees, while Marion rang Mr. Aldridge to let him know his 1:00 PM appointment had arrived. Dana usually knew the reason for every appointment on Mr. Aldridge's schedule, but neither she nor Marion knew why Mr. Cunningham was there.

It wasn't long before Mr. Aldridge buzzed Dana into his office and she learned the reason. Mr. Cunningham wanted to solve his long-

15

standing problem collecting monthly payments for cars he sold to soldiers stationed at Fort Knox, the US Army installation located nearby. As the long-time owner of two of the largest automobile dealerships in the area, Mr. Cunningham sold vehicles to vast numbers of soldiers. But when the soldiers left on field maneuvers, which they did frequently, they sometimes forgot to make their vehicle payments until they returned home. This was costing Cunningham a great deal of time and money to track down the overdue payments, and costing the soldiers' money in late fees. He made note of the fact he didn't care about the cost to the soldiers, but he hated losing money himself. Finally, he decided this had to stop.

Mr. Cunningham told Dana he'd spent many long hours contemplating this problem with no potential solution in sight until the previous morning while eating breakfast at Jerry's Restaurant in Radcliff. Sitting in his favorite booth, eating his daily plate of fried eggs, ham, and a country biscuit, Cunningham picked up a discarded copy of the *Fort Knox Bugler,* a weekly newspaper distributed by the Fort Knox Public Affairs Office to apprise soldiers of current issues at the Army Post. Right on the front page was an article about a new Department of Defense program that would enable military service members to pay some of their regular monthly bills by having the payments deducted directly from their pay before they received their paychecks. Currently, the program was being tested at four sites across the country and Fort Knox was one of them. The program considered only certain types of vendors, and one type included in the test program was a vehicle loan payment. The article also said initial trials for the program were successful and further demonstrated the significant potential of electronic payments. So, he wanted to know if First Citizens Bank could accept the allotment checks from the government each month, and then send that money to his automobile dealership.

Mr. Aldridge confirmed to Mr. Cunningham the bank already was part of the Department of Defense allotment program. And, their bank performed the same function for another client in town — ABCO — a company that provided financing for individuals with sub-standard credit. He told Cunningham it was Dana who managed the program and then

16

called Dana in to explain how the program worked.

Dana remembered describing to Mr. Cunningham the procedure they'd put into place for the Defense Department. Each month the Federal Government deducted the allotment amount from a soldier's paycheck and mailed that money as a check to their bank. A bank employee would take these checks and put them in alphabetical order. Then, the employee would manually log the amount, the date, and the soldier's name into a general ledger and mail the money to the business.

There were hundreds of such entries hand-written in the general ledger each month, and for each transaction the bank processed, it received two dollars. That was until Mr. Cunningham entered the bank that day. Cunningham had hundreds of soldiers making monthly car payments, and he wanted *all* of them to set up allotments for their payments. He desperately wanted to stop spending thousands of his company's dollars tracking down soldiers who stopped making payments, and he also wanted to stop paying the outrageous fees for his attorney's role in the collection process. Mr. Cunningham's face cracked a smile only once during the meeting — when Dana told him the fee for each allotment transaction was two dollars, and it was the soldier who paid the fee. He couldn't sign the papers fast enough to become the bank's next electronic payment client.

A few weeks later Mr. Aldridge had a similar meeting with another business owner from Radcliff, the small town next to Fort Knox, and then another one soon thereafter. Before long, the bank was running a sizable operation collecting checks from the government, entering the transactions in the general ledger, and making allotment payments to businesses around town. And at two dollars a transaction, the bank was making a tidy profit.

The phone ringing down the hallway in her home jarred Dana from her thoughts. She stood up from the edge of her bed and glanced away from her reflection in the closet mirror. She'd managed to lose a few of the baby pounds and was looking more like her old self, but she still had a long way to go. Why does everything have to be so hard — having a job, having a baby, keeping a home running, keeping a halfway decent-looking body? She walked down the hall and into the kitchen. Picking up the phone, she glanced into the living room where Liz was sitting quietly in her baby seat, and Ryan, her sweet-natured, three-year-old son, was playing on the floor with Grandma Adkins.

"Hello?" she said, leaning against the stool next to the wall.

"Hey Hon, it's me. I just want to wish you good luck today. I didn't want to wake you this morning, but I didn't want you to go to your meeting today without saying good luck. I know you're really upset about things at work, but no matter what happens today, we'll be OK. So please remember that, and don't let him get to you. You worked really hard at that bank, and if he doesn't realize that, he's a fool."

Joey's steady voice was an instant comfort. She had to admit, he couldn't have been more supportive lately. "I know you're right, Joey. But now we have two kids, and it's going to be a lot harder for us to get by on a teller's salary if Johnson demotes me today." Dana peeked into the living room to make sure Grandma Adkins hadn't heard her. But Grandma was knee-deep in big yellow trucks, multi-colored building blocks, and a three-year-old demanding all of her attention. "Don't worry, Joey. I'll be fine. I'll call you as soon as the meeting is over."

"OK, Hon. I'll be thinking of you."

"Thanks for calling." Dana hung up the phone. She picked up the cup of coffee she'd forgotten on the kitchen counter 30 minutes ago and poured it down the drain. If there was one thing she disliked, it was cold coffee.

Dana walked into the living room and retrieved Liz from her baby seat. She swung the baby over her head and looked up at her. A smile blanketed Liz's tiny, round face, and she gurgled happily at her mother. "You be a good girl for Grandma, OK?"

"Me too, me too!" Ryan was holding up his arms and jumping at Dana.

"OK, you too!" Dana smiled down at him. She gently handed Liz over to Grandma, then spun around and scooped up the laughing little boy. She swung him around in a circle — his legs flying out like the swings on a carnival ride — until her arms tired and she put him down.

"More, Mommy, more!" he cried out, raising his arms for her to pick him up again.

"Mommy has to go to work now, but I promise I'll be back soon and then we'll play, OK?" Dana bent down and wrapped her arms around his slight frame. She kissed him on the cheek and hugged him tight until he wriggled free and ran off to play with his trucks.

Dana turned toward Liz and Grandma and bent over to hug them both. "Love you. I'll see you soon." She kissed each of them on the cheek, then returned to the kitchen to retrieve her purse.

"Good luck, Hon," Grandma called behind her. "I know in the long run everything is going to turn out just fine."

"Thanks, Grandma, and thanks again for watching the kids." Dana gathered her purse and keys and headed out the kitchen door to the carport. She closed the door behind her and then stopped and stared at her Chevrolet Impala, parked in the driveway. Would she have trouble making the car payment if the bank demoted her to a teller? With two kids now, how would she afford childcare? A family of four couldn't survive very long on Joey's salary as a police officer — not very well, anyway. She felt that familiar knot forming in her stomach. One hour and that dreaded talk with Mr. Johnson would be over and she could move on. She was happy about that, but scared too. Until this morning when she was sitting on her bed, she'd tried *not* to think about how terrified she'd been during their meeting in his office. Remembering made her heart pound.

Dana got into the car and backed out of the driveway. A steady rain fell onto the windshield. She hated rainy days and hoped it wasn't an omen for how the day would proceed. She drove slowly down the familiar road bordered by small, mostly red brick, three-bedroom homes built in the mid-1960s. There were large oak, maple, and pine trees aligned in the grassy median of two narrow asphalt streets. Nearly every yard reflected recent mowing and meticulously trimmed shrubs and flower bushes. She thought of how many times she'd driven down this road on her way to work with a peaceful feeling in her stomach instead of the tightness and burning she now felt. Dana wondered how one person could mess up your life so spectacularly and make you feel incompetent and worthless?

She slowed to a stop at the end of her street. Mrs. Knight, who lived on the corner, was walking down her driveway toward the mailbox. She was wearing her bathrobe and holding an umbrella. She smiled brightly at Dana and waved. Feigning a smile, Dana waved back to her. She sat in her car watching Mrs. Knight and wondering how the world kept turning when her own life had imploded. Not only did the world not stop, it took no notice of her pain and suffering.

Turning onto the main road, she began the three-mile drive to the bank. Usually she was in a hurry to arrive at the office and begin her day. She liked the atmosphere in the bank, enjoyed the daily challenges, and the company of her co-workers. Her days were long, albeit rewarding. But today, she drove slowly. She glanced at the road beside her with cars traveling in the opposite direction and wished she was on her way home. This is silly, she chided herself. I've done nothing wrong. I'm a hard-working, loyal employee, and the bank made a significant profit from the allotment program. Grandma is right; how can that man *not* be pleased about that? But as much as she tried to convince herself of the logic of her argument, worry still nagged at her.

Dana turned into the bank's parking lot and parked in the employee section. She turned off the car and checked her face in the mirror. Her cheeks were still fuller than she was used to seeing, and also a little paler.

She exited the car and walked in the rain across the lot and through the front door of the bank. Her palms were clammy and she shoved them into her pockets. She scanned the lobby and then set her eyes on the open area in the far corner. Her heart sank as she discovered Marie was not at her desk. How could she not be here today? Dana made her way across the lobby, her legs numb and rubbery.

Marion glanced up as Dana neared her desk, her well-lined face smiling warmly. "Well, hello there! How's our little mother doing?" She stood up and walked around her desk to greet Dana.

Leaning over, Dana hugged the much shorter Marion. "I'm doing just fine," she lied, forcing a smile, "and the baby and Ryan are doing well too."

Marion's smile faded as she studied Dana's face. "Are you getting any sleep, or is the baby keeping you up at night?"

"Actually, she's sleeping pretty well now, about three to four hours at a time. At six weeks, that's pretty good. I can't complain." Dana's eyes searched the lobby again. "Is Marie here today?"

Marion walked back to her desk. "Mr. Johnson sent her to the Elizabethtown office this morning to fill in for Carolyn Waite who's having some dental work done. I think Marie will be back after lunch, but who knows, she may be there all day. She'll be sorry when she finds out she missed you."

Dana glanced at the floor and frowned. "Yes, I'm sorry to have missed her too. Please tell her I was looking for her."

"I will, Hon. Do you want to sit down for a bit and wait? You're a little early, but I can see if Mr. Johnson is ready for you." Marion reached over to pick up her phone.

"Oh . . . all right, if you think he won't mind my showing up early." Dana sat down guardedly in the chair next to Marion's desk and waited. She chewed on the side of her lip and soon her right leg was bouncing up and down. The folder with her papers slid off her lap and spilled onto the floor. She quickly bent over and scooped them up, hoping Marion hadn't seen. Dana desperately wanted the meeting to start.

But Marion didn't appear to notice. She'd swiveled around in her chair and was facing Mr. Johnson's door, talking to him on the phone and in a voice that was inaudible to Dana. Finally, Marion turned back around. "Mr. Johnson is just finishing up a few things and he'll buzz when he's ready for you. Would you like a cup of coffee while you're waiting?"

"Oh, thanks Marion, but I'm fine." Dana's throat was dry and her voice sounded small even to her. She wanted the coffee but didn't trust herself to not spill it on her clothes. "I've got some stuff to read. I'll just sit here and wait if it's OK with you."

"Sure, Hon. Make yourself at home. You shouldn't have to wait long."

But Dana did wait. She sat next to Marion's desk for 30 minutes — 20 minutes past her appointment time. Finally, the intercom button on Marion's phone buzzed, and Mr. Johnson was now free to see her.

Dana had locked her legs together for so long, she could barely stand.

21

As she walked stiffly down the corridor, she could almost hear her heart beating. Her throat was so dry she had trouble swallowing. As she passed the water fountain, she leaned down and quickly took a drink, trying to calm her racing heart. Why am I so afraid of this man, she wondered? The worst that can happen is I'm going to be a teller again, and I can live with that. I did it before.

Marion walked ahead of Dana, and when she reached the door to Mr. Johnson's office, she opened it and ushered Dana into the room. At the first sight of Mr. Johnson sitting behind his desk, Dana froze.

"Well, sit down." Mr. Johnson shouted across the room.

Startled by his tone, Dana felt her legs trembling as she moved toward the same single chair in front of his desk that she'd sat in a couple short months ago. Her stomach felt sick. Anyone looking closely surely could make out the veins pulsing in her neck. But Mr. Johnson wasn't paying any attention to her. He hadn't even bothered to look up from the papers on his desk when he'd barked the order for her to sit.

"Good morning, Mr. Johnson," she managed to eke out, as she grabbed the arm of the chair and guardedly sat down.

Mr. Johnson glanced up at Dana without saying a word, and then just as quickly looked back at the beige folder and spreadsheet on his desk. He picked up a pen and scribbled something on the yellow legal pad next to the folder. For several more minutes he continued reading the spreadsheet and making notes, seemingly oblivious to her presence.

She looked around the office. It was as cold and unwelcoming now as it looked then, mirroring the traits of the man inhabiting it. Dana fixed her eyes on Mr. Johnson. She'd seen him only a handful of times. With his dark, thin, oil-slicked hair combed over his bald spot, his pasty complexion, and his grey nondescript suit, he reminded her of the stout, ornery banker in the cartoons she watched on TV as a kid. Only Mr. Johnson wasn't stout. He was just mean. In every other physical aspect, he was as unremarkable as his office. The white walls were unadorned. He'd had the pictures and paintings removed when he took over as president. There were no plants, photos, or personal items at all, and certainly no candy jar or anything else to welcome visitors. There was just a bookshelf with binders full of bank regulations and the single chair in which Dana now sat.

"While you were out on maternity leave, I had two auditors from the main office review the ledgers from the allotment program," Mr. Johnson blurted, without looking up. His tone was animated with sarcasm. "The results were unbelievably embarrassing for this branch! If I remember correctly, all I heard out of you during our first meeting was how *great* everything was, and how much money you were making for the bank. Do you have *any* idea how many discrepancies they found?"

Dana jumped at the first sound of his voice. Her breathing came in fits and starts, her face flushed, and she couldn't move. All she could do was stare at him, her mouth half open.

"Yeah, while you were out on maternity leave, I had your ledgers audited," Mr. Johnson repeated, without waiting for a response. "Do you have *any* notion of how bad your little accounting system is? Any clue how many discrepancies were found? There are too many to count! Some accounts are thousands of dollars overdrawn, and other accounts have thousands of dollars too much. The bank has made somewhere between $10,000 to $15,000 more in payments than it collected in deposits! I've been sitting here for weeks going over these ledgers and the audit reports, trying to figure out how on earth you've been getting away with this for so long!" Mr. Johnson's nostrils flared with every accusation and his face grew redder as the pitch of his voice got higher.

"Mr. Johnson, that's not exactly true," Dana said, louder than she intended. She leaned forward in her chair. "What happened was we upgraded the initial manual ledgers some time ago with an automated system, and right before you got here we started upgrading the automated system."

"Not exactly true? Is that what you said?" Mr. Johnson stood up as he bellowed across his desk. The pen fell from his hand. "Are you saying the auditors' report is 'not exactly true' and I'm supposed to believe you instead?" His face had turned crimson and his eyes were ablaze. Thin strands of hair bounced across his forehead as he shook his head back and forth.

Dana tried to speak, but nothing came out. It felt as if her throat had closed and she could neither speak nor swallow. Her breath came in shallow gasps and she struggled to focus her eyes. Blinking hard, she tried to make out Mr. Johnson's blurry face.

"I've had your belongings put in a box, which now is sitting in the closet next to the lunchroom. I want you to get your things and leave this bank immediately! You no longer work here!" Mr. Johnson turned to his phone and pushed a button. "Marion! I want you to come in my office and escort Dana and her belongings to her car — now!"

Dana sat dumbstruck, gaping at Mr. Johnson. She grabbed the folders from her lap and bolted from the chair. She flung open the office door and nearly fell over Marion, who was about to open it from the other side. Dana flew down the hall, barely able to breathe. Tears spilled uncontrollably down her cheeks. When she reached the closet by the lunchroom, she yanked open the door. Her eyes darted over the boxes filled with holiday decorations until she saw a smaller box with her name written on the top, sitting on the floor next to the wall. She dropped her folders on top and lifted the box with both hands. Then she turned and stumbled out of the closet and down the hallway toward the bank's main entrance. A man entering the bank held the door for Dana as she flew past him, clutching the box tightly to her chest, her eyes cast downward. She tried to thank him, but the words would not come.

When Dana reached her car, she dropped the box and her folders heavily on the wet pavement. Fumbling in her purse for her car keys with one hand, she wiped at the tears cascading down her cheeks with the other. Finally, she pulled the keys from her purse and unlocked the door. After throwing the box and her folders onto the back seat, she opened the driver's side and fell into the car. Holding her hands over her face, Dana cried uncontrollably until there was nothing left inside of her.

4

30 minutes later

Staring over the wet hood of her car and into the holly bushes planted next to the parking lot, Dana sat silent and motionless. She'd cried herself into an unexpected state of solitude. Although there were cars moving up and down the busy road by the bank, and people were all around, she heard nothing but her own labored breathing. Her chest felt as if someone were stepping on it and pushing out all the air. My God, she thought. What am I going to do? I've just lost my job! He fired me! And what will I do with two kids and no way to support them? Tears rolled down her cheeks again.

She sat in her car for a long time, thinking. After being fired for incompetence, no other bank would likely hire her. Word in this small town would get around quickly. But banking was all she knew. Despite what Mr. Johnson said about her, the previous president, Mr. Fugitte, thought she was excellent at her job. The thought of Mr. Fugitte made Dana's stomach churn again. If only he'd taken her with him when he resigned, she'd be working for him now and wouldn't be jobless. She still felt betrayed. But . . . maybe by now he'd figured out how worthless her old partner was and wished he'd asked Dana to join him instead. If he helped her now, she could overlook him hurting her before. The more Dana thought about it, the more convinced she became he could help her. She reached down and turned the key in the ignition. Wiping her tears with the back of her hand, she drove out of the parking lot and onto the street. It was about five miles to her former boss's new office.

As she drove down the rain-soaked street, her thoughts centered on the last time she'd seen her former boss. They hadn't spoken since he walked into the bank that morning nearly four months ago and turned in his resignation without saying a word to anyone — least of all her. All their previous plans about going into business someday vanished without a single word said between them. And to make matters worse, he'd obviously coordinated his exit with her lazy partner in the allotment initiative, because he'd turned in his resignation that day too. There was never any love lost between Dana and her old partner. As far as she was concerned, he was a user. Yes, he had a notable business degree from the University of Kentucky, but he also was arrogant, lacked motivation, and took credit for work she'd done.

Dana let off the gas, and the car slowed. Second thoughts about whether she could face Mr. Fugitte swirled through her mind. She had no idea what to say to him. Maybe the three of them could begin working together now that she too was out of a job? Wonder how that'd go over? If they'd wanted her as part of their team, they would've said something before they'd quit. But they said nothing to her — not a single hint of what they'd planned. Dana wanted to believe they didn't ask her to join them because she had a growing family to support and needed the steady income. But that didn't matter now because she had no job! Pressing the gas pedal, Dana decided she had nothing to lose, except whatever pride she had left. And maybe her old partner wouldn't be there to witness her humiliation.

After driving the last mile, she turned onto the street where Fugitte's office was located. Ahead, she could see his silver Camaro, parked next to the building. Not far away and behind a row of bushes, she glimpsed the tail of her former partner's car. Good Lord! Am I going to get any sort of break at all today, she wondered. She looked up at the sky and sighed out loud. Pulling into a space adjacent to the front door, Dana turned off the ignition. Her head hung heavy, and she stared at her lap for several long minutes, not wanting to get out of the car. I've got to do this, she thought. I've already lost my job, so the worst that'll happen is I'll get back into this car and still not have a job.

Dana opened the door and swung her legs out of the car. She felt ill. Her stomach was in knots, her head ached, her mouth was dry, and her hands were sweaty and cold. Her legs nearly gave way as she tried to stand, and she felt like she might throw up in the parking lot. Leaning against the wet car, she took several deep breaths to calm her racing heart and regain some composure.

Just then the door to Mr. Fugitte's office swung open. A tall, imposing man, with neatly trimmed brown hair, smallish brown eyes, and a big smile stepped onto the front stoop. The jacket to the grey pin-stripped suit he was wearing was unbuttoned and hanging open. His blue tie was lying neatly over a crisp white shirt.

"Well, hello there, Dana! I thought that was your car that pulled up. My office is right on the other side of this window so I've got a bird's-eye view of all my visitors before they enter the office, which of course, I appreciate. It's always good to know who's walking through that door before they actually do!" Mr. Fugitte was as ebullient and personable as always. His cheerful demeanor was one thing Dana had liked best about him — but not today.

"Mr. Fugitte," she said faintly, still leaning against the car. "I was hoping you might have time to talk to me this morning."

Mr. Fugitte's smile quickly faded as his eyes fixed on Dana's face. "Sure Dana, I've got all the time in the world for you. Come on in out of the rain." He held open the door and ushered her into his office. "Here, sit down in one of those two chairs by the window so we can have some privacy and I'll get us a cup of coffee."

"That would be great." Dana staggered toward the window and collapsed into the chair with her back facing the main part of the office. She didn't want her former partner to walk around the corner and see her, but maybe he wouldn't recognize the back of her head. She looked out the window at her car parked outside. The lot was fairly empty for mid-morning. Perhaps it was the rain. But she was glad; she didn't want to see anyone. And in this small town, the chance of running into someone you knew was significant.

27

Mr. Fugitte returned quickly, carrying two coffees in large Styrofoam cups. "Here we go, two cups of hot coffee. And black, if I remember correctly."

Dana startled at the sound of his voice. "Yes, black. Thank you, Mr. Fugitte."

"Call me Jim, Dana. I'm no longer your boss." He smiled down at her as he lowered his large frame into the chair next to hers.

"OK, I'll try." Dana managed a slight smile. She glanced down at the coffee she was holding on her lap. Her hand was trembling. She realized she hadn't thought far enough ahead to know what to say next.

Mr. Fugitte tilted his head, and his eyebrows knitted together. "How are things at the bank?"

"Not . . . not very good." Dana looked up from the coffee she was holding and tried to focus on Mr. Fugitte's face. But her eyes had filled with tears and his face blurred through her blinking. Her cheeks grew hot as she struggled not to cry.

Mr. Fugitte's expression turned sober, and he leaned forward in his chair. "What's the matter, Dana? Did something happen?"

"Mr. Johnson fired me today," Dana blurted, as the tears spilled onto her cheeks.

"What? Bernard Johnson fired you? What on earth for?"

Dana's face was burning red now, and her words erupted in a high pitch. "I really have no idea! That man has disliked me from the first time I met him. I've had *one* meeting with him since he took over and it was awful! Do you remember I was supposed to get my first bonus check in February? The board had already approved it. Well, he called me into his office right after he took over and told me I was not getting anything, and 'no snotty-nosed kid was going to make more money than he did!' I swear those were his exact words! I was totally dumb-founded! I just sat there and looked at him. And basically, that was the entire meeting. He didn't want to hear about anything else. I thought the whole purpose of the meeting was for me to brief him on the allotment initiative!"

Mr. Fugitte was silent. He sat very still in his chair, staring at Dana.

Finally, he leaned over and set his coffee on the table and then sat back in his chair. "Did he give a reason for firing you?"

"Yes," Dana's voice quivered. "He said he was firing me because while I was out on maternity leave, he had the auditors review the ledgers for the allotment accounts and they found numerous discrepancies. He blamed me for everything! Then he yelled at me for embarrassing the bank and him, and said while I was on maternity leave they'd boxed up all my things, and I was to go get them and leave the bank immediately!" Dana struggled to maintain her composure, but by the time she'd finished speaking, tears were streaming down her face.

Mr. Fugitte sat upright in his chair, staring intently at Dana. There was a grim expression on his normally genteel face, and his hands gripped the tops of his thighs. "Was he talking about the discrepancies you and Brenda had been working to fix — the ones that occurred when we went from the manual ledger system to the automated one?"

"Yes, I guess that's what he was talking about," Dana stammered, shrugging her shoulders. "He never gave me a chance to ask questions or tell him anything. He just shouted at me that they'd found numerous discrepancies, and it was my fault, and then told me to leave!"

Mr. Fugitte reached up and rubbed his temple. He turned away from Dana and looked out the window.

Dana stared at him, waiting for him to say something. She searched his face for some sign of compassion or understanding, but saw neither. He simply stared out the window, his eyes unoccupied. Perplexed by his continued silence and detachment, she was no longer crying. Finally, after it became apparent he wasn't going to respond, she asked, "What do you think I should do, Mr. Fugitte?"

"I don't know what you *can* do — other than perhaps talk to an attorney and see if there's some legal action you can take. But if Bernard Johnson had the auditors collect evidence of discrepancies between the two accounting systems, and you were the employee responsible for the accuracy of the data in those systems, I'm not sure how successful you would be with any legal maneuvers."

Dana listened in stunned silence. She could hardly believe what she was hearing! Was he turning against her too? "Are you saying you don't think there's anything I can do?" Her voice trailed off as the realization of his words sank in.

"I wish there was something I could do to help you, Dana, I honestly do. But we both know there were quite a few accounts out of balance that you and Brenda were working to correct. And if Bernard Johnson was gunning for you, which is what it sounds like, I doubt there's anything I can do to help. I suppose I could go talk to him for you and see if I can find out if he's . . ."

Dana drew back sharply in her chair. "I don't want you to go talk to him! That's not what this is about at all!" She couldn't hold back her anger and hurt any longer. "I thought you, my co-worker, and *I* were planning to go out and start up an allotment business of our own! I thought that was the plan we discussed! But you just came in one day and submitted your resignation — you and my co-worker — and never said a word to me!" She stopped suddenly, realizing she might have said too much.

Mr. Fugitte flinched at her words. A pained look crossed his face. "Dana, I wasn't aware there was any plan. We talked about it — yes. Maybe joked about it would be more accurate. But a plan to leave — no. I don't remember there being any plan to leave."

"But we talked about it six months ago at the conference in Hilton Head! Don't you remember? We talked about it at lunch several times as well. Yes, I agree at first it may have been more joking, but later it certainly wasn't — not on *my* part anyway — and I don't think on my co-worker's part either. And I'm sure it wasn't joking when we discussed it in detail in Orlando," she said in an accusing tone.

Jim Fugitte sat stiffly in his chair, listening earnestly to Dana's tirade. He opened his mouth to say something and then stopped. "Dana," he said finally, speaking slowly and guardedly, "I'm sorry you're hurt and upset, and that you lost your job. What happened to you this morning is about the worst example of management I hope you ever experience. And I'm very sorry if you got the wrong impression from our discussions. But there's no job for you here either, if that's what you're thinking."

Dana fixed her glassy eyes on Mr. Fugitte's face and instantly felt her cheeks flaring. She leaned over abruptly, grasping wildly for her purse. "Thank you for your time, Mr. Fugitte. I'm sorry I bothered you." She stood up and bolted for the door.

"Dana, wait!" Jim Fugitte pleaded, while struggling to lift his tall frame from the low chair. "Please come back and sit down. We need to talk because I think there has been a serious misunderstanding between us."

But Dana was already out of his office. She grabbed the handle to the front door and flung it open, bursting out of the office and to the safety of her car. She glanced up at the window where she'd been sitting only a moment ago and saw Mr. Fugitte still standing there, staring at her through the rain-streaked glass.

Hurriedly starting the car, Dana backed up and sped out of the parking lot. As soon as she was a safe distance away, she pulled off the road at the first side street and turned off the car. Covering her face with her hands, she leaned over into the seat and broke down completely.

5

Two weeks later, mid-May 1986

It was an unusually warm morning for mid-May and Dana left the windows of her car cracked at the top before getting out and locking the door. Eager to see Marie, she hurried across the parking lot toward the restaurant. As she approached the door, it unexpectedly swung open from the inside, and out stepped Debbie Hines, a teller from the main office.

"Hi Debbie!" Dana said, surprised at seeing her old friend and co-worker from her early days at the bank.

"Oh! . . . Uh, hi Dana," Debbie replied in a low voice, looking away from Dana's face and over toward the parking lot.

"It's great to see you, Debbie. How are things?" Dana looked earnestly at her friend's face.

"Fine. Everything's fine." Debbie pulled at the sleeve on her shirt, glancing at Dana and then back to the parking lot. "Bob's waiting for me, but it's nice to see you, Dana." She stepped around Dana and then headed briskly toward the parked cars.

Dana frowned as she turned and watched Debbie walk away. The two had become close friends when Dana first started at the bank and Debbie occupied the teller's station next to hers. Dana stood there, fixated on her old friend and trying to comprehend her obvious lukewarm reaction to seeing her. Oh well, she thought, maybe she's just having a bad morning, and it has nothing to do with me. Yet Dana remembered a similar reaction when running into another friend at the grocery store last week. Turning back toward the restaurant, she decided not to dwell on it and have her day ruined. She'd been looking forward to seeing Marie, who never failed to make her laugh and feel better about things.

She stepped into the restaurant and scanned the waiting area. Before she reached the hostess, Dana spied Marie, who was waving wildly in her direction. Perfectly coiffed, as usual, Marie was sitting in a booth near the back of the restaurant. Dana waved back in acknowledgement and made her way through the crowded aisle. When she reached the table, Dana leaned down and hugged Marie tightly, not wanting to let go. Just holding onto Marie made Dana feel comforted and secure.

"I know you've always been attracted to me, Luv, but you're squeezing the life out of me!" Marie said, feigning suffocation. She grabbed Dana's shoulders and pushed her back, gazing intently at her face. "I'm assuming you haven't slept at all in the past week because, girl, you look like a car ran over you — twice."

Trying to suppress a grin, Dana rolled her eyes and sat down on the bench across from Marie. "I think it's time for you to stop holding back, Marie, and start telling me what you *really* think."

Marie crossed her arms and placed her elbows on the table, all the while staring fixedly at Dana. "Well, you look simply dreadful, Darling — bags and dark circles under your eyes, your face is pale as a ghost, and your whole body is slouching. That's the only way to describe what I see here," she replied, with a wave of her hand.

"I'm fine," Dana lied, fidgeting in her seat. She couldn't quite meet Marie's eye, preferring to stare at the middle of the empty table.

"I'm your best friend, Luv. I can see all over your face you're not fine. In fact, your face has 'I'm Not Fine!' written across it in bold font."

"Marie, you do tend toward exaggeration, you know. And if you remember, I have a newborn at home. They have a habit of cutting into your normal sleep pattern, if you know what I mean."

"God no!" Marie hissed, recoiling into her seat. "I hope to never know what you mean. Children and I are like oil and vinegar, dogs and cats, Janis

33

Joplin and Andy Williams . . ."

"Stop! I get it, Marie," Dana said, shaking her head and trying not to laugh. "I'm sure they feel the same way about you. But no, that's not true, is it? Kids love being around you. Why is that?" She tilted her head and gave Marie an inquisitive look, really wanting to know the answer.

"I believe in giving children all the sweets they can manage in one sitting and educating them by watching as much telly as possible," Marie said firmly and with an air of conviction.

"Ah, yes," Dana said, laughing at the mental picture. "Now I remember why I don't let you babysit."

"Well, at least you've perked up a bit since you walked in here. When I first laid eyes on you, I thought you might cry in your soup today. Speaking of soup, where is that waitress? She came by a bit before you arrived and I told her to come back. I suppose we shan't see her ever again." Marie glanced around the restaurant. "By the by, Debbie Hines and her husband are in here somewhere."

"No, she left just as I was about to walk in the door. I talked to her for a minute outside — or rather, I *tried* to talk to her. She acted like she didn't want to be seen standing next to me. She would barely look at me. We used to be really good friends because our teller stations were next to each other. I have no idea why she just acted that way. Maybe she believes the rumor that I messed up the allotment accounting and that's why I was fired." Dana could feel her face turning red and her heart quicken.

"Debbie is a mercurial sort, as you know. A 'tart' is what we would call her across the pond. Her husband probably forgot to put the milk in her tea this morning and now she'll be cross all day."

"Thanks for the thought, Marie, and I might have taken comfort in the semblance of truth in that statement, but the same thing happened last week when I went to Kroger. I ran into Sandy Kent. Remember her from the Elizabethtown branch? We worked together for a long time too. I saw her coming down the aisle and I know she saw me too. Then she turned her cart around and went the other way. I saw her again when I was checking out and she wouldn't even look up. So I know this is *not* my imagination.

People in this small town are usually much nicer to each other."

Marie threw up her hands in dismay. "For God's sake, Dana! Sandy Kent is a daft cow! Don't get your knickers in a twist over anything she said or did. I ask you, when is the last time you heard that wanker make a single comment about anyone that wasn't laced with innuendos or outright lies? She's the most miserable person I know! Not to mention she won't go out in the rain because her face would melt."

Dana looked down at her lap and smiled. "Yes, but she also works in an office that is fairly isolated from the main office. So if *she* knows I was fired, the word must have spread by now."

"Are you ready to order?" A petite, fresh-faced girl stood before the table, smiling down at them.

Dana and Marie looked up at the waitress, both staring at her for several seconds without saying a word.

"Are you ready to order?" she repeated, looking from Marie to Dana.

"Oh, yes; I think we're ready. Do you know what you want?" Marie gestured to Dana to order.

"Yes, I'll have a western omelet, hash browns, toast, and black coffee, please." Dana handed the menu back to the waitress.

"And I'll have two soft-boiled eggs, toast and jam, and can I have a few grilled tomato slices on the side?" Marie batted her eyelashes at the waitress and smiled sweetly.

"I'll check and see. It should be OK, but it might cost a little more than our normal sides." The waitress had a puzzled look on her face.

"No problem." Marie dismissed the girl with a wave of her hand. "Now, where were we?" she asked, turning back to Dana. "Oh yes, I remember now." She glanced back at the waitress, who was hustling toward the kitchen. "Stop dwelling on what someone might know or be thinking. That daft prick unjustly fired you! Anyone with a brain bigger than a pea knows that much. Now, what have you done about it?" Marie added in a demanding tone.

"Noth . . . nothing." Marie's reaction surprised Dana. "Are you suggesting I take on Mr. Johnson?"

35

"Absolutely! You need to see a lawyer and get his arse in trouble! You were a superb employee with excellent performance reviews for over nine years. The bank rewarded your hard work with an incentive contract that was approved by the board. You performed according to your contract, and the bank owes you the reward. It's as straight-forward as that!"

Dana sighed and stared at the table. "I wish it were that simple. But if you remember, last year when the bank transitioned from the paper ledgers we were using initially for the allotment accounts, to the automated ledgers, we found quite a few accounting discrepancies. That part of Johnson's ranting at me was true. When we transitioned, we found some accounts were short of money and some had too much. Brenda Sheppard and I worked many hours trying to reconcile those accounts. We had to call some people and tell them their accounts had too much money and then call other people and tell them the bad news their accounts had too little money. It was a nightmare. We'd corrected a majority of the accounts when Mr. Johnson took over, but obviously we weren't finished. Then, to complicate things, we'd just installed the first update for the software, which highlighted different discrepancies. So we'd been working for quite a while to reconcile both sets of discrepancies. Of course, Johnson never gave me a chance to explain any of this. I never got to say *anything*, or maybe I was too shocked to say anything. But I quickly realized he wanted to blame me for the whole thing and then fire me. I really think he was just trying to find a way to not pay me the incentive fee. I still can't believe he actually said, 'No snotty-nosed kid is going to make more money at this bank than me!' Who says something that juvenile?"

"Obviously the man was weaned on an icicle and hasn't a clue how to behave properly or how to manage people. What a blithering idiot! But I strongly believe you should speak to an attorney because I feel certain something can be done. What have you got to lose? You've already lost your job!"

"True," Dana murmured, looking down at her hands. "I'm sure you're right, Marie. I don't want him to get away with what he did to me, and I don't want him to ever do this to anyone else either. What an asshole!

36

Things were so good before he showed up at the bank. I used to get up every day and look forward to going to work. After he came and I had that first meeting with him, I dreaded going to the bank. What a difference one jerk can make."

"OK, so *do* something about it and stop fannying about!"

"OK, I will. Now, can we talk about something else? Something a little more pleasant and interesting, like who you were out with last Saturday night? Joey said he saw you in the passenger seat of this little gold-colored Datsun 280Z and a guy with blonde hair was driving. Details, lady; I want details!"

Marie's sober expression softened, her eyes narrowed, and the corners of her mouth slowly turned upward. "That, my dear, was the most able-bodied man God ever put on the earth. I might even keep him around a while to have something to play with."

Dana laughed. Marie would keep him around only until she found someone she liked better.

"OK ladies, breakfast has arrived!" The waitress placed the steaming plates in front of Dana and Marie. "Can I get you anything else right now?"

"No, I think we're fine," Marie said, surveying the plates. "Thanks. Oh, and a special thanks for the grilled tomatoes!"

"My manager said there's no extra charge." The waitress smiled, then scurried off toward the kitchen.

Dana looked down at her plate and then back at Marie. She couldn't help but smile at her long-time friend. She looked out the window. The sun was glowing, and the newly planted yellow and blue pansies were sitting up smartly in the freshly mulched beds. For the first time in many weeks, Dana felt better.

6

One week later, late May 1986

"Mr. Goldberg will be with you shortly. You can wait over there." The secretary gestured toward the chairs in the corner. "Would you like some coffee?"

"Oh, thank you, I'm good," Dana said, as she walked toward the seating area. She picked out a chair next to the window, leaned over and set her purse on the floor, and then sat down heavily in the chair. She felt tired, yet anxious, and even a little hopeful at the same time. Talking to a lawyer was going to cost money, but it seemed her only option to getting some resolution on her firing.

Staring out the window, Dana thought about how much her life had changed in the past few weeks. Right before Mr. Fugitte left and Mr. Johnson took over, she and Joey had discussed how finally after eight years of marriage, they felt comfortable enough with their income and savings to take a two-week vacation, or put a down-payment on a car, or make a major household repair, without breaking their budget or having to pay on credit. Now, with only one income for the family of four, they were back into the scrimping mode. And that wouldn't be the worst of it if she didn't get a job soon. There was no alternative; she *had* to work in order to pay the bills and feed the family.

"Hi Dana! I saw your name on Mr. Goldberg's appointment schedule and thought I'd stop by and say hello. How are you doing?"

Dana looked up at the tall, slim, and attractive dark-haired woman standing in front of her. "Hi, Mary! I didn't know you still worked here. I don't think I've seen you in several years." Dana stood up and hugged Mary.

"Oh yeah, I'm still here. Going on 10 years now. I like it here and they treat me really well. We're like one big, happy family." Mary motioned for Dana to sit back down as she perched on the arm of the chair opposite her. "How are Joey and the family? And didn't you just have a baby not very long ago?"

"Yes, I did — a girl. She was born on 13 March, so 13 is now a lucky number in our house," Dana said with a grin. "We named her Elizabeth, but we call her Liz. She's doing great. Actually sleeping fairly well at night already. Ryan is doing great too. He's three now. We weren't sure how he'd handle having a little sister, but he does really well with her. He's always patting her on the head and kissing her," Dana said, laughing at the memory. "Joey is doing fine too. He's still a police officer, working in Elizabethtown. How's your family?"

"The kids are great." Mary shook her head. "Hard to believe they're so old already — six and eight. Tim and I got divorced a year ago. I don't know if you'd heard."

Dana sighed, then reached out and placed her hand on Mary's arm. "Yes, I did hear. You can't keep anything quiet in this town. I'm really sorry, Mary. I know divorce is a tough thing for everyone involved."

"You're so right about everyone knowing everything about you in this town," Mary said, looking up at the ceiling and laughing, "which is the reason I know why you're here. And I hope Mr. Goldberg can give you some useful advice because you certainly got a raw deal, Dana."

Dana felt better hearing at least one person besides her family and Marie was on her side. "Thanks, Mary. I can use the support. I can't tell you how many people I've run into lately who just turn around and walk away when they see me coming. First, I thought it was my imagination, but it has happened too many times. Guess they just don't know what to say, so they avoid me altogether. And even though I know that, it doesn't make it hurt any less, or make me feel less embarrassed."

"Just ignore them, Dana. People automatically assume if you got fired, you did something wrong. It's hard for them to comprehend there really are some terrible managers out there. Just hold your head up and hope the truth eventually gets out there. I'll do what I can to spread it," Mary said in a compassionate tone.

"Thanks, Mary. It means more to me than you know."

"Well, I better get back to my desk." Mary stood up, then leaned over and hugged Dana. "Stand tall. You've done nothing to feel embarrassed about. This too shall pass."

Dana managed a slight smile at hearing Mary's words, but didn't respond. It can't pass quickly enough, she thought.

Mr. Goldberg's secretary finally called Dana into his office after she'd sat fidgeting in the waiting area for another 15 minutes. She followed the secretary down the hallway and around the corner until they reached the closed, heavy wooden door near the end. The secretary knocked on the door, and without waiting for a response, opened it and motioned for Dana to go in. Feeling anxious, Dana walked into the office and quickly set her eyes on the occupant — a short, stocky man with light-brown hair combed neatly to one side. He stood up from behind his desk and walked around to greet Dana. He wore a dark grey suit that looked perfectly tailored for his frame.

"Hello, Mrs. Smolenski. Please have a seat," he said, gesturing for her to sit in the chair next to his desk. "Can I offer you a cup of coffee or some water?"

"No, I'm fine. But thank you."

Mr. Goldberg returned to his chair and sat down. "All right then, what can I do for you today?"

Not even any small talk, Dana thought. That was OK with her. She was happy to get to the point and not waste time and money she didn't have. "Mr. Goldberg, nearly a month ago I was fired from my job at First Citizens Bank, and since I feel I was wrongly fired, I want to find out what legal options I might have."

"All right. Why don't you tell me the circumstances of your firing and then we'll discuss options that might be suitable for your case." Mr. Goldberg picked up a pen and scratched some notes on the yellow tablet in front of him.

Dana settled into her chair and took a deep breath. "I worked at First Citizens Bank in Elizabethtown and at the Radcliff office for the past nine years. Phillip Hayes was the bank president who hired me as a teller in December 1977, and then I worked for Jim Aldridge, and then Jim Fugitte until he resigned last November. Mr. Fugitte wanted to expand three specific areas of business at the bank, and one was the allotment program, which I handled. I was working under an incentive program, which basically meant if I increased the number of allotments at the bank by a certain percentage each year, I would get a bonus based on that percentage. I was due my first bonus — around $100,000 — when Mr. Fugitte resigned and Bernard Johnson took over as president. At our first meeting, he called me into his office and without even asking me about my job or what I had accomplished with the allotment program, he simply told me no snotty-nosed kid was going to make more money than he did — he actually used those words." Dana was talking rapidly, and the pitch of her voice was getting higher. She'd clenched her hands into fists and was pushing them into her thighs. "I went on maternity leave three weeks later, so I never talked to him again after this one meeting. But when my maternity leave was half over, I had a phone call from a woman who worked with me at the bank. She told me they were boxing up everything in my office, and she advised me to come in and meet with Mr. Johnson to find out what was going on, so I did. I called up and made an appointment to see him. When I went into his office, he was quite belligerent, just like the first time I met with him. Only this time he told me — or yelled at me is more accurate — that he'd had an audit done on the allotments while I was on maternity leave and they'd found numerous discrepancies. Then he blamed me for everything, said I was fired, and to get my things that were boxed up in the closet and leave the bank immediately." Dana's voice quivered, and she struggled to control her emotions. "Then he called his secretary to have me escorted out of the building. That's pretty much it in a nutshell."

"What do you know about Bernard Johnson, Dana?" Mr. Goldberg put down his pen and sat back in his chair. "He's not from this area, is he? I've not heard his name before."

"No, he's not. An investment group from Texas hired him to be the bank president. In 1982, this investment group bought and took over management of the bank when the Butcher brothers, Jake and C.H. — who were the owners of First Citizens at the time — got the bank into trouble by making too many bad loans, and also by withdrawing a lot of the bank's capital for their personal use. I don't know how much of this story you know or what was public information. Do you want me to go into a little of the history? I'm not sure if I'm legally allowed to discuss what happened, so can we keep this between us?"

"Yes," Mr. Goldberg said, waving his hand. "What you say in this room is subject to attorney/client privilege. I suspect most of the history was in the newspapers and on TV, but regardless, you don't need to worry."

"OK." Dana relaxed into her chair. "Just as background, federal bank regulations require banks to maintain a certain amount of capital at all times. When the Butcher brothers granted so many loans that went bad and then had to write off those loans — in addition to withdrawing large amounts of cash at any given time for their personal use — First Citizens wasn't able to maintain the legally required level of capital. Basically, there wasn't enough money at the bank at any point in time. First Citizens wasn't the only bank the Butcher brothers owned with capital requirement problems. They owned numerous banks that were in the same situation as ours. Eventually, the bank regulators discovered this and shut down the Butcher banks, which is what we called them, and mandated the banks were to be sold. So this group of investors from Texas bought First Citizens. Actually, the new owners were quite entertaining. They walked into the bank one day wearing Stetsons and cowboy boots! We discovered they were from the oil business." Dana smiled at the recollection.

"Seems like I remember some of this," Mr. Goldberg said, taking notes again on his tablet. "OK, so after the investment group installed Bernard

Johnson as the new president, did he clean up the bank's act and start maintaining the required level of capital?"

"No, that's the odd thing," Dana said, shaking her head. "When Jim Fugitte took over as president, which was four years prior to Bernard Johnson, *he* was the one who was there when the bank received the 'cease and desist order' from the FCC, and was told he was not to approve any more withdrawals of money from the Butcher brothers or make any more loans unless they were premium level or triple A level loans, which basically are loans with a high assurance of repayment. But then Mr. Fugitte suddenly resigned, along with one of the bank's interns, to start up their own bill pay company, since the one we created at the bank had become so successful. Mr. Fugitte had already turned things around at the bank when he resigned and Bernard Johnson took over."

Mr. Goldberg sat quietly at his desk, staring ahead at the wall. After what seemed like a long time, he said, "Dana, I don't want to second guess anyone's motives, but do you think Jim Fugitte and the intern knew there would be someone who would have to take the fall for the accounting errors, and they decided it would be better if it were you than them?"

Dana looked down at the floor and sighed. "Yes, I have thought about that. It's possible, but I don't know. I think eventually I still would've been fired because Bernard Johnson seems to have a genuine dislike for me. He acted incredibly rude toward me at our first meeting, and at that point he knew nothing about the accounting discrepancies. Maybe he simply doesn't like working with women."

Mr. Goldberg placed his pen on the tablet and sat up in his chair. "If that's the case and we can find evidence to support that assertion, we'd have grounds to sue based on wrongful dismissal due to gender bias. If we won, you'd be awarded your former job. There's one other defense to consider. The law says an employer must counsel an employee regarding any identified problems or shortcomings and then provide that employee the opportunity to correct their performance. If the employee still doesn't correct the problem after a specified period, then legally the employee can be terminated. If this is true in your case, we could sue based on wrongful dismissal."

"I can assure you I was never counseled regarding any shortcomings or problems." Dana assumed the comment Phil Hayes made to her shortly after being hired regarding her being a bad teller, but a good employee, didn't count. Suddenly, she realized what Mr. Goldberg had said. "Mr. Goldberg, I don't want my job back."

"Oh . . . well, what is it you *do* want? I thought that's why you were here — to get back your job." Mr. Goldberg peered at Dana, his brows knitted together.

"I want some sort of retribution, something to happen to him so he knows he can't treat people this way and get away with it. But I certainly don't ever want to *work* for him again. He's the worst excuse for a boss I've ever seen!"

"Dana, I'm afraid all I can do for you is try to get back your job using one of those two legal arguments I just explained. I don't think we could sue for damages since, correct me if I'm wrong, it is an accurate statement there were accounting errors within the allotment sector at the bank, and you were in charge of that sector. Is that correct?" Mr. Goldberg studied Dana's face, waiting for an answer.

"Well, yes, technically that's correct," Dana stammered. "But I can't believe those are my *only* choices. I can't believe someone can treat you this way and there's nothing you can do about it!"

"I'm not saying what he did was right, or that it was the best way to handle that problem. I'm only saying that *legally*, there are limited options, which become more limited if you're telling me you don't want your job back. Also, I'm not saying if I were you, I would again want to work for a man who had just fired me. I think it's safe to say he'd probably just look for another reason to fire you, if you really think he has something against you. But Dana, as unfair as all this sounds, legally those are the options."

"What about the bonus I was supposed to get? I'd met the target of the incentive program and earned the bonus. Could we sue for that?"

Mr. Goldberg leaned forward on his desk. "Do you have the agreement for the incentive program in writing, and was it signed by all parties?"

Dana hesitated for a moment and then shook her head. "No, I have nothing in writing. But I was told it was approved by the board and supposedly was written in the board meeting minutes too, although I never saw it. Would something written in board minutes count as being in writing?"

"No, that would be a real stretch to win a case based on something written in the board's minutes. Certainly we can try anything you want — it's your money — but I would advise against pursuing something you don't have in writing and signed by the proper bank authority. I'm afraid a judge would view board minutes as insufficient evidence, and you'd end up wasting a lot of time and money pursuing such a case."

Dana stared despairingly at Mr. Goldberg. The only thing that had given her any reason to be hopeful during the past week was the thought of making Bernard Johnson pay for his despicable behavior. She really hadn't expected to get the bonus paid because she figured Johnson would cite the accounting errors as the reason to not pay it. But the absolute last thing she wanted was to get back her job and have to face *him* again every day in the office!

"Dana, I recommend you go away and think about all this for a while. Pursuing a case in court is a big decision, and a costly one as well. It warrants some thought." Mr. Goldberg put down his pen and sat up in his chair.

"Yes . . . probably a good idea," Dana said, more to herself. "I have to think about it. Thank you for your time, Mr. Goldberg," she mumbled. "I really appreciate it."

"Absolutely, Dana. I'm sorry for your troubles and I wish you the best, no matter what you decide. There's no charge for this initial consult. Just let me know if you want to proceed with anything." Mr. Goldberg stood up and walked around his desk.

After reaching down to pick up her purse, Dana rose from her chair and shook his hand, thanking him again for the information. Then she turned and walked out of his office, her shoulders slumped, staring at the floor.

45

* * *

Joey walked around the small, rectangular kitchen table, placing a dinner plate at each end. "So that's all he said? You could get your job back?" Pausing a minute to look at his wife, he placed a small, plastic plate with a smiling purple dinosaur splashed across the center, and then reached across the table to set down a warm bottle of formula.

"Yep, that was pretty much it." Dana stood at the stove mindlessly stirring a saucepan full of chili mac. She felt utterly drained and numb, and was having trouble concentrating on preparing dinner. She opened her eyes wide and then closed them tight several times, trying to focus on the hamburger meat she was mixing with the water and spice packet. Chili mac was one of her favorite quick meals, and one of the few things her son would eat — besides chicken nuggets and French fries. But she wasn't sure she could swallow anything right now.

Joey walked across the kitchen, pulled open a drawer, and took out a handful of forks and knives. He reached across the counter and grabbed some napkins. "Hon, I couldn't be any sorrier because the whole thing is just so unfair. You're a hard worker and as dedicated as anyone at that bank. You didn't deserve to be treated like that, and if I ever run into that asshole, I'm going to tell him so."

Dana continued to stare into the boiling saucepan. "Joey, you can't do that; you're a police officer. But I appreciate the thought."

Joey paused and stared at his wife. The silverware and napkins dangled from his hands. "Please try not to worry. It'll be tougher for a while, but we'll manage. We're more fortunate than many people, including many people we know."

Dana stopped stirring and turned to look at Joey. "Yes, there will always be someone worse off than us, and we'll be OK for a while. But we need my income, Joey," she said indignantly.

Joey was silent. He walked back to the table and slowly placed the silverware and napkins at each end.

"I'm sorry." Dana put down the spoon and walked over to her husband. She reached up and hugged him tightly. She held on, not wanting to move. Finally, she let go and stepped back to look into his face. Dana had loved Joey's soft brown eyes and ready smile since the first time she'd laid eyes on him.

Joey ran his hands up and down Dana's arms and gazed back at her. "Dana, we've known each other since high school and we've been through hard times before. Yes, things will be a little tougher for a while. But you'll find another job, and maybe one you'll like better. You were miserable working for Johnson, and if he hadn't fired you, you'd be miserable now anyway — and probably *more* miserable because you wouldn't see an end to it. So, maybe this is a blessing in disguise and you'll be happier at some new place. A year from now you might say he did you a favor by firing you."

Dana managed a small grin while looking skeptically at her husband. That was just like Joey, always trying to find the bright side. She was more of a realist, and the realist in her was saying harder times were ahead. Joey's salary as a police officer was $26,000 a year. They had a mortgage, two car payments, and two children to feed beside themselves. Diapers were expensive, and at three months, Liz went through them like crazy. Neither Dana's nor Joey's parents could help them financially. Grandma probably could help them for a while. She'd offered once before, right after they'd gotten married and Joey was in the National Guard and Dana had just started at the bank. They wanted to manage their new life on their own, but it was nice to know they had a safety net if they ever needed one. Dana hoped that time was not now.

Suddenly she remembered dinner boiling away on the stove. "Forgot about dinner!" In three steps she was across the kitchen with her eye on the boiling pot. Comfort food. She was feeling a little better. She gave the pot a quick stir, set the lid on top, and turned off the burner.

"I guess we're ready for dinner," Joey said. "I'll get Ryan. It's hard to believe he's still playing with those Legos alone in his room. Maybe we'll let Liz sleep until she wakes up on her own," he added, as he went down the hallway toward Ryan's bedroom.

Leaning over the kitchen counter next to the stove, Dana looked down at the playpen where her youngest child lay asleep. Liz was lying on her stomach with her head twisted to the side. Her tiny arms were stretched out with hands clenched into tight fists. The thin skin of her mouth resembled delicate rose-colored tissue paper. Dana stared at the fine veins in her eyelids. She looked so fragile. Suddenly she felt overwhelmed with the sense of responsibility for taking care of such a helpless creature. I've let you both down, she thought. I brought you and Ryan into the world and I'm supposed to take care of you until you can care for yourselves. Dana's head hung, and she stared into the gold-colored carpet. Tears welled up again.

"Boo! Mommy, I scare you!" Ryan's head popped around the corner of the cabinet and Dana jumped at the sudden sound of his voice. A smile flashed across her face and she stood up to see him more clearly. He was crawling around the corner on all fours.

"Is . . . is it a dog? No, it's a cat! No wait, it's CatDog!" Dana spoke in her most announcer-sounding voice. She heard giggles from the floor.

"No, Mommy, it's me — Ryan!"

"Ryan?" Dana reveled in his simplicity and innocence.

"Mommy, I'm not CatDog, I'm Ryan, see?" He bounced up and down in front of Dana, giggling loudly.

"So you are!" Dana placed her hands on the sides of her face. "I would've never guessed!"

Liz stirred at the sound of Ryan's voice and soon was squirming in her playpen, trying to lift her head. Dana had noticed Liz was most animated when Ryan was nearby. Her eyes would fix on him, and she'd coo and gurgle until he tired of her attention and left her sight.

"Are you hungry, Hon?"

"No! Come play with me, Mommy! Come play in my room. Daddy's in there."

"I have dinner ready, one of your favorites — chili mac. You remember?

48

The one with the red sauce and the noodles shaped like the letter C?"

"No, I don't want it! I want chicken nuggets and French fries!" Ryan stomped his foot.

Dana bent down on one knee so she was eye-level with the little boy. "We don't have any right now. We only have chili mac. Will you do Mommy a big favor and sit by me and eat that for dinner, please?"

Ryan didn't respond. Instead, he sauntered over to Liz's playpen, kicking at the carpet along the way.

Joey returned to the kitchen and began spooning out dinner. He put a small portion on Ryan's plate. "Come on over here, Son, and have a seat next to your mom."

Dana sat down at the table and smiled at Ryan, patting the seat next to hers. He turned around and wove his way back to the table, climbing onto the chair.

"Maybe we'll get away with finishing dinner before Liz decides she's hungry too." Joey picked up his silverware and began to eat. "You know, Hon, there are lots of other banks in this town. I'm sure any of them would be happy to have you work for them."

"I doubt it. You know how rumors spread in this town. I can only imagine what has been said about my being fired. No bank will hire me if they think I'm responsible for losing $15,000 dollars."

"Give them a chance. Pick out the ones where you'd like to work and talk to a manager. Tell them everything you've done, including the allotment services, and see what they say. Maybe another bank would be interested in starting up that service too. It was so lucrative for First Citizens, I can't imagine why they wouldn't. You can go back and steal away your old clients. Have you thought about that?" Joey reached over and picked up Ryan's fork and held it out for him to take.

"Yes, I've definitely thought about it," Dana said, staring at her dinner, unable to take a bite. "I'd be thrilled to get hired at another bank and take the whole allotment business away from First Citizens. Nothing would make me happier. But I don't think that's going to happen. Everyone seems to know about my being fired, and I'll be lucky to get a job anywhere in this town, let alone at a bank."

"Mommy got fired!" Ryan yelled, sitting up in his booster seat. "Mommy, was it hot? Did you burn?"

"No, Mommy didn't burn!" Joey said laughing. "She won't be going to her job at the bank anymore, that's all. You might like that better, Ryan. She'll probably be spending more time now with you and Liz."

"I won't go to school anymore?" Ryan's smile disappeared.

"Oh yes, you'll still go see Miss Debbie every day at the Montessori school. You still want to go to school, right?" Joey raised his eyebrows at Ryan.

"Yes, I want to go see Miss Debbie every day, and Stephen, and Mike, and Andrew, and David. I want to go to school!" Ryan was trying to stand up in his seat.

"OK, sit down, Ryan," Dana said, as she took his arm and pulled him back into his seat. "You'll still be going to school every day and you'll be hanging out with me a little more too. I'll need to spend some time each day looking for a new job, but I think you and I will have a lot more time together too. Won't that be fun?"

"Yes, I like that Mommy!" He'd returned to pushing the macaroni into piles and then smacking them with the back of his fork.

Dana looked over at Joey. She still had little appetite, but began eating anyway. "I thought I'd start out by trying Fort Knox Credit Union and First Federal Bank, then maybe Elizabethtown National Bank. Those probably are the only ones that could handle the allotment business and might be interested in it. I've been checking the employment section in the News Enterprise. There's not much in it. Marie is keeping an ear open for me too. She knows a lot of people. Hopefully something will come along soon."

"I'm sure it will. In the meantime, you can enjoy being home with Liz while she's still a baby and also with our big boy," Joey said, as he squeezed Ryan's arm.

Dana forced a smile and then looked down at her plate. She hadn't been unemployed in over nine years. Even with all the work involved in taking care of two small children and managing a household, how would she get used to not getting up each day, going to an office, and being around adults? Dana was upset and depressed, and having an increasingly hard time covering it up from everyone who believed new mothers were supposed to be incessantly happy. She couldn't remember a time when she was less happy.

7

Five months later, October 1986

Dana was in a melancholy mood and deep in thought as she drove down the old two-lane road toward her parents' house. The road had needed resurfacing for a good fifteen years, but the county continued to patch new potholes after each icy Winter. Reddish-orange and brown leaves now covered the mottled asphalt, and the distinct smell of Fall spilled over the tops of the half-opened car windows. Even Ryan and Liz, both buckled into their car seats, were staring out the window, uncharacteristically quiet and motionless.

During the 20-minute drive from her home to her parents' house, Dana reflected on the oddness of time and how it seemed to have slowed dramatically the past few months. Any other year, Summer came and went so quickly it hardly seemed possible when Labor Day arrived, along with the first chill in the air. But this year had been anything but typical. Each week dragged out slower than the last, and each day Dana got out of bed a little less hopeful she would find employment again and her life would return to normal.

This year Labor Day came and went with little fanfare, and Fall settled into Elizabethtown. This had been Dana's favorite time of year since she was a child. Fall meant the start of the school year, and unlike a lot of kids, Dana loved going to school. Each year she would feel the anticipation when Summer came to a close. Fall meant the return to all things exciting — her friends, the teachers she adored, the challenge of learning, some boy she had a crush on, band and her clarinet, and the familiar concrete building that was her high school, with its unique and strangely comforting smell. Now that she was no longer in school, there was no reason to get excited when Summer ended and Fall arrived. Nevertheless, she did get excited — every year except this one.

The arrival of Fall had driven Dana into a nervous, self-reflective state. As she drove to her parents' house that day, the crisp, clean smell in the air and the sight of the leaves lying in a colorful blanket across the road triggered doubts about what she'd accomplished since graduating from high school. Most of her friends had gone straight to college, graduated in four years, and now had decent jobs with upward mobility. She'd chosen marriage over college, and then several years later went to college at night after having worked at the bank all day. She wondered if she should've focused more on her career. Mr. Johnson was around her only when she was pregnant. He probably regarded her as a wife and mother, and not as a serious career employee — not that any of it mattered now. She'd been fired and had little to show for the past nine years of diligent work. Dana slowed the car and turned into a short asphalt driveway, stopping behind her parents' blue Pontiac parked in the carport.

"Memaw! We're at Memaw's house!" Ryan sat up in his car seat, pushing against the straps.

"Yes, we're at Memaw's house," Dana said, unbuckling her seat belt and grabbing her purse before exiting the car. She opened the rear door and pulled the wriggling boy out of his car seat and set him down outside the car. "OK, go on in and find Memaw and Papaw and tell them we're here."

Dana closed the door and went around to the other side of the car to retrieve Liz, who was gurgling noisily and kicking her feet in anticipation. She opened the car door and reached down to unbuckle her. "OK, come on baby girl, let's go see Memaw and Papaw."

Walking into the house, Dana breathed in the familiar scent and savored the comfort that enveloped her. She hugged Liz tightly. For a fleeting moment, she enjoyed the warm and peaceful feeling. Then, just as quickly as it had swept over her, the feeling left and the anxiety returned. Dana sighed and wandered toward the muted voices emanating from the hallway.

"Mommy! Mommy! Memaw got me a new train!" Ryan was standing at the end of the hall, proudly holding up a small green metal train in his hand.

"Wow! Another train for your set! Pretty soon you'll have them all." Dana went down the hallway and took the train from Ryan's hand and inspected it. "A pretty green one. Memaw and Papaw certainly are good to you, aren't they?"

"Yes," Ryan said, turning to look back at his grandmother, who'd come up behind him and was smoothing down the back of his light-brown hair.

"Hi Mom," Dana leaned over Ryan and gave her mother a quick hug and kiss on the cheek.

"Well, hello little darling!" Dana's mother beamed down at Liz, still in Dana's arms.

Liz gurgled and cooed at her grandmother, kicking her heels into Dana's sides. "Here, come to Memaw." Mrs. Adkins held out her arms and Liz leaned toward her.

Dana was happy to relinquish the extra weight. She'd been thinking her little girl seemed to get heavier by the week. After ten minutes of carrying her around, Dana's arms and back felt the strain.

Dana's mom looked over her shoulder at Ryan. "Hon, you can go in the TV room and play if you want. I just put 101 Dalmatians on for you to watch."

"OK," Ryan said, running down the hallway with the shiny green train clasped tightly in his hand.

"I need to check on dinner, Dana. Let's go sit in the kitchen." Her mom went down the hallway and into the kitchen. She was clutching Liz tightly to her chest.

"Where's Dad?" Dana followed her mother to the kitchen, canvassing the other bedrooms along the way.

"He's in the backyard, hopefully picking some squash for dinner." Her mom shook her head and laughed. "Your father's lost when garden season is over. He's already getting withdrawal symptoms, you know, standing on the patio staring at the empty rows, not saying much."

Dana went over to the sink and looked out the window. There he was, just as she described, standing at the edge of the porch staring at the garden. The plastic bag, presumably filled with squash, looped over his hand. She grinned at the sight.

"Dana, come sit down and tell me what you've been up to lately. How's the job hunt going?" Dana's mother swung Liz to the back of her hip, quickly stirred the pot of beans, and then walked over to the yellow Formica table at the opposite end of the kitchen.

Dana gave an audible sigh and visibly wilted. "Mom, give me a break! I just got here."

"You look terrible, Dana. Your eyes are sunken in, your face is pale, there's no life in you anymore. You've always been so upbeat and had so much energy. I can't stand to see you this way. It just breaks my heart. And it's not good for the kids."

"I'm not doing this on purpose, Mom," Dana said in a defensive tone. "Things will be better when I find a job. It's hard to be cheery right now, but I don't think the kids sense anything. I'm doing the best I can." Dana stared at the floor. She thought her mother — of all people — would understand and be supportive.

"Oh, I know you are, Hon! I didn't mean to sound as if you weren't. I know you're working hard to find another job, and I know this has been terribly hard on you. Sorry I said anything. I just hate to see you looking this way — depressed and run down." Dana's mother pulled out a chair from the table and sat down, still holding Liz. She patted the chair cushion next to hers. "Come sit down, Dana."

Reluctantly, Dana walked towards the table and slumped into the chair next to her mother. She didn't feel like rehashing the last few terrible months of her life. She stared at the floor, unable to meet her mother's gaze.

"I don't want to ruin the evening, but I've been watching you go downhill over the past several months and I'm worried." Her mother paused for so long, Dana thought she might get off without a big lecture. But then she continued. "I'm worried you think your inability to get another job is a reflection of your worth, your value as a human being and as an employee. Just because you aren't able to get another job right now doesn't mean you aren't a good, honest, and desirable employee. You have an excellent education and you're a hard worker. Someone is going to hire you. You just need to be patient."

Dana looked up at her mother. "I know, Mom. I know I'll get a job eventually, but I need one now. And I know I'm not supposed to feel worthless and dejected because no one will hire me, but I do. I don't know anyone who is even a tiny bit conscientious who wouldn't feel the same way." Dana tried not to sound annoyed.

"I don't mean to irritate you. I just thought I could help you feel better and maybe give you some ideas," her mother replied softly.

"I'm sorry, Mom." Dana reached out and grasped her mother's hand. "I'm such a jerk sometimes. Don't pay any attention to me."

"It's OK; I understand. But maybe I can help, so why don't you tell me who all you've contacted and how you've been going about it." Her mother had laid Liz face down over her thighs and was rubbing her back while they spoke. Liz was making a deep cooing sound Dana hadn't heard before.

Dana could tell her mother was going to persist until she got her way, so she might as well tell her mother everything and get it over with. She took a deep breath and sighed and then relayed the painful litany. "First, I went to the three banks I figured were my best prospects for a job, based on their size and likely interest in the allotment business. I went into each one and asked to talk to the manager. In all three cases I was told they weren't interested right now in starting an allotment business like we had at First Citizens, and they didn't have any openings for anyone with my level of education and training."

"Yes, I remember you telling me that part before," her mother said, shaking her head. "Frankly, I can't believe not a single manager at any of those three banks had the foresight to see how much money they could make doing allotments if they only knew what to do. That part is dumb-founding to

56

me."

"I agree. I'm handing them the business on the proverbial platter and they don't know what to do with it."

Her mother looked down at Liz, staring at her back while still pondering the issue. "But I really don't get the part about no openings for someone with your level of education and training. It almost sounds like you're being penalized for having a bachelor's degree and nine years of work experience."

"Yes, I think I am!" Dana raised her voice. "I never would've believed all those nights I spent for two-and-a-half years, working my tail off at Embry Riddle, would now be a hindrance to getting a job in this town! But apparently, I was wrong to assume a Business Management degree would help. I wish I'd known that four years ago when I started back to school. I could've saved myself a lot of work and stress — not to mention all that money!"

Her mother frowned. "Do you really think they considered it a detriment when you were interviewing? I was just being sarcastic when I said that."

"Yes, I absolutely think they did! None of the banks' managers showed the least bit of interest in my having a business degree. I'm sure they see me as just someone demanding a higher salary and benefits package. That's the problem with living in such a small place as Elizabethtown. Don't get me wrong; I love it here. But there are only so many jobs, and everyone knows everything that happens here. I'm sure that's the real reason I'm not getting hired anywhere. And yes, I actually do think there's a conspiracy against me, led by that asshole Johnson!"

"I'm going to ignore your last comment as un-Christian-like," her mother said, in a disapproving tone. "Where else have you applied or at least looked into?"

"Well, after I realized I wasn't going to get a job offer from any of those three banks, I started looking for anything sort of related to banking, and then I started looking for anything even remotely related. So let's see . . . I looked at office manager positions at several companies in town and at several organizations at Fort Knox. I applied for three different financial

57

planning positions in Elizabethtown and didn't even get a call back from any of them. But in all honesty, my degree didn't prepare me to be a financial planner and I don't have any work experience in that area either. If you remember, my drawer rarely balanced when I worked as a teller," Dana said sheepishly. "So maybe that wouldn't have worked out, anyway. But I'm sure I would've done well at any of the office manager jobs. That's basically what I did when I worked for Jim Aldridge, and thinking back, that's probably where I did my best work and was my happiest." Dana's sudden gloomy expression matched the tone of her voice.

"You and Jim were quite a team, that's for sure." Her mother beamed at Dana. "I remember how much you enjoyed working for him. Well, it sounds like you're doing everything you can to find a job. Have you tried the county and city school systems?"

"Yes, I've applied for so many jobs I have to keep going back to my list to make sure I don't keep filling out the paperwork for the same jobs. After several months of looking, I started forgetting which jobs I'd applied to and which ones I was still thinking about. After I talked to Mr. Goldberg and realized I couldn't do much legally — other than get my job back, which I don't want — I decided I'd have a weekly goal of finding two significant prospects. So I've been getting up each day, I get Ryan and Liz dressed and fed, I drop Ryan at the Montessori school, and then come back to the house. I look through the employment section in the News Enterprise every day and the Radcliff Sentinel on Fridays, which doesn't change much from week to week, and then I make phone calls. I pick up Ryan after school, play with him and Liz until nap time, and then I make more phone calls while they're asleep. That, in a nutshell, has been my life for the past five months. And despite all the effort to find any sort of suitable job, I've got nothing to show for it!"

Her mother paused. "I ran into Roger Cunningham's wife at Kroger yesterday. She told me Roger, Wayne Higgins, and George Redmond had made you an offer months ago to start up an allotment business using their money and their clients, and you turned them down. Is that true?"

"Yes, it's true, but I didn't completely turn them down. I just said I wasn't ready to do it yet, and I wanted to think about it. I'm worried about possibly competing for business with Mr. Johnson and First Citizens. It might be better if I found a job doing something new. Also, you need a bank in order to do allotments so we'd be breaking new ground to find a bank to work with us. I hadn't decided if I wanted to take on those issues and the potential trouble from First Citizens. However, last week I was thinking if I don't find something else soon, I'll have to take them up on their offer. We can't live solely on Joey's police salary much longer."

"Memaw, where's Papaw?" Ryan had wandered into the kitchen, still clutching his new train in his hand.

"He's out in the backyard, Hon," Dana's mother said. "Can you go get him and tell him he actually needs to bring those squash into the house so I can cook them for dinner? I think maybe he'd just as soon admire them rather than eat them."

Ryan didn't answer. He just turned around and ran out the back door.

Dana's mother watched him go and then shook her head and laughed. "I can't believe it took him this long to go find his Papaw, as crazy as he is about him. Guess he really likes that new train!"

"He does love his Papaw," Dana murmured. "He's really a sweet boy. I forget how good he is until I see a bad kid. I try to remind myself how lucky I am in other ways. Both Ryan and Liz are normal, healthy kids, I have Joey, and I have lots of friends and family as support. Still, it's hard sometimes to not get depressed about my job situation. The whole thing seems so unfair to me. And it all happened so fast I didn't have time to prepare, that's all. I'm sorry about being such a grump, Mom." Dana looked down at the vinyl-tiled floor. She could feel the tears welling up, but she didn't want her mother to see her upset, and she was tired of being upset herself. She blinked back the tears and stood up. Forcing a smile, she looked down at her mother. "C'mon Mom, let's go drag Dad out of the backyard and finish up dinner. Joey's shift ends at six and I told him to come straight here and we'd have dinner ready."

"Sounds good to me. I'm not convinced you're as OK as you're trying to sound, but we'll go with it." She glanced at Dana. "Although, I'm keeping an eye on you."

"I would expect nothing less!" Dana bent down and hugged her mother tightly. Thank God I have you, she thought.

8

Four weeks later, November 1986

On the twenty-minute drive to Hardin Memorial Hospital in Elizabeth-town, Dana listened to the Bee Gees Greatest Hits album, her favorite eight-track tape, forcing herself to sing along in attempt to stay calm. It was only slightly working. She could feel the wetness in her armpits, her stomach felt jittery, and her throat was dry. She popped some chewing gum in her mouth and tried to focus on the supportive comments Marie had made earlier in the morning when she called to confirm they would meet at McDonalds right after Dana aced the interview.

Turning into the sprawling hospital parking lot, Dana pulled into an open spot and turned off the car. She sat there for a while, staring through the windshield at the other cars. After several long minutes, she pulled down the visor and peered into the small, rectangular mirror. Large brown eyes with golden flecks stared back. Her dark hair turned uniformly under her chin. Satisfied with her reflection, she shut the visor, got out of the car, and locked the door behind her.

The leaves had mostly fallen from the trees now, but the clear, deep-blue sky made up for any loss of beauty on the horizon. Dana inhaled the fragrant air of a sunny and crisp November morning. For the first time in many months, she felt alive. A job interview — and a promising one at that! It felt good to be wanted again, even if only for another interview. But this job appeared to be the most promising, and it was the job she was the most excited about since she began job-hunting. Most amazing of all, she'd made it to the final gauntlet.

With a smile on her face, Dana walked toward the hospital entrance at a brisk pace, smoothing her hand down her dark suit jacket and skirt. It seemed like years since she'd put on a suit. How she wanted to be wearing one again to a genuine job! She vowed to never again complain about having to get dressed in a suit and uncomfortable shoes to go to work.

This job had sounded perfect for her since the day Marie mentioned it nearly two months ago. Marie had been dating the Assistant Administrator of the hospital until she grew tired of him after her normal three dates. 'Men are like fish,' she would say; 'they begin to smell after three dates.' He, however, hadn't given up on dating her. During one of his perpetual phone calls to her, he lamented about having to find someone to fill a new public relations position for the hospital. Marie perked up enough to find out the details so she could pass them to Dana, who Marie predicted would be a 'smashing fit' for the job. Dana had little experience in public relations, but how hard could it be? She enjoyed talking to people, and everyone said she was friendly. She was exceptionally well-organized and willing to work hard, so she figured she had about as good of a chance as anyone.

Dana pulled open one of the large glass and chrome doors to the main entrance of the hospital and strolled into the lobby. The hospital's familiar aroma of disinfectant and rubbing alcohol greeted her. She took a deep breath, contemplating the peculiar scent. Maybe she'd become inured to the smell after a few months of working there.

She took the elevator to the second floor and turned down the hallway toward the administrative area. The Human Resources department was next to the Accounting office, which she knew only because her lifelong friend, Rhonda Phillips, worked there. Rhonda had asked Dana to come early so they could grab a cup of coffee before the interview, but Dana knew she'd be too nervous and distracted to engage in conversation.

Wandering down the hallway, Dana glanced from room to room until she passed the office Rhonda shared with her boss. She stopped in front of the doorway. Rhonda looked up from her typewriter. Her face broke into a wide grin and she gave Dana a thumbs-up. Dana smiled and continued down the hallway. Near the end, she spied an office nameplate that read 'JoAnn Townsend.' The door was open. A slight, middle-aged woman with a greyish-brown pixie haircut sat hunkered over the desk.

Dana knocked on the doorframe. "Mrs. Townsend? I'm Dana Smolenski. I'm here for a job interview." Her voice sounded timid and lacked the confident projection she intended.

JoAnn Townsend looked up from her papers and smiled. "Hello, Dana!" she said cheerfully. "Please, come in." She pushed back her chair and stood up. She was wearing a dark green pantsuit and white silk blouse with the collar flipped neatly over top of her suit jacket.

Dana approached Mrs. Townsend's desk and shook her outstretched hand. "It's nice to meet you, Mrs. Townsend."

"It's a pleasure to meet you, Dana. Please, have a seat right there." Mrs. Townsend gestured toward the chair closest to her desk. "I'll just push all this stuff aside and find your folder and we'll get started. Can I get you anything? Coffee? Water?"

"Oh, thank you; but no, I'm fine." Dana surveyed the small, but well-organized office. The grey, modular furniture and nearly bare walls gave the office a sterile look, which seemed appropriate for the particular venue. She sat down carefully and took out a small yellow pad and a pen from her purse before placing it on the floor. She looked up at Mrs. Townsend. "Thank you for the opportunity to interview for the Director of Public Relations job, Mrs. Townsend. I've read the job description, and the requirements and responsibilities page, and it sounds like a great fit for me. I believe I have adequate skills and training to do the job well, if given the opportunity." Dana took a deep breath and sat back into her chair, trying to relax. Maybe she'd said too much. She didn't want to come across as too eager, or worse — desperate.

Mrs. Townsend smiled as she continued shuffling through the folders on her desk before closing in on one slim, manila file. "Yes, from what I remember of your application, your job experience from your years at First Citizens would have provided you similar skills. Generally, we look for

63

someone to fill this position who has a four-year degree in public relations, marketing, or communications. However, we're considering your business degree to be a related field. We also look for demonstrated leadership and management, and it appears you have at least six years of experience there. And finally, we look for some type of experience in the health care field, whether it has been in public relations, sales, or something else, just so you're familiar with the particular language and nuances of health care. If I remember correctly, you don't have any experience working in health care; is that right?"

"No, ma'am; unfortunately that's correct." Dana leaned forward in her chair. "I haven't yet worked for a health care organization of any type, but I don't believe that would be a hindrance for me. I'm a quick learner, and my prior boss can confirm I'm a hard worker."

"I have no doubt about that," JoAnn Townsend said with a smile. "I've already spoken with Jim Fugitte and he couldn't sing your praises enough. Also, let me be clear. Experience in the health care field is not a requirement for this position; it's just something nice to have. It makes the break-in period a little easier for you . . . and to be frank, for us as well."

"I understand." Dana had to admit it made sense, and it was something she had concerns about as well. She knew little about health care. She barely knew anything about hospitals, except for her two experiences giving birth. Otherwise, she'd been the picture of health her whole life.

JoAnn Townsend settled back into her chair and flipped through the papers in the folder. She pulled out a single sheet with some typing on it and picked up her pen. "Some people tell me I'm an unorthodox interviewer. But I figure everyone who makes it through the wickets and to the interview probably is qualified, and I'm just here to determine who's the best fit for our hospital. So, a few of my questions may seem unrelated to the position but they do have a purpose."

"OK." Dana placed her hands in her lap and tried to relax.

"Tell me about your favorite day at your last job. You can take a few minutes to think about it."

Dana's mind jumped to one memorable meeting in Mr. Fugitte's office.

64

"I don't need to think about it. The memory of my favorite day is crystal clear. As you know, I worked for Jim Fugitte on a special project to start an allotment program where military service members can pay their insurance or car payments directly from their paychecks each month. Well, after working hard for nearly a year to recruit customers into the allotment program, Mr. Fugitte called my colleague and me into his office for a meeting that was not on the weekly schedule. I took one look at Mr. Fugitte's face and thought we'd done something wrong. Then, he gets a huge smile on his face and tells us the program is making more money for the bank than any of the other special initiatives, that he's very proud of us, and all the hard work we did is paying off."

"And why was that your favorite day?" JoAnn Townsend's eyes fixed on Dana's face.

Dana responded thoughtfully. "It was an ambitious program we weren't sure would even pay for itself in terms of time and capital investment. It involved a lot of creative thinking on our part, and the program allowed me to use the marketing skills I'd learned in my business classes. I remember feeling so good about what we'd accomplished, it made all those years of working during the day and going to school at night seem worthwhile. It was a great day, one of the best in my work life." She smiled at the memory, then her eyes took on a vacant stare.

"The feeling of accomplishment of a job well done, is that what you mean?" JoAnn Townsend put down her pen and sat back in her chair.

Dana pondered the question. "Yes, working hard for something I wanted. But maybe more important was to succeed at a project that was dependent on how well I did in sales. In reality, that was the one thing that was going to make or break the project — how well I did convincing people they would benefit from what we could provide them, which was the assurance we would make their payments on time, month after month, even if they deployed elsewhere in the world. It was a great feeling to succeed at this new project for the bank, and to provide military personnel a service to make their lives a little easier."

"My next question normally would be to ask you about your worst day at a job. But since I talked to Jim Fugitte, I think I can guess what was your worst day," JoAnn Townsend said, in a sympathetic tone. "I've been working a long time and I'm pretty sure it would have been mine."

"Yes," Dana mumbled. She looked down for a moment and then directly at JoAnn Townsend. "Mrs. Townsend, I'm not sure how Jim Fugitte relayed the story to you, but I want you to know I feel I did nothing wrong — certainly nothing to deserve how Bernard Johnson treated me. I believe he had a personal vendetta against me, maybe because I was pregnant when he arrived at the bank, or maybe because I'm a woman. But he never gave me a chance to explain the allotment program to him, or tell him how successful the program had become, and what that success had done for the bank's bottom line."

"I got a good run-down on the situation from Jim Fugitte. No need to ruin your day by having to relive it. Your termination at the bank will not be a consideration in our decision to hire you or not."

Dana's face softened. "Thank you. I appreciate that very much."

"Dana, I'm sure you studied the Requirements and Responsibilities page attached to the job application. If hired for this job, tell me what type of things you might suggest that could improve the hospital experience or its public relations."

"I've thought a lot about what I could bring to the table that would be unique." Dana was thrilled she was asked this question because she felt she did have a talent for seeing things differently and taking on new projects. She certainly didn't mind new challenges, as did some employees. "I've had various bosses tell me I get along well with the customers and I need to be out front, working with them every day. I have significant experience researching new business areas and trends, and creating business plans with built-in performance measures. I've drafted many documents aimed at the bank's employees and customers that would be like the press releases drafted by your Public Relations department."

Dana quickly continued before Mrs. Townsend could inject another question. "One of my primary responsibilities was to improve management and employee relations, and we did this by several means. We had an open door policy, whereby anyone could request a meeting with Mr. Fugitte and within 24 hours the meeting would take place. We had Town Hall sessions where Mr. Fugitte would get everyone together to update us on the status of the bank's various departments, maybe tell us about people who we'd hired or promoted recently, any new programs or expansions at the bank. It was a way to communicate better and provide transparency between management and the employees. If you hired me as your Director of Public Relations, I would hope to implement similar ideas here at the hospital." Dana was leaning forward in her chair now. "One of my favorite management programs allowed the bank's employees 30 minutes each week to just sit and think about how to do their jobs better. For example, an employee could suggest an organization change, or a new or improved service, or they could request to demo an idea. Some great ideas came out of this program."

JoAnn Townsend laid down her pen and looked up. "Yes, I suspect so, and those types of programs are good confidence-builders for the employees. Now, tell me a little about yourself. What makes Dana tick?"

Dana had prepared for this question too. "I'm a definite self-starter. I like to research new ways to do business and then try them out. I like to use spreadsheets to track my own tasks and performance, and the tasks of employees I'm responsible for training and supervising. I'm a big proponent of lists and I have them everywhere — on my desk, pinned to bulletin boards, and all over my house. I even keep a notepad and pen on the night table in my bedroom so when I wake up in the middle of the night thinking about something I don't want to forget, I write it down and then I can go back to sleep. Friends tease me about my lists, but I've found they keep me on top of things."

"I think making lists is an absolute necessity and I do the same thing myself." JoAnn Townsend leaned closer. "But I have to say, I never thought of putting a notepad and pen next to my bed so I don't forget something by morning. I'm going to try that myself!"

Dana felt the interview was going surprisingly well, so she began talking freely. "I don't want to get up each day and just go to a job; I want to get up and continue a career. I love working with people, helping to make their lives easier, and working at the management level where I'm able to use the leadership skills I learned at Embry Riddle."

"From what Jim Fugitte told me, Dana, I imagine you're an excellent manager. Those are characteristics we certainly want in our Director of Public Relations. Since you have no experience in the medical field and only a little in public relations, I want to ask a couple specific questions so I'm able to note those things you do have experience with so you'll get credit for them during our assessment of the candidates."

"Sure." Dana sat back in her chair.

"You said you have no experience writing press releases, correct?" JoAnn Townsend had taken a page out of Dana's file and was busy writing.

"No, ma'am. I've never written a press release, but I have written documents and status reports that might be similar. I do have experience writing professional-level reports, and Mr. Fugitte relied on me to do those in my department."

"Do you have any experience working with the media?" JoAnn Townsend glanced up at Dana.

"No, I'm afraid not. That was Mr. Fugitte's role." Dana tried to smile, but her lack of experience in this area had worried her.

"How about speaking experience?" JoAnn Townsend continued through her checklist. "Did you ever represent the bank at public events and have to speak publicly on the bank's behalf?"

"I'm afraid I have to say no again. Mr. Fugitte represented the bank himself, or someone from the corporate level would attend and speak. I have little experience with public speaking, other than the classes I had in high school and college." Dana sat up in her chair and uncrossed her legs. She was trying to keep her responses upbeat, yet honest.

"Yes, I understand how that works." JoAnn Townsend's facial expression did not give any clues as to what she was thinking. "You said you have some marketing background and some experience there?"

Dana nodded. "I took several college classes in marketing and I did some of that at the bank, yes." Finally she could say something positive.

She hoped Mrs. Townsend didn't ask her to expound on her experience because other than the marketing she did for the allotment program, her experience was thin.

Mrs. Townsend closed the folder in front of her. She laced her fingers together and looked up at Dana. "That's the end of the questions, Dana, unless you have some for me."

"No, the job description is pretty detailed, and I believe I understand what's involved."

Mrs. Townsend scooted back in her chair and sat upright. "Then I want to thank you for coming in today. The hiring committee will probably make a decision early next week, and someone from Human Resources will let you know shortly thereafter. It was very nice to meet you and I wish you the best of luck." She smiled warmly and stood up, extending her hand toward Dana.

Dana stood up and shook her hand. "Thank you for considering me for the job, Mrs. Townsend. I appreciate your time and I look forward to hearing from someone once the selection process is over." She picked up her purse and quickly left the office.

Once Dana was safely down the hall and around the corner, to her own surprise, she blinked back tears. She felt such relief! Until this moment, she hadn't realized how stressed she'd been about the interview. She really needed this job! She'd spent a great deal of time researching the job requirements and truly believed she was a good fit for the job. It was going to be terribly hard to wait an entire week to find out if she got it.

Making her way down the stairs and toward the main foyer of the hospital, she thought of Marie and was glad they'd made plans to meet. Dana wanted to review every last detail of the interview with her. She flung open the hospital's heavy main door and stepped outside. The deep blue sky and crisp November air quickly brightened her mood. Dana breathed in the fresh scent and smiled. Today her luck just might have turned around. She was due some good luck. After all the failures of the past six months, that much was for sure.

69

9

Two weeks later, late November

The rain had stopped, but there was a light tapping sound as water dripped steadily from the roof onto the grill below. Dana sat eerily still at the kitchen table, listening intently to the rhythmic pitter-patter. Unable to pull her eyes away from the brownish-gold tiles on the kitchen floor, she recalled the day she and Joey moved into this house, their first actual home.

The house was a real fixer-upper, as Joey called it. Mr. and Mrs. Holland had owned it for over twenty-five years. Then she passed away from cancer, and nearly six months later he died as well, even though he hadn't been ill. At the time, Dana wondered if there really was something to the notion of true love, and poor Mr. Holland simply couldn't live without his beloved wife. She liked thinking that was the case, anyway. Once Mrs. Holland was diagnosed with cancer, Mr. Holland seemed to give up on everything, including taking care of the house. When it finally went for sale three years later, it was in an unfortunate state of disrepair. But Dana thought the house was perfect and convinced Joey they could put it back together with all the love it had received from the Hollands. She and Joey spent many hours together repairing, rebuilding, painting, and cleaning. It was a hard and long project, but it brought them closer. The house was perfect, Dana thought, as she stared at the gold tiles. She desperately hoped they weren't about to lose it.

The phone rang, startling Dana. She jumped up and reached over the table to grab the receiver off the wall. "Hello?"

"Dana, darling! It's Marie."

"Marie!" Dana nearly shouted into the phone, her heart still racing. "How nice to hear from you. Is everything OK?"

"Of course everything's all right with me. How are you and why are you shouting at me?" Marie's British accent was in full throttle.

"Oh, I'm sorry!" Dana pulled the phone's cord across the table so she could sit back down. "I was sitting here thinking about something and the phone scared the wits out of me."

"And that is precisely why you needn't bother yourself thinking so much and burning up scarce brain cells. It does no good at all and simply wastes valuable time. Now, have you rung the lady from the hospital who interviewed you two entire weeks ago; and if your answer is no, why not?"

When Marie's voice sounded this resolute, Dana knew she didn't stand a chance arguing with her. She hadn't won a verbal battle with Marie in a long time, and well, if she really thought about it, maybe ever. There was something about Marie's constitution and her charm that made you roll over and do whatever she wanted — usually without putting up much of an argument. Dana wished she had more of that herself. "No, I haven't called her yet, but I was about to when you called," she lied.

"Really?" Marie sounded unconvinced. "Then shall I ring off and ring back in fifteen?"

Good Lord, Dana said to herself, rolling her eyes and sighing heavily. "OK, OK, I'll call her right now. You can call me back shortly and I'll tell you what she said. But since I've not heard from her, don't get your hopes up because I certainly haven't at this point."

"Right then! Good luck and we'll chat in a bit!" Marie hung up the phone without saying goodbye.

Dana reached over the table and hung the phone back on the wall. She sat there for a moment without moving. Well, shit! I'll have to call Mrs. Townsend right now or I'll never hear the end of it from Marie. God, she can be so annoying sometimes, Dana fumed. She went to find her purse and retrieve Mrs. Townsend's phone number.

71

Dialing the numbers slowly, Dana contemplated the predictably brief conversation. "Did I get the job?" Mrs. Townsend's doubtless answer, "No, I'm sorry." Should take less than a minute to finish the call and know the truth. Dana believed in the adage of ignorance being bliss. She could go many more weeks without knowing and be perfectly content.

"This is JoAnn Townsend, may I help you?" The voice was firm but pleasant-sounding.

"Good afternoon, Mrs. Townsend," Dana said nervously. "This is Dana Smolenski. I interviewed for the Director of Public Relations position two weeks ago, and I haven't heard if I got the job. I hate to bother you, but I'd really like to know if I'm still in the running. Do you happen to know?" Her heart was racing and she broke into a sweat. She didn't really want to know the answer; that was a lie! She wanted to keep believing she was going to get the job, and they simply hadn't called her yet. What on earth was she thinking by calling and stirring the pot?

"Oh, Dana! I'm so sorry. I thought someone from Human Resources called you a week and a half ago. Then I'm sorry to tell you, no, you didn't get the job. You were in very close contention, but the job went to a woman who had quite a few years of public relations experience in the health environment. I want you to know you were our second choice, though. You gave a great interview and I also believe you would've been a good fit for the position. I hope you find something you like at another place soon. I feel you would be a good hire for many diverse companies." Mrs. Townsend's voice sounded sympathetic and sincere.

Choking back tears, Dana swallowed hard. "Thank you for the kind words, Mrs. Townsend. I appreciate it more than you know. Sorry to have bothered you."

"It was no bother, Dana. Someone should've called you a while ago, and I apologize for the failure in communication. I wish you the best. Goodbye." JoAnn Townsend hung up the phone.

Dana sat very still, holding the phone. She couldn't pretend any longer she was waiting to hear from this hospital about the job. She knew it was not good she'd heard nothing, but wanted to believe no news was good news. Unfortunately, that rarely seemed the case in her life. Her eyes filled with tears and soon they were running down her cheeks. Hopeless, that's how her life felt — hopeless. She had no pending job interviews, no prospects from the employment section of the newspapers, and nothing to give her hope. She thought about calling Joey to let him know the bad news, but the thought made her stomach upset. He would just say it was OK, something would come along soon, and she didn't want to hear it again. She hung up the phone and waited for Marie's inevitable call. It was one of the few times she didn't want to talk — even to Marie.

Ten minutes later, the phone rang. Dana slowly reached across the table and picked it up. "Hello?"

"Oh my God, did they hire someone else?" Marie's tone sounded more like a demand than a question.

"Yes, of course they did," Dana said indignantly, "because that's how my luck has been this whole year. And why should they call and let me know? It's only the decent thing to do, for God's sake! They just don't give a damn! No one seems to do the right thing anymore — no business, anyway. They all treat you like crap!" Soon, Dana was sobbing into the phone.

"Christ, Dana! I'm so bloody sorry! I wish there was something I could do. I would love to fix this whole thing for you. Of everyone I know, you're the one who least deserves this sort of treatment. You're the hardest working, most honest — too honest, I believe — conscientious, person I know. I really thought you had a shot at this one. I know you would've been absolutely marvelous in public relations!"

"I thought I had a shot at this one too," Dana replied through her sobs. "According to Mrs. Townsend, I was the runner-up, which doesn't mean a thing except I didn't get the job."

"Well then, what can I do to cheer you up?" Marie's voice shifted to a jovial, optimistic tone.

"Nothing! There's nothing you can do, Marie. I'll just have to start all over again looking for a job." Dana's crying spree receded as her thoughts turned to what she would do now.

"Look, I know you don't want to hear it, but you do have a rather grand offer from those three business owners to start up another allotment company with them. I can understand why you don't want to do it until you have no other choice, but it appears that time is now. Frankly, I cannot understand what you've been so concerned about. If I were you, I would bloody well jump at the opportunity to stick it to Johnson and the whole bloody bank! You started that business, they've done nothing with it since you left, and the clients were all yours, anyway. So why are you still fannying about?" Marie was nearly shouting into the phone.

Dana was silent for a while, then clenched her teeth and stared straight ahead, realizing the truth in Marie's words. "As usual, you're right, Marie. I have no choice now; I need to get back to work. I've wasted enough time looking for a job. I'll put together some talking points and give Roger Cunningham a call."

"Bloody hell, that took long enough! I'm rather looking forward to having the old Dana back. I much prefer her spunk to this wimpy thing that has invaded her body the past nine months!" Marie's tone had an air of satisfaction.

"I agree whole-heartedly," Dana said, slowly and determinedly. She sat up in her chair and was no longer crying. "It's past time I moved on."

10

December 1986

The conference room in Wayne Higgins' office was not what Dana had expected. It looked more like the conference room of a high-powered attorney in Manhattan, rather than one practicing in small town Kentucky. The broad sweeping design of the dark grey and white custom-made drapes mimicked the border on the large, plush rug that covered much of the floor. The walls were a lighter shade of grey and the crown molding was stained a rich, dark cherry color. Paintings of Kentucky racehorses decorated all four walls, but the large oval table in the center of the room was the crown jewel. The top of the table was made of thick cherry wood with smooth, rounded edges that gleamed in the sunlight. It must have cost a fortune, Dana thought.

Although Roger Cunningham had arranged the meeting with Dana and the three men, he decided they should meet at Wayne's office because there was less likelihood of constant interruption. When Dana arrived at 9:00 AM sharp, it was immediately obvious the men had been there a while. They sat huddled together at the far end of the table and at first didn't notice her standing in the doorway. Roger was wearing his usual suit and tie. Both his light brown hair and mustache were a bit too long for Dana's taste. She thought it made him look shaggy, especially when wearing a suit. She could see the back of a shiny, nearly bald head and knew it belonged to Wayne Higgins. The beige shirt he was wearing was untucked from his dark brown pants and hung over his belt, which was typical for Wayne. Usually his belly hung far over his belt too, but Dana couldn't see his front side. Wayne Higgins owned a mortgage and insurance company in Elizabethtown, and in the past, she'd wondered how he'd secured so many clients when he resembled an unmade bed most of the time. Dana looked over to the third man in the room, George Redmond, the polar opposite of Wayne in nearly every physical aspect. George was tall, black-haired, and handsome. His short-cropped locks were parted on the side and combed meticulously across his forehead. George had been a larger-than-life basketball star in high school and he still maintained an athletic build. Although he rarely wore anything other than dark silk pants and a name-brand polo shirt, he was by far the most elegant, best-dressed man in the room. George Redmond owned the Pontiac and Buick dealership in Elizabethtown and a Honda motorcycle dealership between Elizabethtown and Radcliff, the small town that bordered Fort Knox. With his smooth-talking manner, good looks, and charm, Dana imagined he sold a lot of wheels.

Roger Cunningham noticed Dana first and stood up to greet her. She walked around the table and shook hands with each of the three men, then chose a seat directly across the table from Roger. Her stomach was a little unsettled, but at this point in her life, she was seeking solace. She hated resigning herself to a job she didn't really want, but it was a tremendous relief that soon she might no longer be unemployed and worrying about her finances.

"Dana, we were just saying how fortuitous it was you called when you did because the timing of this thing seems to work well for all three of us." Roger sat perched on the edge of his chair, leaning over the table towards Dana. He spoke in his typical rapid-fire mode, with his glasses resting low on his nose. "Starting things up the first of the calendar year makes our accountants happy, and more importantly, it's usually a slow time of the year for all our businesses."

"Whatever works for the three of you will be fine with me," Dana said. "It really doesn't matter on my end."

Roger stood up and traipsed to the far end of the table. Dana had noticed years ago he walked with a limp, and only later learned he'd lost part of his foot after stepping on a booby trap in Vietnam during the war. His limp was apparent now, as he tried to pace back and forth in a small space. Roger Cunningham was a tall, slender man with a penchant for wearing dark suits, white shirts, and plaid ties. Considering his anxious personality, Dana suspected he preferred to walk while talking.

"Dana, I know you and I talked a little on the phone about how this might work, but for the sake of Wayne and George, and my own edification, why don't you run through how you plan to get started and how this might play out. Then let's talk about how much start-up money you think you'll need. I'm sure after that, George, Wayne, or I will have some questions."

"Sure, Mr. Cunningham." Dana pulled out her notebook and pen and flipped to the page where she'd written an outline and some notes. "I put together a simple marketing plan and a timeline, and since none of you have banking experience, I'll explain in basic terms how the concept would work." She looked up and smiled at the three men.

George leaned back in his chair and laughed. "You'd better be real basic for us, Dana! We all know what people think about car salesmen and insurance brokers!"

"Speak for yourself, George!" Wayne said. "I consider myself a golfer who just sells insurance products on the side."

"Ah, yes, of course, Wayne. I like that explanation. Ditto for me." George nodded his head. "That's why I keep my clubs behind the door of my office and my golf shoes in the trunk of my car. I can make a clean getaway whenever the opportunity presents itself."

Dana laughed uneasily, but recalled hearing George actually did keep his clubs in his office and you could find him on the golf course most warm afternoons. She looked up at Roger, who wore a slight smile but continued to pace. "No offense to anyone," Dana said, trying to smile while glancing down at her notes. "You all know what I mean, so I'll go ahead and explain the concept."

"Yes, please proceed, Dana," Roger said, pulling out his chair and sitting back down at the table.

"Here's a rough plan for the first part of the year," Dana said, handing each man a one-page paper with her approximate timeline, a few typed notes, and a cost estimate. "I'll begin by looking for a bank that's willing to work with us. The bank's responsibilities will include accepting the money that's taken out of the military service member's paycheck, maintaining an accounting of the money, and then sending the money to the business holding the note. The bank will charge us a fee, I'm sure, but they'll also make money on the float, which is the time between the bank's receipt of the money from the military and their payment to the business. Are you with me so far?" Dana looked up and studied each face for signs of confusion. She saw three heads nodding in affirmation, and so continued. "Once we have the bank identified, I'll take each of your businesses one at a time and contact those individuals with current loans, and explain how they can make a payment automatically by setting up a monthly allotment. I'll describe the benefit of automatic payments, how they can travel or deploy without worrying about their payment being forgotten. I'll demonstrate how the allotment process works technically, because some individuals want to know the actual details of when and how their money is moving from one place to another. Finally, I'll explain how they'll get confirmation of the money transfer. This is Phase One, or the first section of the timeline you have in front of you." Dana looked up again to ensure the men were following along with her chart.

"Just doing our current customers should keep you busy for a long time, Dana," Wayne said, studying Dana's face. "Are you planning to do this by yourself?"

"Initially, yes. This is what I did every day for quite a few years, Mr. Higgins. This part I know inside and out, and I've got my sales pitch down to a fine art. It's time-consuming, though. As I'm working on this part with all of your respective businesses, I'll also be doing this same procedure with new clients as you get them. I'm not expecting too many new clients the first three months, and possibly into the fourth month before the weather improves. Come Springtime, business will ramp up and that's when I'll probably need to bring in someone to assist. I would envision that person starting as a part-time employee, then later on as full-time." Dana looked up to see Wayne and Roger studying her chart. George was hammering away on his calculator.

Roger looked up at Dana. "OK, just to make sure I understand your Phase One cost estimate, from January to around April, our costs will be just your salary and maintaining an office for you. Somewhere around May, costs will increase to around 1.5 man-years plus the office operational costs. Is that correct?"

"Yes, but I only have preliminary data on your businesses right now. That could change once I get a closer look at your books. But that's probably a good estimate." Dana leaned back in her chair and gave the men a chance to digest her Phase One estimates. "Should I move on?"

"Yes, go ahead," Roger said, without looking at the other two.

"Phase Two would start only after I've contacted — at least once — all the military members who have loans, and I feel I have a good handle on getting as many of them as possible into allotments." Dana pulled out her notes and placed them on the table. "For Phase Two, my concentration of effort would move toward a marketing approach, where I'll contact businesses similar to yours, and other businesses where debt servicing would be useful — such as electronics, TV sales, and maybe home mortgages — and bid for servicing their allotments. This might entail some travel on my part to other military installations, because eventually we'll want to branch out beyond our customer base here at Fort Knox, which is limited."

"We'll have to talk about the travel part when the time comes," Roger said.

Dana suspected he would be the one to balk on funding any travel for her. Roger Cunningham was long known for his stinginess. Often he claimed he didn't get to where he was today by giving cars away. Dana decided not to comment on his statement and risk irritating him or scaring him off. Right now she just wanted the three men to give her the OK to start work.

George had been fairly silent since she'd started talking. He was making notations on his paper and banging away on his calculator. Finally, he placed his pen on the table and looked up. "Dana, are you finished with your spiel?"

"Just about," Dana said. "To summarize, I would only add that once Phase Two starts, we pretty much stay in a sustained marketing mode. We simply try to expand our service to new market areas. Maybe as the technology gets cheaper and more universally accepted, we expand outside military installations to the general population. I mean, technically, there's no reason we couldn't set up allotments for anyone with a paycheck, right? It's just that right now the military and maybe a handful of other small businesses are the only ones willing to pull the money from their employees' pay before cutting paychecks. However, as allotments become more accepted as a reliable way to pay bills, our business should pick up in other markets as well. I hope we grow the business in many directions." She wanted to give them something positive and exciting to think about after she walked out of the room. She certainly wasn't going to tell them her major concern — because she was fired from her job at the bank, no one would give her *any* business. People might think she'd done something wrong at the bank, and they wouldn't trust her. Maybe Mr. Johnson had told people she'd messed up the allotments so badly the bank failed their audit and lost thousands of dollars. So maybe she wouldn't secure *any* clients.

"It sounds like a good plan to me," George announced suddenly. "I'm in."

"Me too," Wayne said, just as abruptly. "I decided last night if I liked what I heard today, it would be worth my investing just to get my own clients on an allotment basis. Anyone else you can sign up, Dana, is gravy."

Roger was slower to respond. Dana watched as he first looked at George and then over at Wayne.

After a noticeably long pause, George raised his eyebrows at Roger. "Well, Roger? What do you say?"

"I think we need to discuss financing this operation first — you know, come to agreement on what each of us is going to put in. I'd feel more comfortable discussing this before we agree to move forward." Roger was living up to his reputation as the cautious, conservative businessman. "Dana, do you want to go into a little more detail about your estimate of start-up costs?"

"Sure," Dana said. "If you look at the bottom of the paper I handed each of you, there are some bullets that describe what I see as initial start-up costs, as well as what I call maintenance costs for our business. Start-up costs would include my salary and expenses, funding for office space, basic office expenses, office cleaning, that sort of thing. This would be the cost estimate for Phase One. Maintenance funding for Phase Two would include my salary and expenses, and that of a part-time — and later on, full-time — employee, and office operating expenses. You'll note I provided some very rough estimates for both phases. However, after we have a couple months under our belt, I'd be able to provide you better estimates for Phase One and Phase Two based on actuals."

"What are you thinking in terms of office space, Dana?" George was rubbing his chin and looking over the top of his reading glasses at Dana. "Because I'm wondering if one of us might have a spare office that would be suitable. That'd save us some start-up money."

"That's a great idea, George." Roger barely let George finish his sentence. "I'm sure I can find a spare cubicle in either of my auto dealerships, and both are close to Fort Knox, which might be convenient."

Dana thought that sounded like a terrible idea. She couldn't imagine a situation much worse than trying to talk on the phone in a busy, noisy dealership. Since she'd be spending most of her time in an office on the phone, she needed a presentable, quiet place to work.

George was studying Dana's face. "Wayne, of the three of us, your office probably is the most suitable for Dana to meet with clients and spend endless hours on the phone. Your building actually *looks* like a respectable office building. I don't know, call me crazy, but I suspect Dana would prefer working in an ordinary office with a window and a door, rather than an open cubicle in one of our dealerships," he added, with a sly grin.

"Sure, George, I can find something." Wayne nodded his head. "I've got a couple spare offices we use for filing rooms. It may take a few days to have one of them cleared out, but either of them would work fine for our purposes, I'm sure."

81

"Dana, is that OK with you?" George asked.

"Yes, that's fine." Dana nodded and returned the smile.

"OK, so that's settled. Now, how about your salary requirements, Dana?" George appeared eager to get things wrapped up. "That seems to be the last big issue we need to agree on today."

Dana wondered if George had another meeting to attend, or a tee time, since the temperature predicted for this late December day was an unseasonable 62 degrees. "As I told Mr. Cunningham previously, at the time I left the bank, my annual salary was $26,000, plus the incentive bonus. As I'm sure you know, once Mr. Johnson took over as bank president, no one received a bonus. I worked as part of a two-person team at the bank. Here, I'll be working on my own, at least initially. I'm asking for $28,000 for the first year, and if we do as well as I'm expecting, I'm asking that my salary increase to $30,000 for the second year." Dana's heart raced halfway through her answer, but she was determined to not back down from the salary she wanted. Marie had said Dana was worth twice that amount, but it was best to get the job first and then after a year let her proven value speak for itself. Marie also said if Dana were a man, she'd have no trouble whatsoever asking for what she wanted; it was only women who had a deflated sense of self-worth. Dana whole-heartedly agreed, but right now she didn't want to sound self-important.

"We had a pretty good idea of your salary at the bank, Dana, and already had discussed something similar in terms of an annual increase. So I think we're all in agreement regarding salary." George appeared to have taken control of the meeting about fifteen minutes ago. "We added one incentive feature I personally think you'll like. If you get the business to 3,000 transactions a month by the end of one year, we'll gift you 10% of the company stock, so you'll have an equity investment in the business. We're hoping the 3,000 transactions will equate to around 1,000 transactions from each of our businesses, which will result in enormous savings in time and effort on our part collecting payments that are past due. So, what do you say, Dana?" George put down his pen and pushed back in his chair.

Dana's stomach leaped into her throat. "Yes, that would work for me," she said, not wanting to sound too eager. She cleared her throat. "I'm a believer in incentive-based pay, so I'm happy for the opportunity to work under that basis, but also to have an annual salary to rely on."

"Great!" George slapped his hand on the table. "Roger . . . Wayne . . . I'm assuming you agree since this is what we discussed last week. Are you both OK with everything we've talked about and agreed to this morning? Any further issues needing decisions?"

"There's nothing I've heard today that's a show-stopper for me, George. This is pretty much what we discussed." Wayne reached up and rubbed his hand back and forth across his bald head. "Like I said, it'll take me a few days to get an office cleared out and set up. Let's see . . . today's the 22nd. There should be no problem getting things set up so Dana can start work on Monday, the 5th of January. Dana, if you want, you can come in on Friday the 2nd and get yourself set up and oriented. See if you need anything else before you actually start on the 5th. Whatever you want to do."

"Thank you, Mr. Higgins. I really don't need much, just basic office supplies, a phone, and access to a fax machine." Dana was getting more excited with each word. Finally, she was going to be among the ranks of the employed again!

Roger stood up and was pacing again. "I agree with everything we discussed here today too. I ran some figures last night based on George, Wayne, and my discussion last week, and I think we can start by putting in $100,000 — one-third from each of us. Dana, over the next week or so, why don't you take on one task — look for a bank that'll work with us on the allotments and we'll deposit our operating money there too. Seems to make the most sense if we use the same bank for both. Maybe that'll be incentive for the bank to accept the allotments for us at minimal, or maybe even no cost. We'll charge the two dollars per allotment transaction, as the going rate seems to be, and maybe over time that'll cover all the operating expenses. Eventually, I suppose we'll make money off this deal. Anyone have any further questions? If there's something you don't like, speak up now."

"Roger, did you come up with a name for the business?" Wayne had stood up and was tucking in his shirt.

"Unless someone has a better idea, how about Military Services Incorporated? We can call it MSI," Roger said proudly, as if he were naming a baby.

"Sounds fine to me, Roger. What do you think, George?" Wayne shuffled his papers into a pile and scooped them up.

"Sure, I hadn't thought about a name, but that's as good as anything I would come up with."

"Military Services Incorporated — MSI it is! OK then, here's to a long and hopefully prosperous relationship." Roger reached across the table and shook hands with Dana, and then with George and Wayne.

Dana could hardly contain her glee. Grinning broadly, she shook hands with the other two men, and thanked them for their trust and belief in her work. Quickly gathering her belongings before someone changed their mind, she made her way out of the conference room, down the hallway, and out the front door. The sunny Winter day greeted her warmly, and she smiled as she walked confidently to her car. Finally, a glimmer of hope on her horizon.

11

June 1987

A warm breeze was spilling in through her office's half-opened window as Dana peered through the glass and into the parking lot in search of Marie's dark blue Audi. She inhaled the fragrant air of Summer wafting by and then exhaled slowly. Her eyes fixed on the newly planted red and white impatiens and the freshly trimmed holly bushes that surrounded the flagpole near the front of the building. Only six months had passed since that nerve-wracking meeting in Wayne Higgins' conference room — the same conference room she now used several times a week to meet with prospective clients. But it seemed like much longer, given all that had happened.

Marie was 20 minutes late and that was not typical for her. Dana chuckled when she thought about Marie's intolerant behavior toward lateness. If her date showed up over 15 minutes past the allotted pickup time, she would turn off the lights in her apartment and pretend she wasn't home. And one thing was certain — that would be the last time his feet would grace her doorstep.

Surmising something must have occurred to cause Marie's delay, Dana turned back around in her chair, picked up her can of Tab, and glanced around her office. Neatly stacked piles of papers and files were sitting side by side across the top of her oak credenza. The credenza itself was full of files. She'd created a file for nearly every man and woman who had a loan with the various businesses belonging to Roger Cunningham, Wayne Higgins, and George Redmond. A few people had transferred to other military facilities, and she didn't have their forwarding addresses yet, but otherwise, Dana had contacted them all. She felt good about the progress she'd made.

Most notable, however, she was feeling like the old Dana again — well, almost. She was working long hours each weekday and often worked part of Saturday and Sunday. Joey hadn't complained yet. He knew how happy she was simply to have a job again. But she figured it was only a matter of time before he reminded her she did have two children who missed having their Mom at home. And truthfully, she missed being with them too. Being home most of the time had been the only part of unemployment that she'd enjoyed, and it was particularly nice while Liz was a newborn. Dana reflected on her tiny, innocent face when she dropped her at daycare this morning. Liz was clinging to her mom's neck when Dana bent over to place her on the blanket with the other babies. Dana looked at Liz's big round eyes and her flushed cheeks, and it was all she could do to walk away before the tears rolled down her face.

"Bloody hell! You've got quite the place here, Luv! If I'd have known it was this nice, I'd have come for tea sooner!" Marie's excitement punctuated the silence in the office.

Dana jumped in her chair, dropping the can of Tab onto her desk. Soda shot out of the top of the can about a foot high and landed all over a large spreadsheet on the desk.

"Good God, so sorry! I should've made a less-grand entrance." Marie yanked several tissues from a box on Dana's desk and dabbed at the wet spots on the spreadsheet. "But I'll bet you can't do that again — drop the soda can onto your desk and not have it turn over and spill."

It took Dana several moments to regain her senses. "Marie! I was getting really worried. You're never late. Oh, man, my spreadsheet! Don't let anything happen to it! This is the only place I keep all my updates."

"Not to worry, Darling, all cleaned up! You barely notice a thing." Marie was blowing on the damp spots.

Dana took the spreadsheet from Marie, looked over it quickly, and set it back on the desk. "It's fine; don't worry about it. Did you have a problem getting here? I really was getting worried."

"No problem getting here; something much more disturbing. I've been busting a gut to tell you, but I didn't want to ring you from the bank due to big ears Martin round the bend from my desk. By the by, I love that shirt and those trousers you're wearing." Marie flopped into the black leather chair alongside Dana and tossed her purse onto the desk. She folded her hands neatly over her lap and looked around the office.

"Oh . . . thanks Marie," Dana said, glancing down at her dark blue pants and still having trouble regaining her wits. "What did you say about disturbing news?"

Marie sat up abruptly in her chair and leaned forward. "That wanker Johnson gave Gloria the boot this morning! Can you believe it? She has been at the bank for 12 years! Rumor has it she wasn't as outgoing and helpful to the customers as she's supposed to be, which is total bollocks! She was absolutely destroyed. She came out of Johnson's office weeping, but you could tell she was mad as hell too. That man needs to flush his head down the loo — his entire body, actually. Except it would be a waste of good water. Gloria is one of the few people who knows how to do nearly every task at the bank. He's going to realize that soon enough and miss her . . . hell, I'm going to miss her!"

Marie was talking so fast Dana was having trouble keeping up. "Johnson fired Gloria? She has been there forever! I can't believe it! She must be devastated. I know exactly how she feels too . . ." Dana's gaze fell to the desk and she stared at the spreadsheet.

"Anyway, with the shakeup this morning — and as you can guess — all the gossip and upheaval, it was a bit of a struggle to get away." Marie pushed up the sleeves of her cream-colored silk blouse, and then adroitly adjusted her brown and tan striped skirt underneath her legs. "I've half a mind to quit as well, but then I remind myself of my excellent situation."

"As you should," Dana said, rolling her eyes. "I wouldn't do anything to jeopardize that, if I were you. It appears no one's job is safe. I'd be extremely careful not to give that jerk a reason to take some other depraved action."

Frowning, Marie nodded her head slowly. "I absolutely agree. And it may be just a coincidence, but I've noticed a pattern here. So far, only women have been let go — not a single chap. I'm getting the feeling Johnson might not enjoy working with women. Or, maybe he's gay. But dodgy, don't you think?"

"Yes, I do," Dana said thoughtfully, staring at Marie. "Suspicious for sure. I wouldn't put it past him to try to fire all the women. He's such a slimy creep with a 'holier than thou' attitude." Dana took a deep breath and leaned back in her chair. "Keep me posted anyway. Poor Gloria. I feel awful for her."

"So, moving right along to a cheerier subject; I totally *adore* your office! This entire place is fabulous! Why didn't you tell me you were living like the Queen here? The only thing that would make it more brilliant is if you told me they served bangers and mash across the street!"

Laughing, Dana surveyed the office. "Yes, it's a great office. Mr. Higgins outdid himself when he said he'd find me something suitable for conducting business. Hard to believe they used this space as a file room! Can you imagine all this beautiful crown molding and lush carpeting wasted on file cabinets? It's also really nice and quiet, and has a great view from the window — heck, it actually *has* a window! In nine years at the bank, I never had a window of my own. And everyone pretty much leaves me alone. The only time I see anyone is when I go to the break room."

"Sounds fabulous to me, Darling," Marie said, still examining the solid oak furniture. "I think I'll take your word on how lovely the rest of the place is and move straight on to lunch. Now, where shall we go?"

"Well, since the weather is just about perfect today, I walked across the street awhile ago and got us two chicken sandwiches, some chips, and two Mr. PiBBs. We can eat outside at the picnic tables. See, over there?" Dana swiveled around in her chair and pointed out the window to the far side of the parking lot where two wooden picnic tables were sitting in the shade of a large chestnut tree.

Marie looked sideways at Dana and raised her eyebrows. "Do you mean *real* chips or your thin, hard American things?"

Dana laughed. "Real chips, Marie, just for you!"

"Splendid! Let's off!" Marie stood up smartly, grabbed her purse, and headed for the door.

"OK then!" Dana said, laughing. "Guess you're hungry!" She picked up the white paper bag sitting next to her desk and led the way down the short hallway and out the glass front doors. She breathed in the warm fragrant air and felt a rush of satisfaction. "Wow, Marie. I'm working my tail off here, but it feels so good to be doing something useful again. You know . . . before, I worried that the success I'd had with the allotment program at the bank would disappear when I tried to do it somewhere else, and with no help from anyone. But you know what? That hasn't been the case at all. Do you remember my old partner — that management trainee at the bank who worked with me for a while? Well, over the past few months, I've realized how little he actually contributed."

Marie stopped and rolled her eyes. "Honestly? You're surprised at how *little* he contributed? So, what you're saying is all those times I told you he was basically a skiver and waiting for *you* to do the work, you weren't paying any attention to me at all? Is that what you just admitted?"

Dana grinned. "I listen to everything you say — doesn't everyone? Mainly we listen to your cute accent and forget to pay attention to the substance." She reached the picnic table first and sat down at the end, placing the bag on the redwood-stained top.

Marie sat across from Dana and picked up the bag. "I smell those lovely chips from here! Since you were so thoughtful to get them, I'll forget that last statement of yours." She popped a few fries in her mouth and flashed her brilliant white smile.

"I've thought that before, you know, that he was more talk than action. But you also know I tend to underestimate my worth. This is not a new topic for us. Many times I thought how nice it would be if I had *half* your self-confidence, Marie. That would be enough for me — just half. But fortunately, what I lack in self-confidence, I make up with hard work. So I've had more success taking back some of my old clients and I'm also getting a lot of new clients from the businesses of my three sponsors." Dana picked up the bag and dug down to the bottom, retrieving the two chicken sandwiches. She handed one to Marie and unwrapped the second one for herself.

"That's the most splendid bit of news I've heard all day! Great chips by the by, and delicious-looking sandwich. Thanks for fetching lunch. It's really quite lovely out here and just what I needed to lift my mood after what happened this morning." Marie was staring, blank-faced, at the blue sky streaked with wispy thin clouds. "I couldn't be happier for you, Dana. You work so hard. It's nice to see a woman in this business get ahead for a change."

"Thank you. I feel like I've gotten the shaft from so many people this past year — people I thought I knew and could trust. I still can't get over Mr. Fugitte quitting the bank like he did without telling anyone, except my old partner, obviously. I don't know if I'll ever get over that one. And then Mr. Johnson — the biggest jerk and worst boss I've ever seen." Dana stopped talking long enough to bite into her sandwich. She ate slowly, deep in thought. Putting down her sandwich, she turned to Marie. "But you know what, Marie? I noticed something different about myself the other day. I've discovered I'm not nearly as naïve and forgiving as I was even a year ago. I hate to think I'm becoming jaded so soon in life, but I think that's what's happening. I've had so many people dump on me lately because they think I'm young and a pushover, and they can get away with it. Well, it's not going to be so easy now. 'Dana the door mat' is learning to fend for herself!"

Marie raised her eyebrows and stared at Dana with her mouth half open. "Let's hear it for you! It's about bloody time! No more Mrs. Nice Girl."

Dana grinned from ear to ear. "Absobloodylutely, as you say across the pond! I started yesterday, as a matter of fact. A car tried to cut in front of me on my way from Elizabethtown to Radcliff, and I wouldn't let him. Normally I would back off and wave for them to get in front of me. But this time I sped up and wouldn't let him in — and I gave him the evil eye too. It felt so good!" Dana was sitting up straight, looking pleased with herself.

Marie simply stared, sandwich in one hand and chips in the other, with her mouth still open. "I'm pleased as punch to hear this . . . and also trying to determine if this is your way of humoring me."

"I'm dead serious, Marie! I've had enough of people walking all over me. I'm going to get back as many of my old clients as possible and work my ass off to meet the one year goal my bosses set, so I get that 10% equity gifted to me as they promised — not to mention getting back my self-esteem."

"I believe you've retrieved a lot of your self-esteem already, and your spunk." Marie picked up her Mr. PiBB can and held it up to toast Dana. "Cheers to you!"

Dana smiled in satisfaction. She reached over and picked up her soda can and tapped it lightly against Marie's Mr. PiBB. "Thanks, Marie. I think I'm finally getting things on track, and it's good to be back!"

12

January 1988

Although nothing had changed in the past year, the conference room in Wayne Higgins' office building looked less formal and felt significantly less intimidating this time around. The grey walls seemed softer, more inviting. The large oval cherry wood conference table still looked elegant and beautiful, but somehow less imposing. And the place where Dana was planning to sit was at the end of the table, not in the middle.

She congratulated herself on being the first to arrive at the meeting. Admittedly, working just down the hall gave her an obvious advantage. Wayne Higgins, who also had an office just down the hall, hadn't yet surfaced today. She rarely saw him anyway. He was out and about more than he was in the building, which suited Dana just fine. She didn't need or want oversight from any of her three bosses.

Placing her note papers and handouts on the table, she turned and walked toward the window just behind her chair. Looking out across the front yard of the building, she decided it was a typical-looking January day in Elizabethtown — nothing but varying shades of grey. The sky, the trees, and the ground — all were grey. The only thing that made one distinguishable from the other was they were different shades of grey. There was a whitish-grey hue to the sky, the ground was a darker tint — sort of brownish-grey, and the trees were darker still, more blackish-grey. Dana hated the depressing look of Winter. She missed Fall. She missed the beautiful red and orange colors, the warm, less-humid days, and the crisp, cool, clear nights. Now, it was just cold, grey, and ugly.

She stared at a huge, gnarly oak tree not far from the window. A small grey squirrel slowly climbed down the trunk of the tree and then stopped two feet from the ground. His head bobbed as he surveyed the ground below. After a minute, he meandered further down the tree and leapt to the ground. He sat upright on his hind legs, his head darting back and forth. Dana's face relaxed as she thought about his simple life. His home was an enormous tree with many inviting limbs. There were plenty of nuts to keep him well fed all year, and there appeared little in his environment to cause him anxiety. There could be worse things in life than being a squirrel.

The sound of men's voices alerted Dana to reality. She recognized Roger Cunningham's voice first, making small talk about the weather to George Redmond. No doubt George was wondering when the sun would come out enough for him to retrieve his clubs from behind his office door and skip out to the golf course. As their voices grew closer, Dana turned and walked toward the conference room door to greet them.

George entered the room first, his face still showing a Summer glow. "Top of the morning to you, Dana!" He stretched out his hand and grabbed Dana's in a hardy shake.

"Good morning to you, Mr. Redmond! Nice to see someone so cheery on such a dreary, grey day," Dana said with a smile. She turned to greet Roger as he followed George into the room. "Good morning to you too, sir. I was just thinking I've hardly seen either of you since our meeting a year ago in this very room. Is Mr. Higgins with you?"

"Good morning, Dana," Roger answered in his typical staccato voice. "No, I've not seen Wayne yet this morning, have you George?" Clearly Roger was not nearly as cheery as was George.

"Nope, I came in right before you did. I suspect he'll show up soon. Wayne's not usually late without a reason, and he always calls first. My guess is he'll show up soon. We can wait awhile before starting, if that's OK with you, Roger."

"Sure, no problem." Roger surveyed the conference room, trying to decide where to sit. "As we both are painfully aware, this is not the busy season in our world." He limped to a spot across the table from Dana's papers and lowered his tall frame into the burgundy-colored leather chair.

George strolled to the other side of the table, choosing a seat close to Dana. "You're absolutely correct, Roger! And that's exactly why I keep telling myself I need to be living in a warm climate during the Winter. I could improve my golf game and accomplish something this time of year."

Dana laughed. "Well, as you'll soon hear, there always seems to be something to do in my line of work. I don't think there *is* a slow part of the year . . . although I keep hoping!" She glanced down the hall for some sign of Wayne Higgins, but the hallway was empty.

"He'll be here soon, Dana. In the meantime, how's the family doing?" George stretched back in his chair, clasped his hands behind his neck, and flashed his famous lop-sided grin.

"Everyone is fine, Mr. Redmond, thanks. Joey's still with the police force, and recently got a promotion, so he's happy. My son and daughter are doing great and growing like weeds. I just wish they wouldn't pick up every germ they can find from every sick kid at their school. That makes this time of year tough for everyone in our house."

"Yep, I remember those days!" Roger emitted a rare laugh. "They just spread the germs from one to another. As soon as you get them off the antibiotic, they catch something again and it keeps going in a vicious cycle. And, of course, you catch everything they get. Where do they go to school?"

"I've been taking them to a Montessori school. I don't know if you're familiar with those. They have a novel approach to learning that's more hands-on and play-oriented compared to traditional daycare centers. Both kids love it there, which makes me feel less guilty about working long hours here." After glancing down the hallway one last time, Dana walked back to the table and sat down next to her papers. "Not that I'm griping about working long hours," she added quickly, with a grin. She hoped they didn't think she was complaining. She still was happy just to have a job.

"Actually, I've heard of that school," George said, rocking back and forth in his chair, and ignoring her comment about the long hours. "One of my golf buds used to take his kid there. Supposedly the kid loved the place and was way ahead of other kids his age who were in public school. But *all* parents think their kid is smarter than everyone else's, don't they, Dana?"

"I can only speak for my own kids, Mr. Redmond, but I can verify they're way smarter than the average kid," Dana shot back with a grin.

"Good on you, Dana," Roger said, leaning back in his chair and unbuttoning his suit jacket. "I recently read this is the most important time for getting their brains in tune for learning — when they're young, and the younger the better. Wish I'd known that when my kids were little." He ran his hand down the front of his checkered tie, smoothing out the paunch near the middle.

"Good morning, everyone!" Wayne Higgins said, hurrying into the room. "My apologies for being late." He quickly selected a seat next to Roger and tossed his briefcase on the table. "My first meeting this morning started late and went downhill from there. But I have a feeling this meeting is going to make up for it, right Dana?"

"Good morning, Mr. Higgins, and I imagine the answer to your question depends on what your expectations were a year ago." Dana smiled at him, but she was never sure how to interpret Wayne. She'd misread him more than once. Now, if Roger had asked that question, she would've known he was serious. He never joked about business or money.

George leaned over toward Dana. "Our expectations are beyond reasonable, Dana, because we know what you accomplished at the bank — before, as we like to say, the hostile takeover." He flashed a grin and sat back in his chair.

Dana forced a smile, hoping to conceal her anxiousness. She picked up her small stack of papers and passed them to the three men. "I'll get started and then you can decide for yourselves. What I've put together is a graph that shows a timeline over the past year and the number of allotments set up for each of your businesses along the line. The first quadrant on the timeline depicts the number of allotments set up for what were your current customers. The second quadrant shows the number of allotments set up for your new customers during the past year. The third quadrant shows the number of allotments set up in new business areas. And the fourth quadrant is what I'm projecting to occur over the next calendar year, based on this year's results." She sat down in her chair and gave the men a few minutes to absorb the information.

A few moments later, George was the first to break the silence. "I'm not sure what I expected to see for the first year results, Dana, but if I'm interpreting your chart correctly, I'd say you did pretty well for yourself — or maybe I should say you did well for us!"

Wayne repositioned his sizable frame in the leather chair. He looked up at Dana, revealing a slight smile. "I agree. Dana, superb job! I don't know what *your* expectations were, but you've beaten mine. Probably more important to you, it looks like you've also met the threshold for the incentive plan we agreed to last year — 3,000 monthly allotments within our first year, so you're entitled to 10% of the stock and now have equity in MSI too. George, Roger, do you agree?"

George peered through the lower half of his glasses at the paper Dana provided him. "I agree, Wayne. It appears Dana has met our best expectations, and then some!"

Roger continued to scrutinize the page with the chart until Wayne raised his eyebrows and said again, "Well . . . Roger? What do *you* think?"

After several more minutes of scrutiny with no response, Roger finally looked up at George. "Oh . . . yes . . . I agree. Excellent work, Dana. Congratulations."

The tone of Roger's voice was less convincing than his words, Dana thought. She decided to proceed through her pitch as planned. "Rather than take up everyone's time going through the numbers for each of your businesses, I thought I would go over the total numbers with you for each quadrant, and then I can meet separately with each of you to review the numbers for your respective businesses. The numbers vary a little for your individual businesses, but not significantly. Does that sound OK to everyone?"

"Sure, that's fine. Go ahead." Wayne had taken it upon himself to speak for the group, and Dana thought he appeared in a hurry to get the meeting over with. He was rubbing the top of his bald head back and forth quickly, which usually meant he was anxious about something. He probably had another meeting soon.

"OK," Dana said, glancing at George and Roger for confirmation, but neither of their faces provided any sign of what they were thinking. "As Wayne just mentioned, my goal for the year was to set up a minimum of 3,000 monthly allotments prior to the end of 12 months from the date we started MSI, which is 5 January 1988. If you take a look at the chart I passed out, during the first three months I set up 1,277 allotments with your current customers. As you know, on April 1st, I brought in a part-time employee, Brenda Sheppard, to take over what I'd been doing January through March — setting up allotments for your current customers. This allowed me to focus on setting up allotments for new customers as the loans were being processed. So, in the next quadrant on the chart, the number you see comprises the allotments Brenda set up with your current customers, which is the blue section on the quadrant, and the allotments I started with your new customers, which is the red section. As you can see, we had 2,253 allotments started during the second quarter of the year, for a total of 3,530 by 30 June." Dana looked up to see if there were questions, but the three men remained fixated on their handouts. "By the end of the third quarter we added another 2,415 allotments, and by the end of the year we'd added another 2,689 for a year-end total of 8,634."

"The third quadrant depicts new business areas. This is the area that's the hardest to get started, but also the most promising. This year, I had little time to spend in this area, and Roger, you expressed concern about spending money on travel, so I did only a little. I did drive to Hampton Roads, Virginia — twice — and those trips are starting to pay off. They refer to this area as Tidewater Virginia and there are literally thousands of men and women stationed there from all the military services. This is a potential blockbuster area for us. I initiated contracts to set up allotments for two car dealerships in Norfolk, not far from the Naval base there, and I'm close to signing a deal in this same area with an electronics business. They sell TVs, VCRs, stereo systems, and those sorts of things. The potential market in this area is huge, but I'll need to spend more time there to capitalize on it. However, with just touching the surface, I was able to sign up 483 allotments from the two car dealerships." Dana glanced up again at the three men. George was the only one who looked up at Dana when she stopped talking. The other two men continued to examine the chart in Dana's handout.

"The fourth quadrant depicts what I'm forecasting for next year. There will be a steady decline in new allotments for your existing customers. We expect this, of course, because anyone who wanted to set up an allotment probably has done so already. But we'll pick up a few more customers because current ones will tell their friends and co-workers that having an automatic allotment to make their monthly vehicle payment made their life easier." Dana shifted in her seat, smoothing her skirt under her thighs. "We'll continue to gain customers from your new sales, so I'm expecting the second quadrant to show similar results next year, or possibly even an increase. As allotments become mainstream, consumers will set them up for lots of different commodities, and over time they'll simply become comfortable having them. Therefore, it's likely we'll see an increase here."

Dana picked up her notes, pushed back her chair, and stood up. She knew the next issue was going to be contentious with at least one of the three men, and standing and looking down on him made her feel more powerful. She took a deep breath, glanced down at Roger, and began laying out her case. "Finally, regarding the third quadrant and setting up allotments for new businesses, this is where I'll spend the bulk of my time, while Brenda Sheppard continues her part-time employment working on the allotments for your existing companies. As I've said before, we have a limited market here in Elizabethtown and Radcliff. I can continue trying to lure away some of my former clients at the bank and also work on picking up new business locally. But we won't see great returns like we'll see if we expand our business to new geographical areas and into new markets. So my intent is to use some small percentage of the profits each year — maybe 5% or 6% — for business development in new areas. This will entail a certain amount of travel throughout the year, but as I've mentioned, it . . ."

"I would prefer you to stay in town and continue to concentrate on our local businesses." Roger's face was flushed, and he was talking quickly. "If you can keep generating these sorts of results every year without wasting time and money on speculation or having to hire more people, I'd be content. What about spending next year expanding to new market areas here in Elizabethtown and Radcliff, and maybe even into Shively? Seems much less risky to me. George, Wayne, what do you think?" Roger turned in his chair and looked back and forth from Wayne to George. Dana noticed he never looked at her, either to gauge her reaction or ask for her input.

"I have no problem setting aside 5% or so every year for business development, Roger," George said casually, still leaning back in his chair with his legs stretched out in front of him. "Dana's right; as much as everyone in this room is taken with Elizabethtown and the Fort Knox area, we have to be careful not to allow our small-town mentality, which we all harbor to some degree, to put blinders on us. There are limited markets here, and our prospects are limited *within* those markets. I think we all agree our desire for this company is sustained growth, which means we have to go outside this limited geographic area we're comfortable in, and into new, and potentially larger, locations. So I'm going to disagree with you, Roger. I think it's a good idea to work those other areas, if Dana has time."

Good old George, Dana thought. Someone needed to temper Roger's stinginess. Roger would rather mortgage the future of the company than spend a little money on business development. "I think it's important enough for the growth of the company that my hope is to make it a priority every year." Dana threw in that last part for good measure.

George turned around in his chair until he could see Wayne. "You're awfully quiet back there. What do you think?"

Wayne sat back in his chair and crossed his stubby arms over his chest. He tapped his left heel against the leg of the chair and finally nodded his head. "I agree with you, George. I think Dana has done an outstanding job this first year — better than I'd hoped. But as she said, the market here is limited. We can keep doing what we've been doing, or we can use a bit of the profits to see if anything takes hold somewhere else. Relatively speaking, it's a small sum of money, so we could try it for a year or two and see what happens. If it doesn't pay off, we'll stop."

George spun around in his chair toward Roger. "What do you think about that idea, Roger? Try it for a year or two and see what happens. Can you live with that?"

Roger ran his fingers through his short, brown hair and then laced them behind his head. He looked over at Dana. "How much more money are you going to need this next year to keep yourself and your helper going?"

Dana looked at Roger for several moments, her eyebrows knitted together. "How much *more* am I going to need? Do you mean what's the total budget projected for the year, or what is the budget for this business development quadrant?"

Roger reached down and picked up the handout Dana had given them and waved it in the air. "This is what I'm talking about," he said impatiently. "How much is all this going to cost us this year? How much do we need to increase the line of credit? Last year we set it at one hundred thousand. How much more do we need this year?"

"We don't need any more money, Mr. Cunningham," Dana said carefully. She was taken aback by his inquisition, then slowly realized he hadn't understood her chart. "There's no need to increase the line of credit. The company made money last year from around our second month in business. We haven't had to tap into the line of credit since the end of the first quarter, when we began making deposits of the profits into our account at the bank. I guess the quarterly profit margin isn't clear on the chart," Dana added, in an apologetic tone, although it had been crystal clear to the other two men.

Wayne rolled his chair over to Roger and pointed to the section on the chart that showed the quarterly profits. "Right here, Roger. As we said earlier, it was a profitable first year. Dana exceeded her incentive goals, made us an admirable first year return, and earned 10% of the company for herself."

Dana glanced at George to gauge his reaction to Roger's strange line of questioning. But George sat expressionless, silently watching Roger and

Wayne over the top of his reading glasses.

Roger stopped rocking back and forth in his chair and studied the chart.

Dana stood still, fixated on Roger and not sure what to make of the situation. She found it hard to believe that 30 minutes into their meeting, he hadn't grasped the fact they were making $2.00 on every allotment, every month. Not only did they *not* need to increase the line of credit, he hadn't realized all three of them had made a significant return from the allotments over the past year, and the rate of return was only going to increase with each subsequent year.

"OK, I get it . . . guess I missed that part of the discussion. Sorry Dana," he said sheepishly.

"No problem, Mr. Cunningham. There are lots of numbers on that chart and it can be confusing." Dana wanted to make light of the situation.

After another minute of silence, George turned back around in his chair toward Roger and asked, "So, back to the question of the day, Roger. Are you OK with taking a little of the profits each year and using them for business development?"

Roger looked up at George and then over at Wayne. "If that's the profit margin for the past year, I have no problem taking a small amount of it and using it to develop the business. But I still think we should focus primarily within our local area, and as someone said earlier, if we can't show much profit for the business development efforts after a year or two, then we should stop it entirely."

"Well then, Dana, guess you have your marching orders for the next twelve months!" Wayne seemed eager to end the meeting. "This has been quite a successful first year. I want to thank you for your efforts and congratulate all of us for making the wise decision to pursue this business venture with Mrs. Smolenski! Anything else we need to discuss before we adjourn?"

Roger glanced up from his chart long enough to shake his head. "Nope, I'm good," he said in a quieter tone.

"I'm good too," George said. "And, I want to second what Wayne said. Dana, I think you've done an outstanding job — better than any of us imagined for our first year of operations. You've definitely earned your 10% ownership. I suspect this is just the beginning of a very successful business venture for all of us. I'll go out on a limb and make a projection that four or five years from now we'll be sitting in this room and won't recognize the business anymore because it'll have grown and morphed into something we couldn't have imagined. That's how much faith I have in you, Dana."

Dana stood still, listening to George's surprising praise. "Thanks for the vote of confidence, Mr. Redmond. I wasn't sure how we'd fare this first year, since all my old customers were still at the bank, of course. But I had some early wins and got back some of them, and I'll be pursuing more in the coming year. I appreciate your comments, and Brenda and I will keep at it."

"Ditto from me, Dana." Wayne stood up, and clasping his briefcase and her handout, lumbered around the table towards her, his hand extended. "It's obvious you've been working hard, and there's no reason to believe your success won't continue. I'll be looking forward to seeing where we are in another year or two."

Dana shook Wayne's outstretched hand. "Thank you, sir!"

Wayne turned and continued towards the door. "Gentlemen, Dana, I'm off to another meeting. Please keep me informed of anything significant." With a brisk wave of his hand, he disappeared from the room.

"See ya, Wayne," George hollered behind him. He gathered his papers from the table and stood up. "Roger, what's on your plate for the rest of the afternoon? It's not a bad day out there. Want to tee up some golf balls and play a round?"

"No thanks, George. I have a cut-off point of 50 degrees. If it's colder than that, I don't go anywhere near a golf course. But my guess is you'll be fine. You're probably still getting some heat from that suntan." He picked up his papers and briefcase. "Dana, keep up the good work. I'll be looking forward to hearing how things are going at the mid-year brief."

"Absolutely, Mr. Cunningham." Dana smiled at him as he turned and limped out the door. She hoped the mid-year brief showed that she was right and he was wrong. There was a lot of work ahead for that to happen. "I hope you enjoy the afternoon, Mr. Redmond. Thanks for coming."

"Thank *you*, Dana. Great job today, and an outstanding first year! In spite of the pushback you got today from Roger, I have no doubt your instincts are correct and next year you'll be off to a promising start with your business development efforts. Just keep plugging away like you've been doing. We have faith in your judgment," George nodded his head and smiled.

Dana breathed a sigh of relief and relaxed. "As I said, I appreciate the vote of confidence. I believe I'm right about expanding the business to new areas, even though we're just starting the second year. Thanks for your support, Mr. Redmond, and have a good time on the golf course!"

"I've never had a bad time out there, only some better than others." George Redmond pushed his chair back under the table. "Take care, Dana, and again, great job."

As he left the room, Dana turned and stared out the window. It was still grey out there, lots of shades of grey. But the grey seemed a little brighter, a little warmer. And the view outside the window appeared less forbidding and unfriendly. Maybe she just needed to give things a chance.

13

Six years later, July 4th 1994

Marie picked up the large bowl of potato salad and carried it out of the kitchen and into the backyard, setting it down on the picnic table. She smoothed out the red-checkered tablecloth and began rearranging the bowls of food. "Dana, I'm positively thrilled to be experiencing my first American 4th of July picnic, with all the trimmings — burgers and American hotdogs on the grill, cold potatoes mixed with mayonnaise, and sweets, loads of sweets! Thank you again for inviting me!"

"I've invited you for years, you know, but you've always been on vacation. We're happy you're finally here too. And for the third time, we're not having sweets, we're having apple pie — good old American apple pie."

"Oh yes, that too! But Liz spilled the beans and told me your mum always brings these chocolate oatmeal cookies that are boiled in a saucepan and are SO wonderful. I also heard something about peanut butter fudge. I can't remember the last time I ate peanut butter fudge!"

Dana stopped, her hands on her hips. "It's unfair you can eat like this and still look like that."

Marie's smile faded. "Speaking of unfair, I've not had the chance to tell you the latest news. Two days ago, Johnson fired Katie McMillan. No one can figure out why, because she was a superb employee. Everyone loved her, especially the customers. That man is a beast, a cow, an absolute wanker! Including you, Johnson has fired *six* women since arriving at the bank eight years ago, and not a single chap! He's mad!"

"You're kidding! He fired Katie McMillan? I can't believe it!" Dana stared at Marie, her mouth open. "You're right; everyone liked Katie, and she really was an excellent teller. What did she do wrong, have too many kids?" Dana asked, sarcastically.

Marie shrugged her shoulders. "Perhaps she should have tried wearing trousers and talking in a baritone voice. One thing for sure, I'm relieved I report to the corporate office and not to him."

"I just can't believe it." Dana was peering at Marie, unable to move. "Why doesn't someone do something? It's clear Johnson doesn't want to work with women. After firing six of them, hasn't anyone put the pieces together? It seems so obvious, especially if you know how good all those women were at their jobs . . . how hard they worked."

"Yes, I think they have." Marie pulled up a lawn chair and sat down. "But as you are keenly aware, it's a difficult thing to prove — even if someone is willing to take him on — and I suspect none of the women would go to court over it. As you learned, they only would win back their jobs, and then they'd have to work with the horse's arse, but the arse would be angrier now and seeking revenge. I cannot imagine subjecting myself to that!" Marie reached over to the table and grabbed a handful of chips.

"Dana, your folks are here." Joey had emerged from the house and the screen door slammed behind him.

"Fabulous! That would mean my sweets have arrived!" Marie was up and making her way to the back door before Dana had turned around.

"You're going to be sorely disappointed if my Mom made something else this year, aren't you?" Dana hollered at her.

"Not a chance," Marie yelled over her shoulder. "Mummy would never break tradition, and she is keenly aware how much I love her sweets!"

"That's true, she loves to feed you." Dana followed Marie into the house.

"Hello Mummy!" Marie was already across the kitchen and hugging Dana's mother before Dana was fully in the kitchen. "Let me help you; you're loaded. Oh, and happy American 4th of July!"

Mrs. Adkins' face lit up when she saw Marie. "Happy 4th to you too,

Marie! I was thrilled when Dana told me you were coming today! I had no idea this was your first time celebrating the 4th of July. It's really about getting a day off work and eating, you know — like several other American holidays." She handed two grocery bags to Marie. "The deviled eggs, vegetable tray, and some special cookies are in there."

"Oh, I know all about those cookies! Liz told me about them as soon as I arrived, and I must have one before she shows up and wants one and her mum says no."

"You just help yourself, my dear. They're small, they won't spoil your dinner one bit." Dana's mother pointed to the bag Marie had just set on the cabinet. "They're in that one."

"Geez, Mom. I don't recall you ever telling me I could have a cookie before dinner — just Marie — and the kids, of course!" Dana rolled her eyes at her mother and walked over and kissed her on the cheek.

"That's because you never asked," her mom shot back. "You just helped yourself."

"Oh, is that how it happened?" Dana turned toward Marie. "Give me one too."

"No problem, I hate dining alone." Marie opened the Tupperware bowl and took out a cookie for Dana and two for herself. She sunk her teeth in and chewed slowly. "My God, these are fabulous! Oh — look — I see oatmeal in them! Health food!"

Dana bit into hers. She'd forgotten how good they were. "Thanks for bringing them Mom. Liz and Ryan have been asking all morning when you're going to get here. I swear, you can't fill them up these days."

"Maybe they just wanted to see their Meemaw," Mrs. Adkins said with a mischievous look.

"I wanted to see their Meemaw too," Marie said, looking lovingly at Mrs. Adkins, and then returning to examine the cookie's contents.

"Meemaw!" Liz yelled, as she bounded into the kitchen, followed by Ryan.

Mrs. Adkins turned to greet them. She leaned over and wrapped her arms around both, holding them tight. "How are my darlings today?"

"Hungry!" Liz said. "Waiting for you and Papaw to get here."

"Did you bring the cookies?" Ryan asked.

"Of course I brought your cookies!" She rubbed their backs and smiled at them.

"Can we have one now?" Liz asked, wearing her sweetest face.

"You'll have to wrestle them away from Marie, but it's OK with me if your Mom says OK." Mrs. Adkins looked over at Dana for affirmation.

"Sure, but just one until we've eaten," Dana said, looking over at Marie, who was clinging to the bowl with one hand and holding the remnants of her second cookie in the other.

"What? You two want one of these?" Marie asked, holding the cookies just out of their reach. "All right, but you've got to help set the table and clean up when we're done — deal?"

"Yes, we'll help!" Ryan yelled.

Marie got out two cookies for them and another one for herself. "Handling fee," she announced, and stuffed the cookie into her mouth. "OK, eat up and let's be off. We've got some serious noshing to do as soon as we get things set up."

They grabbed their cookies and headed for the back door.

"I'm sure I'll not see them again until it's time to eat," Marie said. "Dana, Mummy and I will take her bags and everything from the fridge outside to the table, and then we'll fetch the drinks. You can round up the rest of the family."

Dana did as Marie instructed and went to find her Dad and Joey. Walking down the hallway, she smiled to herself. Crazy Marie. She brightened the day and made Dana forget about the argument she had with Joey earlier that morning. Their arguments were occurring more frequently these days. Dana needed to work long hours and typically six days a week. Joey thought eight hours a day was enough time to spend at the office. Since he often worked nights, he wanted her hours to be more consistent for the kids' sake. But she had too much work to get done in eight hours a day, even with Brenda and four additional employees working full-time now. There didn't seem to be a solution they both could agree to, and most of the time she was too busy and too tired to think about it. Marie was a great distraction from their troubles. The kids were too. Ryan and Liz were the light of her life. At least she could thank Joey for them.

Finding no one in the house, she walked back through the kitchen and into the garage where she found her Dad and Joey deep in conversation about the new lawn mower. "Hey, are you two ready to eat?"

Dana's father looked up at Dana and smiled. "I don't know about Joey, but I'm starving! I had to watch your mother bake all morning, and she barely let me have anything. I only wanted to make sure they were good enough for everyone else to eat," he said, with a wink. "Just give me a minute to wash up and I'll be right out."

"I need to wash up too." Joey pushed the new lawn mower back into the corner of the garage and went into the house.

"What do you think about the lawn mower, Dad? Like it?"

"Yes, it's a good one. I hope it works longer than your last mower, but I'm happy to come over and help again. Seems I don't see much of you all lately. You and Joey are busy working and the kids are involved with their activities. They look a couple inches taller every time I see them. Time just flies, doesn't it, Hon?" Dana's father was staring at her face, but his eyes were miles away.

"Yes, it does, Dad; it really does," Dana said, contemplating his absent gaze. "I was telling Joey this morning I can't believe I've been working on my own for over eight years now." Dana turned to walk back into the house and her dad followed.

After they finished at the sink, Dana pushed the screen door open and went outside to see if everything was ready. Marie, her mom, and the kids were already sitting at the picnic table. Liz and Ryan were swinging their legs, making their heads bob up and down. Marie and her mom were laughing about something. The sight of the happy foursome made her smile, despite her melancholy mood.

Joey and Dana's dad emerged from the house together and joined them at the picnic table. "Shall we say grace?" Joey asked.

Dana glanced at her Dad. "Do you want to say it, Dad?"

"Sure. Lord, we thank you for this beautiful day of freedom you've given to our country; we thank you for this wonderful food you provided for us; and most importantly, we thank you for each other, amen." Dana's father raised his eyes and ginned. "Let's eat!"

As everyone passed the bowls of food and filled their plates, Dana relayed Marie's news regarding the latest firing at the bank. "It's unbelievable," Mrs. Adkins said indignantly. "Six women in eight years! Does anyone see a pattern? What are they saying at the main office in Elizabethtown?"

Marie put down her hotdog and wiped her mouth on her napkin. "While I don't know specifics, I've heard a few people are asking questions. It should seem unusual to anyone with half a brain that only the women are disappearing. The other odd thing is Mr. Johnson typically holds several meetings each week, and it's unusual for a woman to be included. I think he simply does not like dealing with women and views them as wives and mothers who're there to earn a few shillings to help at home, while men are the real workers and money-earners."

"In this day and age, that's hard to believe," Mr. Adkins said.

Joey nodded his head. "Yes, it's unbelievable, but it looks like he's going to get away with behaving this way because the women are too afraid, and probably don't have the money, to take him on. Maybe someone in the corporate office will figure it out and fire him, or maybe they'll put pressure on him to quit."

Marie shook her head. "Not a chance. He has no guilt or shame."

Dana took a bite of potato salad and stared off toward the rose bushes lined against the back fence. "I'm getting my revenge against Johnson each time I take away one of First Citizens' allotment customers. Over the past eight years, I've taken away a lot who tell me MSI provides much better service."

"That's my girl!" Marie said, still munching on her hotdog. "They're infinitely better off with you and it's good they know it, which is why you've been able to build MSI into quite the allotment business."

"I agree," Mrs. Adkins chimed in. "One thing about you, Dana, when you put your mind to something, you work until you get it right. When a business is performing a service for someone, that's the most important thing — other than honesty, which you have in spades over Johnson."

Mr. Adkins looked over at Dana. "Have you thought any more about going on your own? I remember the last time we talked, you said one of your clients had told you to stop working this hard for someone else."

"Yes, she's thinking about it," Marie said, before Dana had time to open her mouth. "Your daughter would be much happier and wealthier if she'd leave those three sharks and set up her own business. They're complete ingrates who're taking every bit of profit from the business each month, dividing it amongst themselves, and refusing to put any money back into the business. The only reason business is booming is because Dana and her staff are working their arses off! Not to mention the fact they won't pay her what she's worth."

"Right," Joey said. "The only good things about the arrangement are the guaranteed salary — even though she deserves much more — and the job security, which I suppose there's something to be said for both."

"That's true, Dana." Mr. Adkins' face softened. "I'm sure you haven't forgotten what it was like eight years ago when you went jobless for the better part of a year."

"I can assure you I won't ever forget it," Dana murmured, staring at her plate. "I never want to feel that way again. It was scary and humiliating, which is why I haven't taken my client's recommendation too seriously. Believe me, nothing would make me happier than to reap the benefit of my long hours rather than give it to three men who don't know a thing about the business and don't want to be involved — except to take all the profit, of course. But I don't want to put our family at financial risk again — not to mention I'm afraid of the likely reaction of my three bosses once I told them what I was doing. I don't think I could do it."

"Bollocks!" Marie said, flashing Dana a stern look. "You've already proven you can do it. Look how quickly you had MSI up and running, and turning a remarkable profit! After the first year, you brought on a full-time employee. Less than a year later, you needed two more full-time employees. You've changed offices twice in the past eight years because you'd outgrown the space. You have a knack for befriending your clients and building their trust because you work hard and don't make mistakes with their money. That's what building a good business is all about. Of course you can do it!"

"Thanks for the vote of confidence, Marie, but where do I get the money to start a new business in this town? No bank is going to lend a 34-year-old woman with virtually no collateral the money to start a business." Dana reached for the apple pie.

"What about asking your grandfather to talk to someone?" Mrs. Adkins suggested. "I imagine he still knows quite a few people around town who could help."

"I agree with your mom, Dana." Mr. Adkins reached across the table and patted Dana's arm. "You work so hard and I hear all the good things you've done with MSI. If that's what you'd really like to do, you owe yourself the chance. Your mother and I will help any way we can, which probably isn't much, but we can watch the kids occasionally, maybe bring over dinner once a week. I imagine you've got several friends who would help you and Joey while you're getting things up and running."

Dana looked at Joey, who hadn't spoken in a while. She knew how he felt. While he'd always been supportive of her career, they needed her salary to make things work. They'd have to make some dramatic changes in their lifestyle if they had to live on Joey's salary alone. No, she didn't want to go back to those days! Not only was it hard financially, it was hard emotionally. Yet she also wanted to be compensated commensurate with her level of effort and success. It was only fair! She was determinedly fair in her dealings and expected the same from others. She hated when people said life was not fair. "What do you think, Joey?" She felt guilty asking him in front of her family.

Joey didn't hesitate. "Dana, if you want to do it and you think you can make it work, then you should try. First, we'd need to do some planning and save money, but you've done the work successfully now at two different places, so that's a good indicator." The tone of Joey's voice changed. "But like you, I have some concern about a potential backlash from your three bosses. They've got a cash cow right now, and they're unlikely to give it up

111

without a fight. I'd hate to see my wife as a defendant in a costly lawsuit. So if you decide you want to do this, we'd need to have time to save money, and maybe find someone who has been through this to give us advice." Joey glanced at Marie. "And now I'll take a few of mom's cookies before you consume them all, so hand them over, girl."

Marie hesitated and then rolled her eyes at Joey. "All right then, but they're not good for your figure, so best you not eat too many." She slowly passed the container to Joey, then turned to Dana's mother. "Mummy, would you pass the fudge, please? Your son-in-law has taken my cookies and I suspect I shan't see them again."

"Sure, my dear, eat as much as you want. If you don't get your fill, I'll make more this week and have Dana deliver them to you. And Dana, make sure you put together a doggy bag for Marie to take home."

Dana chuckled to herself. There was no better compliment you could give Mrs. Adkins than to ask her to make you something to eat. And Marie knew how to suck up to Dana's mom as well as any family member.

Marie sat up straight and her eyes widened. "I would love a doggy bag!"

"I had every intention of giving her a bunch of leftovers, Mom." Dana reached across the table for her Mom's homemade bread and butter pickles. "Here Marie, have a pickle to go with your fudge."

"Thank you, but I've had several. Onward to dessert." She put a large piece of fudge in her mouth. "Blimey, that is pure heaven!" She closed her eyes slowly. "Back to the subject at hand. I agree with Joey about your approach. Maybe I can assist. I'll look for someone to help with the loan and someone who can provide legal advice."

"Thank you," Dana said. "I have no idea what to do, but before I do anything I'll want to learn as much as I can. I appreciate any advice I can get."

"Absolutely, Darling! Happy to help!"

"I think I'll make an appointment with Shane Sanders, my client who thought I should start my own company. I'm working on a new contract for him now, anyway."

"Excellent idea!" Marie put her hand on her stomach and her eyes widened. "I can't remember the last time I ate so much."

"You did well, Marie," Joey said, laughing. "You kept up with me for sure. I don't know where you put it! You must have a stomach like a cow, with four compartments."

"I believe I've filled all four compartments." Marie stood up and stretched. "I'll take some of these dishes into the house and help you clean up, Dana."

Mr. Adkins stood up and patted Dana on the back. "Everything was wonderful, my dear, as always. Thanks for the hard work you all do every year putting together this terrific meal."

"You're welcome, Dad."

Mr. Adkins looked down at Dana and grinned. "Who knows, maybe next year when we sit down to eat our July 4th picnic, you'll be president of your own company!"

"From your mouth to God's ear, Dad." Dana stood up from the table and picked up a tray to carry into the house. One can always dream, she thought.

14

Three weeks later, late July 1994

The late afternoon sun cast long shadows across the parking lot, making it easy for Dana to find a shady spot to park her car. She picked up her briefcase from the seat, swung open the door, and hopped out of the car. There was a lilt in her step as she set out for the front door of the one-story office complex near the edge of town. For days, she'd thought of little else than this meeting.

"Good morning, Mrs. Smolenski." Jan Harris sat perched on the edge of her receptionist chair, behind a small but stylish desk in the middle of the foyer. Her crystal clear, blue eyes swept over Dana. Impeccably groomed as usual, she wore a cream-colored linen suit, and not a platinum blonde hair was out of place. "You're here for your nine o'clock appointment with Mr. Sanders."

"Good morning, Jan," Dana replied, not sure if Jan was asking her a question or telling her she had an appointment. "Yes, I have a nine o'clock with Mr. Sanders. I know I'm a little early so I'll just sit over there and review my notes," she added, motioning toward the window.

"Mr. Sanders is still with his eight o'clock appointment, but they should finish soon. Can I get you something to drink?"

Jan Harris's voice was as smooth and elegant as her appearance, and Dana would've delighted in having Jan get up and wait on her. But she didn't want to go into her meeting juggling coffee, her briefcase, and a purse.

"Thanks, Jan, but I'm fine," she said reluctantly, and then immediately felt guilty about her less-than-charitable thoughts.

Dana picked out a Queen Ann chair closest to the window and sat down, placing her briefcase on her lap. She pulled out her notes and sat back into the soft chair. After several weeks spent contemplating a prospective business plan and the financials, Dana broke down and called her former boss at her old bank — Jim Fugitte — to ask his thoughts on her idea. She'd run into Jim several times since starting MSI eight years ago and had tried to remain friendly. Yet, it was hard. Her pain was still raw, despite the eight years that'd passed. She'd forgiven him for hurting her, but she'd been unable to forget his unwillingness to help her the day she was fired and went to see him. Despite all that, she'd decided it was OK to pick his brain for all the information and advice she could get. He owed her that much.

Her intuition had proven correct. The lunch meeting she'd arranged with Jim Fugitte turned out to be most insightful. As she'd expected, Jim thought Dana's idea to buy out the three men was an excellent one — and long overdue. He seemed less certain *how* to do it. Offering money to them — sizable sums of money — was his only suggestion. Since Jim had spent six years working for the FDIC, the most significant thing he could offer Dana was an introduction to a banker he knew, who might help secure a loan for her. Besides convincing the three men to relinquish ownership of the company to her, Dana figured securing a loan would be her next biggest hurdle.

Other than getting advice from Jim Fugitte, Dana had relied primarily on Marie and her points of contact, and Joey's assistance with family financial planning. Marie had arranged for Dana to have a lunch meeting with one of her many cast-off boyfriends, who by chance was a contracts attorney practicing in Louisville. He told Dana since there was scant paperwork involved when they set up MSI, there was not much for him to review and little advice he could provide. The only way she would know the likelihood of having to go to court to secure ownership of MSI would be to talk to each of the three men individually and gauge their reaction to her plan. The attorney was more helpful with ideas for setting up the new company.

However, Dana thought the whole meeting was worthwhile, and little by little she was learning what she was up against. Unfortunately, the poor attorney clearly was still smitten with Marie, who ignored his glances the entire time and instead munched her way through a burger, fries, and an enormous slice of strawberry pie.

Joey's primary concern was having enough money to pay the bills. They'd decided on a savings plan that would allow them to build up six months of living expenses, but it would take at least 18 months to build up that amount of money. Dana had hoped to secure ownership of the company in six months to a year. They'd worked to create a reasonable plan though, so she'd agreed to it. And if absolutely necessary, she figured borrowing money from Meemaw was an option, even though Joey was likely to nix that idea.

The top piece of paper on Dana's lap had a line drawn down the middle. On the left side were the steps she'd identified as necessary to achieve ownership, and a timeline next to each step. On the right side were issues she was likely to encounter with each step. Looking down at the paper, the magnitude of the endeavor seized her for the first time. She broke into a sweat, her heart raced, and her throat became dry. Soon, she couldn't focus on the words. She looked up to see if Jan Harris was watching her, but Jan was flipping through papers on her desk, oblivious to Dana. Sitting upright in her chair, Dana took several deep breaths. This is ridiculous, she thought. If I don't like what I hear today, or it looks like it's going to be too much for me to deal with, I'll just forget the whole thing. But deep down, she didn't want to forget the whole thing. For months she'd thought about how wonderful it would be to get up each morning and go to work for herself. There would be no boss telling her what areas she could or couldn't focus on. There would be no one to siphon off the profits. No one could tell her she didn't need to hire more employees. How good it would feel to make all the decisions she knew were the right ones, for the right reasons! Dana knew no matter how hard taking control of MSI would be, it was the right decision for everyone — except for her three bosses.

The door to Shane Sanders' office swung open and a tall, fit man with dark blonde hair and a handsome face strode into the foyer. "Dana, come on in here! I've got a surprise for you."

Dana looked up at the sound of Shane's voice. She quickly returned her papers to her briefcase and stood up. "Good morning, Shane! I was admiring the gorgeous view you have here." Dana picked up her purse and briefcase, and followed Shane into his office. She was surprised to see a short, stocky, fireplug of a man standing in the middle of Shane's office.

"Dana, I want you to meet an old and dear friend of mine, retired Marine Corps Colonel David Lockwood. And Dave, this is Dana Smolenski, the woman I've been telling you about who runs MSI — the company that manages our allotment program."

Dana stretched out her arm and received a hardy handshake from the colonel.

"Great pleasure to meet you, Dana. I've been hearing from Shane a lot of good things about you and your company." The colonel's voice was deep and gruff. His blondish-brown hair was cropped short, and he wore military-style, black-framed glasses.

However, what caught Dana's eye were the sharp creases ironed into his khaki-colored pants and also into the short sleeves of his polo shirt. "Very nice to meet you too, Colonel Lockwood." She was mystified why this meticulously dressed man was in Shane's office and why they'd been discussing her.

"Dana, Dave, why don't you both sit down at the table over there," Shane said, motioning toward the other side of the room, "and Dana, I'll tell you why I've asked Dave to join us this morning."

The colonel walked toward the round conference table and pulled out a chair for Dana. She sat down and he scooted her chair up to the table. "Thank you, Colonel Lockwood," Dana said, looking up at the colonel with a bewildered expression. She couldn't fathom how Shane had become good friends with a retired Marine Corps colonel. Fort Knox was the only military facility nearby, and it was an Army post. Unsure of what else to do, she reached into her briefcase and pulled out her charts and notes.

Shane took a seat next to the colonel. "Dana, the reason I asked Dave to join us today is because he was an attorney in the Marine Corps for 30 years and has extensive experience with family law, tax law, reviewing contracts, defending clients or serving as their advocate, drafting correspondence, negotiating, and about any other legal matter a Marine might need help with while on active duty. He's a sort of legal Jack-of-all-trades. Our families were friends and neighbors many years ago, and Dave and I have stayed in touch. After Dave retired, he moved back to Kentucky. He can't practice law in Kentucky because he's not licensed here, but he can provide you advice and help regarding your desire to buy out MSI. I've given him some background on the subject, but told him the information would be a lot more accurate coming from you."

Dana looked at Shane and then over at Dave. "Yes . . . thank you so much for this introduction. And Colonel Lockwood, thank you as well for being here today and giving me some help. I appreciate any advice you can provide. I suppose Shane told you I'm pretty clueless about the entire process."

Colonel Lockwood grinned. "First, call me Dave. Second, let's see how much help I can provide before you thank me."

"OK," Dana replied sheepishly, smiling back at him. She was a little intimidated by his crusty manner, although he seemed kind enough. And he was a close friend of Shane's — one of her favorite clients — so he must be OK.

The colonel leaned back in his chair and crossed his arms over his chest as if he were giving himself a hug. There was a legal pad and pen on the table in front of him. "Dana, I know it has been quite a few years since MSI started and your memory may be vague on some of these issues, but why don't you start by telling me the circumstances of your agreement with the three owners, what documents you signed, and who provided the start-up money. Oh, and also if you remember whether there were any attorneys involved in the start-up."

"Sure," Dana said, relaxing a bit in her chair. The colonel seemed genuinely interested. Maybe he could keep her out of legal trouble. "I don't know what Shane has told you, but I worked for nine years at First

Citizens Bank, mainly in the Radcliff branch. The last several years I worked there, I managed the bank's allotment initiative, which was a new service the bank had started in order to generate revenue. This was not what you would think of as a traditional function for a bank. Primarily, we targeted the military — soldiers at Fort Knox — although we also processed allotments for a few other local companies. Basically, I would go out and find businesses that sold products — cars, insurance, televisions, or pretty much anything a soldier would purchase — and offer to set up an automatic monthly payment plan for the purchaser. The way it worked was DFAS — the Defense Finance and Accounting System — which you're probably familiar with since it's the military's payment activity, would deduct the monthly payment from the soldier's paycheck before he received it, and send the money to our bank. We'd log it into a paper ledger — later we developed a computer program to do the accounting — and then we'd send the money to the business. The bank charged two dollars to execute each transaction. As you can imagine, both the business and the soldier liked this service because the business was assured of getting its money, and the soldier knew the payment would be made, even when he or she had deployed. There was a 95% margin on these allotments, so after a year or two, the bank was making money hand over fist. Our president at the time believed in rewarding people in non-traditional ways too, so he created a profit-sharing incentive for my co-worker and me. We met our targets — actually, we exceeded them — and were about to receive a substantial bonus when the bank sold, the new owners brought in a new president, and according to him, he wasn't about to pay such a substantial bonus to someone my age. So while I was on maternity leave, he went looking for a reason to fire me and then did so right before I returned to work. Incidentally, I understand he has fired six women since becoming the president, eight years ago. No men have been fired — just women — but that's another story."

The colonel frowned and his jaw set. He shook his head and looked down at his feet.

"Hard to believe in this day and age, isn't it Dave?" Shane Sanders said, with a sarcastic chuckle.

Dana continued. "An attorney told me I probably could sue the bank for wrongful dismissal, but the likely result would be I'd get my old job back. I decided I'd rather not work there at all if I had to work for him again. So, I started job-hunting. During my job search, three local businessmen approached me to work for them. One was a car dealer, the second sold cars and motorcycles, and the third was a mortgage and insurance broker. When I managed the allotment program at the bank, I worked with each of their companies, so they were familiar with my work. Apparently, they realized what a profit-generating business this was for the bank. So essentially, they wanted me to open up an office and provide the same allotment services for their businesses, and other local businesses, just like I did for the bank. Only *they* would receive the profit — not the bank. The only difference was I had to find a bank willing to accept the money deducted from the paychecks. Once I found a bank, I could do the rest of the work."

"So you took them up on their offer," Dave said, taking notes on his pad.

"Not initially. I spent three more months looking for another job. I really didn't want to stay in banking and just felt I needed a career change. So I interviewed for a public relations position at Hardin Memorial Hospital in Elizabethtown, but didn't get the job. When that happened, I decided it was time to call back Roger Cunningham — one of the three businessmen who'd talked to me initially — and tell him I was ready to take them up on their offer. Shortly thereafter, I met with all three men. We came to an agreement on pretty much everything during our first meeting, including my salary and a 10% equity deal if I grew the business to a certain level in the first year, and I started work a week or two later. It all happened fairly fast."

Colonel Lockwood shifted in his chair and then picked up his pen again. "What sort of agreement did you sign following this meeting?"

"The only document I signed was a short and simple Offer of Employment, laying out my salary, a basic benefits package of paid sick leave, vacation, that sort of thing, and the 10% equity deal. There wasn't much to it. I can show you a copy if you'd like," Dana offered.

"Yes, I'd like to look at the agreement. Now, where did the start-up money come from?"

"As I said, my first task was to find a bank that would accept the money being deducted from the paychecks. This wasn't too hard. Once I found a bank, I obtained a signature loan for the company that was secured by the three men. I borrowed against the loan for only a couple months before the company began turning enough profit to pay expenses." Dana looked down at her papers and smiled at the memory. "Initially, I thought I'd need a cash infusion from them to fund the first year of operations, but as I said, we were making money nearly from the start. So, the three of them actually never invested a dime of their own money. The current procedure is for me to disperse anywhere from $30,000 to $40,000 out of the company account every month to each of them. And at every annual performance meeting, I ask them to put just a fraction of the profits back into the company so I can hire more people, get better offices, and grow the company faster or maybe in alternative areas. But they'd prefer to siphon away every bit of the profit for themselves. It's hard to swallow, because I know the company could perform so much better with some investment money."

"And as a client and friend, it's hard for me to swallow too," Shane said, shaking his head. "It's hard to watch. Dana does all the work and they take all the money. You'd think they'd feel *some* obligation to give her even 25% or 30% of the equity, but apparently they have no moral conscience or sense of fairness."

Dana thought Shane sounded like a big brother. She couldn't imagine him treating his employees so shoddily. "Initially, I was just happy to have the job. But after a few years, it was hard not to believe they were taking advantage of me, and treating the company like their personal cash cow. So, when Shane recently suggested I consider taking over the company or buying them out, I thought seriously about the idea. I've been researching the process, and I've talked to several people who have experience in this area. But honestly, I haven't learned enough to convince myself I can do it legally."

"Are you aware if there was an attorney involved in the start-up of the

121

company?" The colonel seemed more interested in this aspect.

"Not that I'm aware," Dana replied. "Of course I wouldn't know if they were receiving advice on the side, or from a friend. But there was never an attorney present at our meetings and they never mentioned one."

"It would be good if we could be certain there was no attorney involvement. There's a much greater chance of finding a loophole or oversight in the paperwork if they didn't have help from an attorney," the colonel said. "Why don't you gather up any paperwork you have from the start-up period and give it to Shane the next time you're here. I'll get it from him, take a look at everything, and let you know what I think. Sound good?"

"Absolutely," Dana replied. "I appreciate any help or advice you can provide. I'm not in any hurry to do anything. If I decide to go forward with this, I want to do it knowing all the potential hurdles and pitfalls. I don't want any surprises."

"I can't promise there won't be surprises because that's always a risk," the colonel said. "But I'll try to get you as much information as I can and prepare you for the potential challenges I can envision."

Dana sat quietly for a moment, looking down at her papers. Finally, she looked up at the colonel. "Dave . . . I'm afraid MSI never paid me enough to have much savings. I know how much attorneys normally charge, and I don't think I'm in a position to . . ."

The colonel held up his hands. "I understand, Dana. Since I'm not licensed to practice law in Kentucky, coupled with the fact I now consider myself retired, I'm not in a position to charge you for my services either. So that works out well for us both," he added, smiling at her. "Sometimes it works out where I can provide a little assistance to someone, get them started, and before you know it they're off and running. I'm hoping it's going to be this way with you too. Not to mention it'll feel pretty good to correct some past wrongs you've experienced, don't you agree?"

Dana smiled at the idea. "Nothing would make me happier. I can't thank you enough, Dave. I'll get all the relevant documents to Shane and then wait to hear from you. You both must have other things on your plate today, so I won't take up any more of your time. But I want to emphasize how grateful I am for all your help. Whether or not it works out, I've definitely learned a lot."

Gathering up her papers, Dana stood and shook hands with both men, thanked them again, and left the office. What a nice man, she thought, as she briskly walked to her car. How many attorneys would offer their services for no fee? Certainly no attorney she'd ever met — or probably ever would meet in the future! There weren't scads of jokes about lawyers being sharks for no reason. How fortunate for her that her client had a retired lawyer for a friend. She may be unable to pay for his services, but she could pay him back in some other way if she could pull off a buyout. The thought gave her great satisfaction as she drove back to her office at MSI.

15

Three months later, Halloween night 1994

"Blimey!" Marie hollered, after struggling for a good five minutes to help Ryan put the Superman boots overtop of his sneakers. "Why do they have to make these things so bloody tight? You'd think they'd stretch! Whose bloody idea was it anyway to make them go overtop one's own shoes!"

"Ryan's boots aren't bloody, are they Marie?" Liz asked, her eyes open wide.

"The boots are not bloody, Liz," Dana said, scowling at Marie. "We've talked about this before, remember? Where Marie is from, they often use strange words to describe things. Just ignore her like we often do."

Marie rolled her eyes at Dana. "Oh, all right! A poor choice of words considering today is Halloween. But Lizzy, one day when you're older, Auntie Marie will give you British lessons and you'll be a hit with all the boys at school!"

Liz looked at Marie with a blank expression.

"Right, then! Run along and find your jumper — your sweater, I mean. I'll have Ryan's boots fixed in a snap and we'll be off," Marie said, with a wave of her hand.

"Hmmm . . . you seem pretty eager to go." Dana was looking at Marie, her head cocked sideways. "You're not allowed to eat the majority of Liz's candy again. She's onto you, Marie. She remembers last year."

Marie feigned an offended look. "I've no idea what you're talking about! I ate merely a third of her candy last year — and only the pieces I knew would remain stuck in her teeth until *next* Halloween. And Ryan was more than happy to give me all the chocolates he didn't fancy. I admit that may have been a lot, but if he didn't want it, what was I to do — say no? I couldn't disappoint like that . . ."

Dana nodded her head and patted Marie lightly on her back. "OK, sure; whatever you say." She turned and headed down the hall toward the kids' rooms, smiling to herself. "You guys about ready to go? I don't think Marie can wait much longer."

Ryan and Liz bolted out of the bedroom, past Dana, and into the kitchen. "Marie, did you fix my boots?" Ryan peered at Marie.

"Yes, my dear chap. The trick is to put your tennis shoes into your boots *before* you put them on. So, let's give it a go and see if this works better. You sit in the chair and put your foot into this whole bit," she added, placing the boot on the floor.

Ryan did as she instructed and his foot slipped into the boot. "Marie, it worked!"

"Fantastic! Now, let's get the other one on and we're ready to go fetch candy! My, I do love this holiday!" she said excitedly.

"Marie, you know it's not really a holiday, right?" Dana said. "Trick or treating is an American thing, which you don't do as part of Halloween in Europe. You also don't decorate houses in Europe like a ton of people do here. People here seem to get into Halloween more and more every year. I have no idea why."

"What? You really have no idea why?" Marie rolled her eyes at Dana and sighed, as if she were talking to a child. "You don't see that there's something uniquely fabulous about knocking on as many doors as you can manage in one night, holding out a bag and saying, 'trick or treat,' and having it filled with any sort of chocolate and countless other sweets? Then you return home, dump all your treats on the table, and behold — it's as if someone set out a delicious buffet for you! I think it's an absolutely brilliant

125

American tradition!"

"I like Halloween too, Marie," Liz said, gazing up at Marie and grabbing her arm. "Can we go now?"

"Absolutely, my darling!" Marie reached down and straightened her tiara, and then smoothed her hands over Liz's hair. "You look heavenly! And Ryan looks very cool in his Superman costume."

Dana handed Ryan the flashlight. "You guys have fun and I'll see you in an hour or so. And remember, no candy until you get home. I have to check everything to make sure it's safe, OK?"

"We promise, right kiddies? Now, onward march!"

Marie, Ryan, and Liz made their way out the front door, and Dana watched them cut across the lawn toward the house next door. It seemed like only a few months ago since last Halloween. Joey had worked on Halloween night for the past several years, so Dana stayed at the house and doled out candy while Marie had been more than happy to take the kids trick or treating.

She picked up the basket of candy and sat down on the couch nearby, prepared for the doorbell to ring any minute. Her thoughts wandered to the subject she'd spent endless hours contemplating over the past several months — what, if anything, to do about MSI. She'd heard nothing from the colonel since their meeting three months ago. Week after week, she was losing hope he'd come up with a plan for her to gain ownership of the company. She'd come up with nothing new on her own. There were no more people she could think of to call and gain information. Slowly, she was resigning herself to the idea she wouldn't be able to take ownership of MSI, and there were only two options left to consider. First, she could keep working there and hope over time to negotiate more and more equity from the three men. Or second, she could quit MSI and start up her own company, taking as many of the customers with her as she could manage. There was little chance of the first option succeeding, since the three men had scant incentive to relinquish much equity. Trying the second option could bring on a lawsuit against her, not to mention a potentially long, hard period of growth for the new company. So, every time she

126

considered the two options, and then the likely outcomes, she got no further toward deciding what to do. Now, three months after her meeting with the colonel, nothing had changed. She still worked long hours at MSI, received marginal compensation, and felt taken advantage of by her bosses. The whole situation was deeply depressing.

The doorbell rang, and Dana remembered her task at hand. She jumped up with her basket and turned toward the front door.

"Trick or treat," three small bodies yelled when Dana opened the door. They were decked out as tiny monsters.

"Oh my goodness," she exclaimed, covering her mouth with her hand. "You three scared me to death!" She bent over and held out the basket of candy. "Would you like to pick out your own candy? Maybe one or two pieces?"

"Yes, please!" they shouted. One monster slowly picked out two pieces and the other two grabbed a handful. "Thank you, Mrs. Smolenski!"

"You're welcome, my dears. Have fun and be careful." She watched them run across the lawn to the lights next door, then she walked back into her house, closing the door behind her. It was almost too quiet without Ryan and Liz — not to mention the affable and spirited Marie. There were so many times Dana wished she were more like Marie — more assured of herself, less stressed, more carefree. Marie didn't take herself or her life too seriously. Unfortunately, Dana was keenly aware she was not like Marie in nearly every way. Dana was serious, she was painstakingly thorough when considering her options in life and work, and she certainly was not carefree. Sometimes she felt the weight of the world — or more precisely, the weight of her family — on her shoulders. She hated to let people down. Besides, didn't every parent want more for their children than they had growing up?

The doorbell rang again. More small children dressed up and excited. As soon as she came into the house, the doorbell rang again. She decided to sit outside on the front porch in the wooden lawn chair her grandfather had made for her many years ago. It was a clear and cold night, but Dana didn't mind. She laid her head back on the wooden slats of the chair and stared up at a black sky full of bright stars. Every so often an adolescent voice punctuated the silence. It seemed a lifetime ago she was trick or treating herself, not far from here, with two or three of her childhood friends. That was one nice thing about living in a small town; she still had the same friends today. They didn't see much of each other now, as everyone was busy and there was little time for your own friends. Now, the people with whom you shared your time were the parents of your kids' friends.

There would be four or five groups of Trick or Treaters at a time, then nothing for 10 minutes or more. They traveled in packs, it seemed. This was the new norm — safety in numbers. We never had to think about such things when we were out trick or treating, Dana thought. Sometimes change was good, and sometimes it was just sad.

Finally, Dana spotted the familiar image of two children bouncing along the sidewalk, one holding the arm of a tall, slender woman. There was no sign of the flashlight Ryan had been eager to hold earlier in the evening. Guess the novelty wore off. Soon Dana could see three smiling faces in the yellow glow of the streetlight. Despite Marie's purported dislike of children, she sure had a way with her kids, Dana mused. Sometimes she worried about the effect of Marie's lively language and antics on the kids, but they seemed to know that their family rules regarding behavior rarely applied to Marie. She was uniquely special, which made her particularly fun. What it must be like to be fun again, Dana thought. She couldn't remember the last time she had any real fun. Between the kids, her job, and trying to work harder on her marriage, she had no time at all for herself.

"Mom, we got tons of candy!" Ryan yelled, bounding up the steps to the front door and holding out his bag.

"We did!" Liz held open her bag for Dana to admire.

Dana looked up from their bags and laughed. "Great job, kiddos! You were out long enough. I figured you were gathering a huge stash. How did Marie make out? Did she get to sample a lot of candy to make sure it was OK for you to eat?"

"She had a lot for sure!" Ryan said.

"It's only fair, you know," Marie retorted. "Payment for a job well done!"

"I'm not saying anything!" Dana chuckled to herself. "OK, time to go in, shut off the outside lights, and sort through your stash."

"I'll come in for a bit, but then I must get back to my place," Marie said, holding the door for everyone. "Lots to catch up on before work tomorrow. By the by, forgot to ask earlier, have you heard anything from the colonel?"

Dana shook her head and sighed. "Not a word. I'm really disappointed. I thought he'd come up with something by now. All I can assume is he can't find anything."

"How long has it been since you met with him?" Marie plopped down in a kitchen chair and pulled off her leather boots, stretching her long legs and massaging her toes.

"Over three months now. If he was going to find something, I would think he'd have done it by now, wouldn't you?" Dana sifted her hands through the two bags of candy the kids dumped on the kitchen table, inspecting each piece for signs of tampering. "OK you two, you can pick three pieces of whatever you want now, and then you can have three pieces a day until it's gone."

Ryan and Liz grabbed their loot and ran down the hallway toward their rooms.

"Yes, but he hasn't rung you back to tell you he *hasn't* found anything either, has he?" Marie asked.

"No, but it's the same thing. He doesn't want to disappoint me, I'm sure."

"I agree; it doesn't look promising." Marie bent over and kneaded her left foot. "But don't give up hope, Darling! Not until you know absolutely for sure there's nothing you can do."

"I'm not, well, not completely anyway." You can never give up hope, Dana thought. If you don't have hope, there's not much point to living.

129

16

February 1995

Joey cleared off the last few dishes from the table and placed them next to the sink. Dana methodically picked up each piece and rinsed it, placing it carefully in the dishwasher. "You OK?" Joey asked, craning his neck to see the front of her face.

"For the third time this evening, Joey, yes, I'm fine." Dana threw her dishcloth into the sink. She wiped her hands on the towel and sharply turned and went into the living room. She didn't feel like continuing the conversation they were having this morning before she left for work.

Ryan and Liz were sitting on the floor, Legos strewn from one end of the room to the other. Dana plopped down on the couch and put her feet up on the coffee table. She picked up the News Enterprise and sunk back into the couch.

The phone in the kitchen rang.

Dana flung the newspaper onto the couch beside her. "I finally get to sit down and relax for *one* minute and the phone rings."

"I'll get it, Dana," Joey said from the kitchen. "Sit still."

Dana picked up her newspaper again and tried to relax — something she found harder and harder to do these days. Between the stress she felt at work and the more frequent disagreements with Joey — no doubt caused by their equally stressful jobs — sitting down and relaxing was one of the hardest things for her to do.

Joey stuck his head around the corner of the kitchen. "It's for you, Dana," he said in a low voice. He covered the mouthpiece of the phone with his hand. "Colonel Lockwood. Maybe he found something."

Dana stared at Joey for several moments before his words registered. Colonel Lockwood! After all these months! This was going to be good news, or it was going to be bad news. There would be no in-between.

"Dana, he's waiting!" Joey said louder. Liz and Ryan stopped talking and looked up at their father.

Dana leaped off the couch and was in the kitchen in four steps. She grabbed the phone out of Joey's hand. "Hello? This is Dana."

"Good evening, Dana. Dave Lockwood. I hope it's not too late to call. I wanted to wait until you were home from work and finished with dinner."

His baritone voice was salve to Dana's ears. "Hi Colonel . . . Dave. No, it's perfectly fine. Dinner is over and we were sitting in the living room. It's nice to hear from you!" She tried not to sound anxious.

"I apologize for taking so long to get back with you. You probably gave up on me, didn't you?" the colonel said with a chuckle.

"Oh . . . no . . . not at all," Dana lied. "You told me you'd get back with me after you'd looked over all the papers I'd provided and had some time to research the issue. I figured you were busy, or you didn't find anything." Dana's voice sounded unusually high-pitched, and she felt out of breath and light-headed.

Colonel Lockwood cleared this throat. "Actually, it was a little of both. I was busy with a couple cases I'm helping research for a former colleague, but I wasn't having much luck coming up with anything on your case either. So, I talked with a couple acquaintances whose backgrounds are more aligned with corporate law, and they gave me some ideas and reading assignments. I've done enough research now I think I've come up with a plan that might work. Would you be available sometime tomorrow to sit down and talk?"

"Yes, absolutely!" Dana couldn't get the words out fast enough. "And tomorrow is my husband's day off. If you don't mind, I'd like to bring him along so he can hear your plan as well. Would that be OK?"

131

"Sure, I'd be happy to have him join us. Do you want to meet during your regular lunch hour so it's easier for you to get away? I suspect our discussion won't take longer than an hour."

"Yes, that'd be great. There's a small coffee and sandwich shop in the Lincoln Trail Plaza off 31W. Usually it's not too crowded, and the food is pretty good. Do you want to meet there at noon?" Dana could feel the excitement in her stomach now creeping into her throat. She was finding it hard to talk.

"I know the place. Noon sounds great. I look forward to meeting your husband too. See you then. Goodnight."

Dana heard a click on the line as the colonel hung up the phone. She stood in the kitchen holding the receiver to her ear, frozen in place. Her heart was pounding in her chest. She'd wanted to yell at him, 'tell me now!' How would she be able to sleep tonight?

"By the sound of things, I'm assuming the phone call was good news?"

Dana turned around to find Joey standing in the doorway, hands on his hips, and a smile across his face. "He said he has a plan he thinks might work! He wants to meet tomorrow during lunch to talk. Since tomorrow is your day off, I asked if you could come too and he said it was fine. I thought we both could take notes, which would help if it's a complicated legal strategy."

"Sure, I'd like to hear what he has to say."

"If this works out, it might be the last lunch we're able to afford for several years," Dana added pensively, gazing across the room. "I hope I'm making the right decision."

"Look, we've talked about this a lot. We laid out all the pros and cons, and we made the decision. So, don't start having second thoughts already." Joey's voice was steady and firm. "Your first reaction was the right one — cautious optimism!"

"You're right," Dana said, the frown easing from her face. "I hate the way things are now. Something has to change or I'm going to have to find something else to do."

"And, before you start to worry about anything, let's wait and hear what the colonel has to say tomorrow."

"Yep, I agree. No sense getting worked up at this point. I think I'll go back in the living room and try to read the paper again. Besides, it's a little too quiet in there. They must be up to something," Dana added, with a grin. If only she could take her own advice. She knew she'd be up all night, ruminating on what the colonel was going to tell her tomorrow.

* * *

Dana forced herself to stay in bed until the sunrise peeped through the cracks of the blinds. She'd hardly slept at all — maybe a couple hours at best. It surprised her that she didn't feel tired. Instead, she was raring to go — straight to lunch, in fact. Unfortunately, first she had to get through the morning at work. There was her weekly meeting at 9AM with her small staff, and then a more important meeting at 10AM with a potential new client. She'd have to be on her game during the new client meeting, which probably would be about the time her body would realize it had about two hours sleep the night before, and it didn't want to process any more information. And then, she'd really have to be on her game when she met with Colonel Lockwood, or he might think she was not worth his help. She still couldn't believe her luck — having an attorney help her and not charge for his work! But maybe he wouldn't be able to help her at all. Dana squeezed her eyes tight and tried to dismiss all the negative thoughts swirling around in her head. She just needed to get through the morning and in about six hours she'd know a lot more about her future — one way or another.

Folding back the heavy covers, Dana swung her legs over the edge of the bed and sat up. She turned around to see if she'd disturbed Joey, but he was still lying motionless next to her in the bed, breathing heavily. Poor man,

Dana thought. I'm sure when we got married he never imagined he'd be living with such a crazy person.

Standing up silently, she walked over to the closet and pulled out a pair of black pants and a black-and-white striped sweater. She picked out a pair of trouser socks and some underwear and tiptoed down the hallway toward the bathroom. 20 minutes later, Dana emerged — dressed and coiffed — and thinking about that first cup of coffee.

The sunlight was streaming in the small window above the sink by the time she rounded the corner and walked into the kitchen. She'd prepared the coffee the night before and set the timer for 7:30AM, but it was only 7:10AM. Dana sighed and turned on the pot. She slumped into a chair and waited, wondering how people survived the day when they didn't drink coffee.

"I thought I heard you up already." Joey's voice pierced the morning solitude. "Too excited to sleep?"

Dana sighed and looked up at him. "Good morning — I hope it is one, anyway. I didn't sleep much, but I feel OK so far."

"You seemed to toss and turn a lot, but hopefully you got enough sleep in between to function today. I'll be with you at lunch to take notes, but I'm afraid you're on your own in the office."

"Don't worry," Dana said. "I've got all this adrenaline to make sure I do. I'll just grab a banana and coffee and head to the office so I can get everything done before our meeting."

"You don't want breakfast before you go? It'll help you think better, get your work done faster."

"Thanks, but I'm fine. I don't have any appetite right now. We have snacks in the office. I'll grab something later." Dana stood up and returned to the bedroom to get her purse. On the way back down the hall, she peeked in Ryan's and Liz's bedrooms to make sure they were still asleep. They looked so precious and innocent when they were sleeping. A stark contrast from how they could be when they were awake, Dana thought.

She fixed her coffee, grabbed a banana and an apple from the fruit bowl, and said goodbye to Joey. Dana was out the door before he could say

134

anything else. Peaceful solitude — that's what she wanted this morning. Time to reflect and prepare. It was going to be a long day.

* * *

"It was great to meet you, Mr. Valimont," Dana said enthusiastically. "I hope I've answered all your questions about our services and you now feel comfortable about doing business with us. Call me anytime if you have any further questions or concerns," she added, handing her business card to him.

"Thank you, Dana." Mr. Valimont took the card, and then gave her a hardy handshake. "I suspect we'll be seeing each other soon. I'm impressed with what I've heard from colleagues in the business and from our meeting today. We'll come up with an equitable arrangement for both of us, I'm sure."

"Thank you, Mr. Valimont. I appreciate that. I'll wait to hear from you. Have a great rest of the day." Dana closed the door behind him. She walked back to her office and sat down in her chair, smiling the entire time.

"Productive meeting?" Brenda Sheppard was leaning against the door-frame of Dana's office with a cocky grin on her face.

"I think so!" Dana couldn't contain her excitement. "I would be thrilled to lure him away from First Citizens after all these years. And it's only fair since I was the one who got him as a client for the bank in the first place. Oh, and Brenda, he told me the bank makes processing mistakes all the time now. He said he really hasn't had good service from the bank since *we* left, and he's tired of all the errors. He wants to turn over the allotments for someone to manage and never have anyone call him about errors again. I told him we were that company. Do you think we can deliver on my promise?"

Brenda didn't hesitate. "Absolutely we can! It's the only way we know how to do business. And that's why you pay me the big bucks! Oh wait, scratch that last part . . . it slipped out accidentally." She laughed sarcastically. "That's why you're *going* to pay me the big bucks one day."

"Brenda, I swear if this meeting today goes well and I ever manage to buy the company, I will pay you what you deserve — and that's a promise!" Dana glanced at the clock on her wall. "Is that the time? I've got to run!"

"OK then, good luck — and I mean that even more now! Don't come back here without a plan. I need that pay raise!"

"Got it!" Dana yelled over her shoulder. She'd already grabbed her purse and was halfway out the door. Jumping into her car, she took off toward the Lincoln Trail Plaza. It was a 15-minute ride, at most. She glanced at the clock — 11:50 AM. There was time to get to the restaurant without risking a speeding ticket, so she took a deep breath and let her foot ease off the gas. One day — probably decades from now — she was going to stop running from one thing to another all day long. At least in the smallish town of Radcliff, traffic was rarely an issue.

She pulled into the shopping plaza and found a parking spot close to the front of the restaurant. Joey's car was already there. She didn't know what car the colonel drove, but she suspected he was there too. Once a Marine, always a Marine — wasn't that the saying? He was certain to arrive early.

Dana's suspicions were correct. As she got out of the car, the front door to the restaurant opened and Dana could see it was the colonel inside who was holding it open for her. Joey stood nearby. "Well, thank you, Colonel. Sorry if I'm late. My meeting just ended, and I literally jumped in the car and drove here."

"No, you're not late. Joey and I arrived early and were getting to know each other. Marines and police officers usually can find a sufficient number of things to talk about." Colonel Lockwood ushered Dana to their table and pulled out a chair for her.

"Thank you again," Dana said, as she sat down neatly in the chair. She wasn't used to such old-fashioned manners. She took out her notebook and pen and placed her purse beside her on the floor.

Joey took a seat next to her and opposite the colonel. His pad and pen were sitting on the table. "How'd your meeting go this morning, Dana — good?"

"Yes, it did," Dana said, without hesitation. "And it was quite entertaining too, which I'll tell you about tonight."

The colonel pulled out his notes. "Hopefully, we can build on that momentum with another productive meeting. If you don't mind, and you're not too hungry, I'd like to conduct the business part of this meeting first and then we can eat."

Dana was happy to concur. She'd found it difficult to concentrate on a business discussion and to eat at the same time. One of those two things would get the short stick every time.

"I'll try to explain the issue, or the plan I'm proposing, with as minimal legalese as possible. But stop me if I lose you, Dana, because it'll be crucial for you to have a complete understanding of the legal issue we're going to cite when it's time for you to talk with the three investors," the colonel said, studying Dana's face.

Dana nodded and picked up her pen.

"The basis of our argument is this." The colonel placed his hands on the table in front of him. "There really isn't a company for you to buy because the investors never properly — meaning legally — set up a company by issuing shares and filing the required reports. As owners of a company operating in the Commonwealth of Kentucky, they were required to register the company, issue shares to each of the investors, document this issuance of shares by completing and filing the required reports, and have annual meetings and file annual meeting reports — all with the State." The colonel looked down at his notes. "My understanding is none of the three investors put any start-up money into the business. You, Dana, simply opened a line of credit in their names — but for which they signed — and then you used this line of credit to fund the operations of the business. After a few months, you began to turn a profit, and once you did, you used the profits to pay down the line of credit. It wasn't long before you paid off the line of credit, at which point you deposited the profits into a money market account. These profits being deposited monthly into the money market account quickly added up to some serious money. Once the investors found out how much money was being made, they had you set up regular monthly withdrawals from the money market account into their own personal bank accounts, essentially raiding the account each month of most of the profits. Is that a fairly accurate rendition of the events?"

Dana stared at the colonel, trying to absorb his words and connect the logic. She was unfamiliar with corporate law, so she didn't understand what the three men had either done wrong or failed to do, and why it was important for her ability to get the company. "Yes, in terms of the sequence of events, that's what happened. I'm sorry, but you're going to have to explain in simpler terms the part of your argument regarding failing to set up the company legally and failing to file the required reports."

"Of course," the colonel said, adjusting his chair. He looked over at Joey and smiled. "Are you able to follow any of this corporate legal jargon?"

"Some of it." Joey looked down at the notes he'd been taking. "But like Dana, I'm fuzzy on the part about the necessity of issuing shares and filing reports. Correct me if I'm wrong, but based on what you said, I'm assuming if you want to start a corporation in the Commonwealth of Kentucky, you must get the correct forms from the State, and then file these forms with the proper authorities. You need to hold annual meetings and then file an annual meeting report. These actions make a corporation legal in the eyes of the State. What you're saying is because MSI's owners never did this, there really isn't an actual company the three men can sell to Dana."

"That's the gist of the argument in a nutshell, yes," the colonel said, pulling a folder from the briefcase beside him and sliding it across the table toward Dana. "I took the liberty of obtaining a copy of the necessary filings and an instruction booklet from the courthouse so you can read about the legal requirements. This will give you enough background on the subject to sound as knowledgeable as any authority. If you want to do any further reading, you can go to any library and research Kentucky's requirements for establishing a corporation. A librarian can direct you to the right reference books. That's essentially what we attorneys will do when we need to conduct research on a subject like this one."

Dana picked up the folder and opened it, quickly thumbing through the contents. She closed the folder and placed it back on the table. "So if they never set up MSI in the first place as a legally registered corporation, how am I going to buy it? I mean, how can they sell something to me that doesn't exist legally? Because now it *really* seems like MSI should belong to me, since they did nothing other than have me set up a line of credit in their names, and then allow me to use it. I could have done that myself!" Dana was feeling many conflicting emotions.

The colonel nodded his head in agreement. "The situation is complex, and it's also ambiguous, which makes our argument and our options less clear cut as well. I've given a lot of thought to the option I'm going to suggest to you, and I've also run it by several attorneys. It's not a given that it'll work by any stretch of the imagination, because you can never predict with certainty how people are going to react, and I don't know the investors at all. But I think it's the *only* option that *might* work with the least chance of attracting a countersuit in return for our efforts."

"A countersuit?" Joey asked, in a startled tone. His eyebrows raised and his mouth hung open.

"There's always that possibility," the colonel said. "Our objective is to reduce the risk of a countersuit to a tolerable level. Dana will need to decide how far she's willing to go before she jeopardizes her current situation at work or risks a countersuit. But before you let your concerns get the better of you, allow me to lay out the case, and then we can discuss the various things that could go wrong."

"Sure, go ahead, Colonel," Joey said with a chuckle. "You just scared me a little with the 'countersuit' word."

"And that's OK," the colonel said. "Because you need to go into this thing with your eyes wide open as to the different scenarios that could result."

Dana didn't say a word. At this point, she wasn't sure what to think, but she hoped the conversation didn't make her heart and her stomach sink any further.

The colonel leaned toward Dana, his forearms resting lightly on the table.

"Dana, I think your best option is to meet with each of the three investors individually and feel them out — and you and I can sit down at some point and go over how this might occur. You could start by telling them you've worked very hard for them for the past nine years and grown MSI into a successful business, making a significant amount of money for each of them every month. However, because you're limited to an annual salary with a very modest equity holding, you'll never be able to make the amount of money *they* are making. You only want for yourself what you've made possible for them. Emphasize the unfairness of the current deal for you."

Dana was listening intently now, nodding her head and thinking. That seemed reasonable. She just wanted an equitable deal from them — the same thing they'd been getting for years. Fairness — who could argue against that?

"Since you know them pretty well after working with them for nine years, I suggest you select the most reasonable one to approach first," the colonel continued, looking straight into Dana's eyes and speaking slowly and deliberately. "Again, emphasize that you've worked hard for them for nine years and now you need to think about taking care of your family. You're no longer satisfied working under the current arrangement. Provide them the legal background we just discussed, explain how they never legally incorporated MSI as a business and thus there really is no 'business' to sell. But in the spirit of working together, you'd like to present them with two options. The first option would be the easiest for everyone, which is they 'sell' the business of MSI to you, and you present them with a monetary offer. The second option would be to tell them you'll be quitting MSI to start your own, similar business, and they'll need to hire someone to fill your position. However, over time you no doubt will take a lot of MSI's current clients away from them because the clients are used to working with you and your staff, and you've built up a relationship with them. Therefore, you'd prefer to work with them, and you hope they see that option number one is best for all parties."

"What if they say no to both options?" Dana could feel her face was hot and flushed. "What if they say they won't sell me the business, and if I try to take away the clients, they'll sue me?"

Joey was uncharacteristically quiet now. His face had grown pale during the first mention of a lawsuit.

"There's always the possibility of being sued," the colonel replied calmly. "As I said, you never know how someone is going to react to being threatened. And essentially, that's what you're doing. You're presenting them with two options, neither of which they'll like. But most businessmen know all the time and money that can be sucked up in a legal battle, not to mention a public spat in a small town, which can be harmful to a business as well. So, you're betting they'll take the money and not do anything that'll attract negative attention to the matter. It may take them a while to get to that point, but you've got time. They'll no doubt be angry at first, but hopefully they'll come around in a short amount of time."

"Will you be with me in the room when I present the options to them?" Dana was pretty sure she knew the answer to her question.

Colonel Lockwood grinned. "I can sit in the room with you as your business advisor, but since I'm not a licensed attorney in the Commonwealth of Kentucky, I cannot be there as your legal counsel."

Dana smiled sheepishly. "That's OK. I'd be content with just the moral support, or a friendly face, or even a warm body on my side of the table."

The colonel laughed. "I'm sure all this sounds plenty confusing and daunting. But I think if you read the material in this packet I put together for you, you'll start to feel more comfortable, and then you'll feel confident about presenting your case. Now, when I said I could sit at the table with you as your business advisor, I was referring to the deal-closing meeting — not the initial, informal meetings you'll need to hold with each of the investors individually. I believe you need to have those meetings privately, because as businessmen, I'm confident they won't appreciate an outsider being in the room when they're presented with options for the demise of their business. This meeting needs to take the form of a friendly discussion where you use your collaborative and persuasive skills to convince them that accepting your monetary proposal is the best choice for everyone involved."

141

Dana stared down at the table, her eyebrows knitted together. After a long pause, she looked up at Colonel Lockwood. "I guess at our first meeting I should have clarified I don't have a sizable amount of money saved to purchase MSI. Maybe if I owned the business, and no longer had to give them nearly every penny of the monthly profits, I could use that money to pay them off over a several-year period. But why would they agree to that when they already receive the profits now *and* the company belongs to them?" Dana instantly regretted her sarcastic tone. "Sorry, Dave. I didn't sleep well last night, and I guess I'm a little short on patience. I know you're trying to help me, and I'm incredibly grateful. But I don't see how I can make an offer to pay them off when I have no money."

Colonel Lockwood smiled and then reached across the table and patted her arm. "You did tell me, Dana, at our first meeting. You apologized for not having any money to pay my legal fees, and then I told you I wouldn't be billing you because I'm not a licensed attorney in Kentucky. I assumed since you had no money to pay legal fees, you also had no money to pay off three investors for their ownership in a very successful business. The answer is you would obtain the money by applying for a signature loan, and MSI would be used as collateral for the loan, probably along with any other capital assets you own, such as your home."

"Oh!" The idea she could get a large signature loan when she had barely an asset to her name — other than her personal belongings — astounded Dana. Her mind sprinted through the small number of capital assets she owned. The drill took about eight seconds, even when factoring in her entire shoe collection. "We don't have much equity in our home yet, we have two fairly new cars, and that's about it. I can't imagine a bank would give me a signature loan based on my assets," Dana said gloomily.

"This might surprise you, Dana, but you're wrong," the colonel said, with calm assurance. "I checked around a little, using some papers you gave me at our initial meeting, and I was told if you're able to use MSI as collateral, you probably could get a signature loan for half to three-quarters of a million dollars. So, as part of your and Joey's decision process regarding if, and then how, you want to proceed, you should contact some banks and figure out how much of a signature loan you would quality for, and then ask for a loan guarantee letter for that amount. We'll need that guarantee letter in order to proceed."

Dana sat in stunned silence, gaping at the colonel.

Joey was the first to speak. "Are you serious? She could get a signature loan for up to seven hundred and fifty-thousand dollars? I don't know whether to be thrilled with that piece of information of scared out of my wits!"

"No kidding! My thoughts exactly!" Dana's eyes darted from Joey to the colonel. "I can't believe *I* could get a loan like that with the tiny amount of things I own! And if I could, I'm not sure I want to — especially if they aren't willing to sell and I have to open up my own business. I'm afraid that might be too much risk for us to swallow."

Colonel Lockwood shook his head. "If they forced you to quit, and you then started your own company, you most likely would *not* qualify for a large signature loan. This would work only if the three investors accepted your offer to buy them out, in which case you'd then be able to use MSI as collateral for the loan."

"Oh, I see." Dana nodded her head slowly. "Basically, this entire plan works *only* if I'm able to convince the investors that accepting the money I can get from a signature loan is the best option they have, correct?"

"That would be correct, yes." The colonel sat back in his chair and crossed his arms.

Dana leaned forward against the table and crossed her ankles tightly under her seat. She blinked several times and then rubbed her eyes. They felt like sandpaper. She wanted to lay her head on the hard table and take a nap. She felt drained — physically, but mostly emotionally. "All of this is a lot to consider, Colonel. As you said, I have some homework to do regarding the legal issues, and I need to find out more about a signature loan. But honestly, I can't thank you enough for all the work you've done to figure this out and give me an option to consider. It means more to me than you can imagine."

"And I second everything Dana said," Joey added, offering his outstretched hand to the colonel. "We may decide this is too much risk to add to our lives right now, but at least we know the options and what the risks are for each one so we can make an informed decision. I'm fairly sure we would not have started down this path without your help."

"That's certainly true," Dana said. "I would've continued along the same path for who knows how long. It's already been nine years."

"I'm happy to help, Dana. My daughter is not much younger than you. I'd hate to see anyone taking advantage of her like you're experiencing. I can appreciate this was a good deal for you in the beginning. But after two or three years, they should have adjusted the business arrangement more in your favor. I suspect simply making you an equal partner would've kept you happy indefinitely, and they still would have made a lot of money. But the fact they've been taking all the profits, and haven't offered you some sort of profit-sharing arrangement since that minuscule one you received after meeting your first-year goal, is simply appalling. If I'm able to help in some small way, I'm happy to do so. We'll call it my good deed for the year," he added, with a laugh. "Now, how about we order something to eat?"

"Good idea, I'm starving!" Joey stood up halfway and waved over the waitress. "And we insist on buying lunch. It's the least we can do to thank you for all your time and effort."

"Fair enough, Joey," the colonel said, with a smile. "Thank you."

Dana was so exhausted she wasn't sure she could eat anything. The prospect of gaining ownership of MSI thrilled her. But the thought of confronting the three investors scared her out of her mind. She worried she could lose her job by pursing this and was afraid she might hurt her family by spending all her time on this endeavor. Confused by all the conflicting emotions, she didn't know what to think. Shell-shocked — that's how she felt.

"Dana, you ready to eat?" Joey asked, peering at her.

"Yes . . . sorry . . . just thinking about everything." Dana forced a smile.

"It's a lot to think about." The colonel reached out and patted Dana's arm again. "The good news is you've got whatever time you need to make the right decision for you both. No one is pushing you to do anything. So relax, do some research, think about it, and then call me if you decide to move forward. At that point, we'll work up a detailed plan."

Dana's face relaxed, and she managed a grin. She took a deep breath. "You're right, there's no hurry to do anything. I was a little overwhelmed for a minute or two." She smiled at both men and then picked up the menu and perused the sandwich section. It would take a lot of research, thought, and planning — not to mention a boatload of confidence and fortitude on her part — to pull this off. Moxie and grit weren't characteristics she came by naturally. This was small-town America. Her parents and grandparents had taught her to treat others with the utmost kindness, that she was more likely to get what she wanted by using honey rather than a stick, and to 'get along' by 'going along.' Fighting fire with fire wasn't going to be easy for her, but she knew it was going to be necessary.

17

June 1995

Summer was in full bloom and the flowers planted outside the Willis and Keyham building resembled big puffballs of purple, pink, and white. Each morning when Dana pulled into her regular parking space, she sat for a moment observing how the flowers had grown or changed, and admiring the sheer beauty of something sprouting from dirt. She was too busy this year to grow her usual spread of flowers at home; so these, planted all around the perimeter of her office building, were serving as a substitute.

However, this particular morning Dana hardly glanced at the fetching blooms. She'd tossed and turned all night, something she was experiencing with increased regularity. This was the day she'd been dreading for four months — ever since the colonel told her she needed to be alone when she spoke to her three investors individually. There was no sugar-coating it; today was going to be agonizing. Thankfully, her first meeting was with George Redmond, and she'd always liked Mr. Redmond more than the other two men. He was smart, personable, and as far as she could tell fair in his business dealings. Still, she was a bundle of nerves this morning, trying to muster the confidence to deliver a persuasive and compelling presentation — not to mention the most important part — convincing the men they must allow her to purchase the company.

Picking up her folders and purse from the passenger seat, Dana threw open the car door and swung her legs onto the pavement. At 8AM, it already was warm and muggy outside — mid-70s and about 80 percent humidity. It was not Dana's favorite time of the year. Of course the office temperature, regulated by Willis and Keyham, would be about 65 degrees. Being able to regulate the thermostat in her own office was going to be a wonderful perk once she owned the business.

As she approached the front door, it swung open ahead of her. "Good morning, Boss!" Brenda Sheppard held open the large metal and glass door with one hand and greeted Dana with a cup of coffee in the other. "I've known you long enough to predict with one hundred percent confidence that you'll be stressed out to the max today. So being the fabulous — although significantly underpaid — employee that I am, I'm starting you off right at the door with your favorite cup of hazelnut coffee! Now I ask you, can your morning get any better than that?"

Dana looked at Brenda and laughed. "That's so sweet! You're right; you know me too well. I ran off and forgot my coffee on the kitchen counter this morning, of all days! And I didn't sleep well either, so I really needed it. Thank you. Oh, and good morning."

"Yes, good morning," Brenda replied. "It might help to remember that hopefully in a few brief hours, you'll be a third of the way to fulfilling your career dream."

"Hopefully," Dana said, straight-faced and with little enthusiasm.

Brenda cocked her head sideways. "What do you mean? Is there something I don't know?"

"No, don't pay any attention to me," Dana mumbled, rolling her eyes and shaking her head. "I'm just being my usual pessimistic, less-than-confident self."

"Then consider today the first step toward a new you! And you can practice your new skills on George. You know he's a big teddy bear, and he likes you. That should make today a lot easier."

"You're right. If I have trouble today with George Redmond, I'll never make it through the next two meetings, so this will be it. At which point I'll have to suck it up and hope I still have a job after today, and also that George doesn't rat me out to Wayne and Roger . . . especially Roger."

"Let's not go down that path right now," Brenda said. "Let's keep moving toward your office and get you situated and thinking positive thoughts. I'm available to help you with anything you need, like being a guinea pig for you to practice your talk, a coffee boy — or girl, actually — to keep you caffeinated and upright, or maybe just an employee who needs to go back to her office and get some work done!"

"I'm fine, Brenda," Dana said with a laugh. "But thanks for the cheering up. I needed it. You can go back to your office and I'll get ready for my meeting. I'll manage today just fine, but thanks for the concern. I do appreciate it."

"OK Boss, whatever you want. I'll be in my office if you decide you need something."

"Thanks, Brenda." Dana continued down the hall to her office and dropped her files and purse on her desk. She sat down and rubbed her forehead and eyebrows. It felt so relaxing she closed her eyes and laid her head on the desk. How nice it would be to drift away to a peaceful slumber.

Suddenly the telephone sitting next to Dana's head rang loudly in her ear, jolting her upright in the chair. "Scare me to death!" she said aloud, while picking up the phone. "MSI, Dana Smolenski."

"Morning Sunshine! I'm ringing to make certain you didn't oversleep this morning and ruin the rest of your life." Marie's voice was a rude awakening.

"Hi Marie," Dana said, still groggy and disoriented from her 15 seconds of solitude.

"Blimey! Perhaps it's good I rang, since you sound as if you actually *were* asleep!"

"Of course I was not asleep," Dana said indignantly. "Well, only a little . . . maybe," she added, groaning. "Geez, OK, I put my head down on the desk for a moment and might have nodded off. I'm dog-tired, Marie. I didn't sleep well, of course, and then I forgot my coffee at home and haven't had a chance yet to drink half the pot here and wake up. So, only small talk, please. I'm not up for anything else."

"Then may I suggest you drink up quickly, Darling? You do recall the most important meeting of your life thus far is a mere 47 minutes away, right?" Marie's voice was full of piss and vinegar as usual.

"I can tell you've already had *your* coffee this morning. Maybe you should be a real chum, as you say, and come over here and help me through my meeting. George has had a particular fondness for you since the day you two met. That could come in handy right now."

"No, not happening. I remember specifically you telling me the colonel wanted you to meet with each man alone. And George is a pussycat, by the by. You can manage him splendidly. However, it is a shame you don't play golf. There have been many deals cut over 18 holes, and if I remember one thing about George, he loves golf nearly as much as he loves his business."

"If I played golf, Marie, I wouldn't be in this position at all. I'd be like my old partner, remember him? He and Jim Fugitte now have an extremely successful business because they're both men, and they play golf with each other and with their clients. Because I'm not a man and I don't play golf, or go have a drink after work, or do any of the other things men do, they're not as comfortable with me and they don't treat me the same way. I'm an outsider, a woman who has two kids to take care of and no time to play golf and bond with my male colleagues. And that's why, even though it's just George, it's still going to be an awkward, tough meeting for me." Dana stood up at her desk, fully awake and charged.

"Right then!" Marie's voice had perked up even more, if that were possible. "I could tell straight away I needed to light a fire in your knickers this morning. My work here is done. Good luck, Darling! Break a leg and all that nonsense, and ring me when it's over, yes? Ta!"

Dana heard a click and realized Marie had hung up. She sat down, staring at the wall in front of her, the receiver dangling in her hand. After a moment, she wondered if the phone call from Marie had really happened or did she fall asleep and dream the whole unpleasant conversation? It seemed real, but Dana was so tired she wasn't certain. She reached across her desk and picked up the coffee Brenda had handed her, taking a long drink.

Pulling out her papers and briefing charts, Dana settled into her chair and thought about her impending meeting. She didn't know how much George remembered of their first encounter nine years ago when they created MSI and agreed to her salary and the incentive deal. Roger Cunningham, the only one interested in saving pennies, had worked out most of the details. The other two men had focused on getting the allotments set up quickly and running smoothly for their own businesses; turning a profit was secondary to eliminating the need to track down missed payments. One thing Dana remembered explicitly was that it was George who made sure she received a decent salary and the one-year incentive program that enabled her to earn 10 percent of the company. Unfortunately, his interest in seeing her get a fair shake didn't extend beyond MSI's first year. In fact, over the last five or so years, George and Wayne Higgins seemed to have sat back and let Roger make the operational decisions and deal with Dana. Not that there was much for him to do; the company ran well on its own and needed minimal input from anyone. Dana was certain Roger's only concern was to ensure nothing interfered with his, George's, and Wayne's monthly deposit of MSI's profits into their respective bank accounts. If Dana were to gain ownership of the company, all three would surely miss the money, but Roger most of all.

Dana quickly flipped through her charts and briefing notes, then closed the folder. Staring at the grainy manila cover, she rubbed her hand over it slowly, unable to pull her eyes away. There was utter quiet in the office. She sat upright in her chair, her breathing slowed, and she contemplated what was at stake today. A peaceful, serene stillness crept through her body. Surprised at her own calmness, a grin crossed her face. She *must* be tired! Maybe she was so thoroughly exhausted she couldn't muster the appropriate amount of fear anymore. Whatever the reason, she was grateful for the anxiety respite, however long it might last.

"Dana, George is here!" Brenda's voice rudely disrupted her newfound placidity. "He's 30 minutes early. I told him to wait in my office and I'd let you know he's here. What do you want me to do with him?"

Dana dropped her head and sighed. "Give me two minutes to grab another cup of coffee and then bring him in. At least I won't have time to get nervous; it's too late for that."

"Sure, Boss. Now remember, all our jobs and livelihoods depend on your performance for the next hour, so good luck." Brenda winked at Dana and laughed out loud. "Just kidding! You'll be great, and whatever happens, we'll all survive. I'll go small talk with George and then bring him back."

"Thanks, Brenda." Dana picked up her coffee cup, patted Brenda on the back, and made her way toward the kitchen. Before she got back to her office, Dana heard Brenda escorting George down the hallway. So much for small talk.

"Good Morning, Mr. Redmond," Dana said in her friendliest voice. "Thank you for coming here to meet. I hope it wasn't too inconvenient for you this morning."

"Not at all, Dana. I often think I should drop by here more and check on things. But you seem to have had everything under control for many years now, so I figure why bother you, right?" George strolled into Dana's office and casually sat down in the chair closest to her desk. "By the way, sorry to show up early, but I had a meeting pop up on the calendar so I was hoping I could take care of your meeting a little earlier and took a chance you'd be free," he said, with a wave of his hand.

"Yes, absolutely," Dana replied, relatively sure what popped up was a tee time. George wore light khaki slacks and a Nike polo shirt. The office or golf course — he could frequent either. She could feel her pulse quicken and she reminded herself to breathe and relax. It was just George, after all.

Dana picked up her notes and charts from the desk and sat down in the chair next to George. She'd thought about sitting at her desk and looking down at him. It might've been more intimidating and possibly benefited her. But at the last minute, she decided not to appear threatening or pushy; that wouldn't work with George. She needed him to see the injustice of the situation and then become an advocate for her cause. She handed him a copy of her slides. "Mr. Redmond, these are for you to review either now or later on, and serve as a validation of my numbers. But you won't need them to understand our discussion today because it's pretty straightforward."

George had maintained a friendly smile on his face, but it was fading. "OK, Dana," was all he said.

Dana looked directly into Mr. Redmond's eyes and began her well-rehearsed speech. "First, I want to make sure you understand how grateful

I am that nine years ago you, Mr. Cunningham, and Mr. Higgins had enough faith in me to allow me to start MSI and to grow it as much as we have. I'm very proud of what we accomplished."

"I'm proud too of what we've achieved, Dana, but this is sounding ominous. Tell me you aren't planning to leave and go somewhere else." George's voice had a solemn tone.

"The issue is a little more complicated, Mr. Redmond. I'm not sure how much you remember about our original arrangement, but I had a starting salary of $28,000 with an incentive arrangement of 10% equity in MSI if we hit a certain number by the one-year point."

"Yes, I remember. You made the goal, and you received the equity — well, on paper anyway. Since we still have MSI, your equity is tied up in the company, just like it is for the rest of us."

"Yes, I have a piece of paper that congratulates me for making the goal, and also states I now own 10% equity in MSI. The problem, Mr. Redmond, is I work very hard every year, yet I receive only small annual pay increases, usually just cost-of-living increases, and no further incentives for me to earn additional equity. In other words, I've expanded the company about 1,500% over the past nine years and the three of you are doing very well from that expansion, but I'm only marginally better off. Also, I see no prospects for this situation to change much in the future. I want what you, Mr. Cunningham, and Mr. Higgins have now with your companies. I want the ability to work hard and then to reap the benefits, not to disperse them in near totality each month to the investors." Dana's hands were trembling, but her voice was clear and controlled. The more she spoke, the more confident she felt. How could anyone not see the unfairness of her explanation underlying the ultimatum she was about to levy?

"Hmm, I'm sensing you're not as happy with the arrangement as I'd assumed. I suppose I can understand your frustration. I've let Roger deal with your salary and benefits, and just assumed you were content, since I've heard nothing to the contrary. Obviously, this was an incorrect assumption. So, you've got my attention. Where is this going? Are you planning to go work for a competitor?" George Redmond had lost his jovial countenance.

"I don't want to leave and go work somewhere else, Mr. Redmond. I want to buy MSI." Dana's voice was steady and firm. Her eyes fixed on George's face and she refused to look away.

George said nothing. Finally, he blinked several times and then frowned. "You want to buy the company? I'm not sure what you mean by that. As far as I know, MSI is not for sale."

"I know, Mr. Redmond, that MSI is not for sale. But I've worked very hard for nine years to build it into what it is, and *I* want to receive the rewards from that work instead of giving all of it away every month to three people who are not working at all for it. So, the only options I see are to start up my own company, which would take away most of MSI's business, or you, Mr. Higgins, and Mr. Cunningham sell MSI to me. I've talked to several banks about obtaining a loan and at some point soon I'll be able to tell you what I can pay each of you. But I wanted to begin the conversation about this now and hopefully agree on how to proceed." Dana's confidence was growing with each word. She was happy to have the initial shock over — at least with George.

There was no change in George's expression as he sat motionless, listening to Dana. "What if we decide we don't want to sell, Dana? Then what?"

"I hope you don't decide that, Mr. Redmond. I hope you see that the three of you have made quite a lot of money from no initial investment at all, since our $100,000 start-up money was from a signature loan, and that money was paid back within just a few months. You've had to make no investment in MSI, nor have you had to do any work. I've done it all. So I'm hoping you'll see the unfairness of this situation over the past years and understand why I feel it's only right I become the benefactor of my long hours and hard work." Dana chose her next words carefully and spoke slowly. "But to answer your question, Mr. Redmond, if you decide not to sell MSI to me, I'm prepared to force a sale legally. I had an attorney look into our situation. In his opinion, in order to have a corporation in the legal sense of the term, the owners must file an application with the Commonwealth of Kentucky to form that corporation. Once the State has approved the

153

application, the corporation then must issue shares, hold annual meetings, and meet other legal obligations. But because the required paperwork was never filed and shares were never issued, MSI is not a legal entity. In other words, there's no actual corporation for me to buy. However, I want to make an offer to buy the business of MSI because I think it's the right thing to do, rather than me set up a corporation now and then come in and take away MSI's customers." Dana decided to stop talking and give him a chance to respond.

However, George didn't respond for what seemed like many long minutes. Instead, he continued to stare at Dana, and then gazed over toward the window, rubbing the side of his jaw, still impassive. Finally, he took a deep breath. He removed his reading glasses, folded them up and tucked them into a small black case that resembled something meant for a cigar. He leaned forward in his chair toward Dana and looked her squarely in the eyes. "Dana, I have to say I'm disappointed in this turn of events. First, I never knew you were this unhappy. I thought you enjoyed working at MSI, and I thought we paid you well for your efforts. Second, I'm going to wait and see what your offer is before I decide what to do. Have you talked to Wayne and Roger about this?"

"No," Dana replied quickly. "And if you don't mind, Mr. Redmond, I'd like the chance to make this presentation to them before you mention anything. I think it would help if I could answer their questions as I'm presenting the case rather than you trying to explain it."

"No problem there, Dana!" He let out a sarcastic laugh. "I'd *much* prefer you break this little piece of news to Roger than me tell him!"

"What do you mean?" As soon as the words were out of Dana's mouth, she regretted them. She didn't want to know, really.

George stood up and slowly picked up the papers Dana had prepared for him. He looked down at her. "Roger tends to get fired up when he thinks someone is treading on his turf. He thinks of MSI as his brainchild, if you haven't noticed during the past nine years. I suspect he'll see things differently."

George turned and walked out of Dana's office toward the front door of

MSI. Dana following closely behind, unable to utter a single word. When he reached the front door, George stopped and slowly turned around to face her. "I hope you know what you're doing, Dana, and you don't create any unforeseen consequences you'll regret." He reached out to shake her hand. "As you said, MSI has been very successful, and there are a lot of businesses and people who depend on it."

"I certainly don't intend to do anything that would jeopardize MSI's success," Dana said indignantly. "I've thought about this for a very long time. I just can't see myself continuing year after year under our current business arrangement. I want something more for myself."

"I get it, Dana, I do. We'll see if Wayne and Roger get it." George pushed open the door. "Have a good day."

"Thank you, Mr. Redmond. You too." Dana slowly turned around and walked back to her office. She felt completely spent, physically and emotionally. Slumping into her chair, she laid her head down on the desk and closed her eyes. Lord! That didn't go as well as she'd hoped.

"Uh oh . . . why is your head on your desk again? Don't tell me George gave you a hard time!" Brenda Sheppard was standing in the doorway, hands on her hips.

"Well, it didn't go as well as it could have, that's for sure!" Dana slowly lifted her head off the desk and gave Brenda a somber look. Normally, she'd be crying by now, but she was even too tired for tears. "Of all people, I thought George Redmond might be a *little* supportive. He didn't say he would fight me; but he didn't say he wouldn't either. And he seemed particularly skeptical of what Roger and Wayne will do — especially Roger."

"Well, you expected Roger to be a problem, right? That shouldn't have been a surprise."

"No, that part wasn't, but *what* did surprise me was George's sober reaction. I guess I've never seen him like that. I thought he liked and respected me and I was hoping he'd be a little more supportive." Dana stared at the floor in front of her desk, her shoulders slumped, and her arms hung at her sides.

"It's just business, Boss," Brenda said grimly. "It's all about money and he gets a lot of it every month from the way things are now. Why would he be happy about losing that? You really didn't think *any* of them would be *happy* about this, did you?"

"No, of course not." Dana said, as if the question were absurd. "Well . . . I don't know . . . maybe. I thought George might be happy for me. Guess that was naïve. Story of my life," she added, glumly.

"I'll agree with you on that, Boss." Brenda crossed her arms and leaned against the doorframe. "You are way too trusting of people and way too nice for your own good."

"Thank you . . . I think." Dana rolled her eyes and then turned in her chair to stare out the window.

"Sorry. Didn't mean to kick you when you're down. But honestly, I predict George will come around after he sleeps on the idea. Might take him a few nights to get there. But he's a pretty reasonable guy, and as I've already pointed out to you several times today, he likes you."

Dana swiveled her chair toward Brenda and gave her a look of resignation. "Yes, in my ridiculous — and mostly hopeless — optimism, I'm counting on that to be the case. I just need to get my head in the right place and keep moving forward with the plan. That's what Colonel Lockwood would tell me."

"Absolutely! Who's the next victim? Roger or Wayne?" Brenda rubbed her hands together.

"Wayne. I've got to work my way up to Roger."

"OK, well, good luck with that! I'm glad it's you and not me. That's why they pay you the big bucks . . . or *you* will pay yourself the big bucks!" Brenda smiled at Dana. "I'm going to finish some things before lunch. Holler if you need anything."

Dana watched her turn and walk away. For a moment she felt envious of Brenda's carefree work life and lack of responsibility. She wondered why she couldn't be like most people who live in small town America and just be happy with a respectable job that pays the bills. Feeling drained, Dana leaned back in her chair, stretched out her legs and crossed her ankles. Life had to get easier at some point. Probably not any time soon, though. She sighed, rested her head against the back of her chair, and began to prepare mentally for her next battle. There was no going back now.

18

One week later, late June 1995

"Thank you, Diane," Dana said, reaching across the counter to pick up her coffee and bag of donut holes. She rarely stopped for coffee on her way to work, but she needed gas. Then she decided to splurge for donut holes because she needed the sugar today. Just a couple more stressful days during the next few weeks, she figured, then she'd be able to breathe again without feeling like someone was stepping on her chest. But one of those stressful days was today — her meeting with Roger Cunningham.

She walked back to her car, got in, and opened the bag of donut holes. The wistful aroma of fried yeast balls and glazed sugar improved Dana's mood substantially. It reminded her of Grandma and the many times they'd made fried bread sprinkled with sugar and cinnamon. Grandma. Although they spoke by phone several times a week, Dana didn't see her as much now. She was too busy working at MSI. And when she wasn't working, she tried to spend her time with Liz and Ryan. They were growing and changing so quickly that sometimes Dana simply stared at them, wondering where her two babies had gone. Time was zipping by and she felt like her life had gone nowhere. Yes, she had two wonderful children to show for it and a nice roof over all their heads. She wasn't sure what to think of her marriage anymore. Not that she and Joey fought a lot, or that they didn't see eye-to-eye on the most important things; they just had little to say to each other anymore. There wasn't the spark, the feeling in her stomach she used to have when they were together. She stared at the glazed donut hole between her fingers and dropped it back into the bag. She'd lost her appetite.

Peering across the dashboard, Dana took a deep breath. She laid her head back against the headrest and closed her eyes. Twelve hours from now she'd be stretched out on the couch, relaxing in the living room with Ryan and Liz, and all this would be over. Roger Cunningham was going to blow a gasket today when she told him she intended to buy MSI with or without his approval. George Redmond had warned her Roger would not take the news well, and Wayne Higgins had said the same thing a few days ago when she met with him. Wayne was pretty unhappy about her proposal as well, but had agreed not to fight her as long as she continued to take care of the allotments for his clients at the same dollar rate per transaction. But Roger would be another story. With the operation of MSI, he'd pinched pennies for the past nine years solely to suck off every cent of profit in order to disburse it monthly to himself, George, and Wayne. There was no doubt he was counting on that distribution indefinitely. At least she had the two practice runs with George and Wayne under her belt. Well, there was no sense sitting in her car and brooding about it further. It was too late for that.

Placing the key in the ignition, she started the car and backed out of the parking spot. The bag of donut holes sat on the seat next to her. If she survived the day, she'd celebrate by eating them on the way home.

Ten minutes later, Dana pulled into the parking lot of her office. Good Lord! Parked in the front row was Roger Cunningham's car! Their meeting wasn't for another two-and-a-half hours. All Dana could assume was he'd discovered the purpose of their meeting and was too upset to wait!

She retrieved her folders and purse, locked the car behind her, and hurried into the building. Before she was completely through the front door, Dana saw Brenda Sheppard sprinting down the hallway towards her.

"Dana! Roger Cunningham showed up 20 minutes ago! He's in your office, said he'd wait there for you. I called your house, but no one answered. I didn't know how to get ahold of you." Brenda was out of breath by the time she'd finished.

"Yes, I know. I saw his car in the parking lot," Dana replied in a hushed tone. "This is not a good sign — to say the least."

Brenda lowered her voice as well. "Look at it this way. You'll get all this over with sooner rather than later." She flashed Dana a reassuring smile, backed away, then turned and hurried down the hallway toward her own office.

Dana noticed her heart rate had quickened and her mouth was dry. She took a deep breath and tried to calm herself. Brenda was right, she thought. Now I won't have to worry about this for the next two hours. One way or another, it'll shortly be over.

She walked down the long hallway and turned into her office. Roger Cunningham was standing at the window with his back towards her. "Good morning, Mr. Cunningham."

He jerked around and looked at Dana with an expressionless face. His cheeks were red and his hair looked either wind-blown or uncombed, Dana wasn't sure. His plaid tie was askew over a white button-down shirt that bunched around his belt. He wasted no time with formalities. "Obviously our meeting is not for another two hours, but I see no point in waiting. I've been told you're unhappy with the way things are now and want to *buy* MSI — whatever the hell that means — and if we don't agree to sell it to you, you're going to buy it out from under us? Are you going to tell me what the hell is going on?" Roger Cunningham's voice hit Dana like a machine gun.

"Yes . . . yes, I'm going to explain everything. That's the purpose of our meeting today. Only I'd have preferred to explain it to you myself rather than you hear it from someone else, who may not have represented it the way I would've wanted." Dana's voice was calm and firm. She knew this was going to be hard, but she'd also mentally prepared for it. "Would you like to sit down, Mr. Cunningham?"

Roger glared at her for several moments, then turned sharply and flung his tall, thin frame into the black leather chair in front of Dana's desk. "Let's hear it then," he demanded. "Let's hear your version." He placed his elbows on the armrests and knitted his fingers together, staring at her across the top of his fingertips.

"All right, Mr. Cunningham. But please give me a minute to find my notes. Would you like a cup of coffee?"

"No, I would not!"

Dana reached into her briefcase and pulled out her files, fumbling through them until she found the one she wanted. This time she sat at her desk. She repeated the speech with Roger Cunningham that she'd used on George Redmond and Wayne Higgins. "Mr. Cunningham, I want you to understand how grateful I am that the three of you had enough confidence in me and in the allotment concept to create MSI and turn it into what it is today — something I'm most proud of. I hope you feel the same way." There was only a hostile stare from Roger, so Dana continued. "If you remember our original agreement, I had a starting salary of $28,000 with an incentive of 10% equity in MSI if I met a certain goal by the one-year mark."

"Of course I remember!" he said indignantly. "You made your goal and you'll get your equity, if, and when, we decide to sell the company. However, that day is not here yet — unless you know something I don't!" His eyes narrowed, and he glared at her.

"What I don't know, Mr. Cunningham, is if you're aware of how much time and effort have gone into building MSI to what it is today, and that I've received only small pay increases every year, mostly just cost-of-living increases. I'm sure you recall during every annual review I've requested you give me additional incentives to work toward with the goal of my earning additional equity, but you've only given me the small pay increases. As I've explained to both Mr. Redmond and Mr. Higgins, I've worked extremely hard putting in many long days and have expanded MSI about 1,500%, which has enabled significant profits dispersed to each of you every month. I want the ability to work hard and reap those profits for myself. I also want to take a small amount of the monthly profits and use them to grow the company. Basically, I see no prospects for the current situation to change and I want more for myself and for my family. I want to *own* a company, just like you, Mr. Redmond, and Mr. Higgins, and make the decisions and be rewarded with the profits. I feel the current situation is unfair, and after nine years of asking, I don't see it changing." Dana stopped talking. She was physically and emotionally drained.

Roger had been glowering at Dana throughout her speech, his mouth half open. "Is this a joke? Suddenly you've decided you're not happy? And you're going to what — *take* the company from us? Is that what this is about?" He spat the words at her.

Dana's heart pounded. She hated confrontation and had been through too much of it lately. "I would like to buy the company, Mr. Cunningham."

"MSI is not for sale," he said nastily.

"As I explained to Mr. Redmond and Mr. Higgins, I believe there are only two options for me. I can start my own, similar company, which I'm prepared to do, but I believe this would lead to many of MSI's clients moving with me. Or, I can purchase MSI from the three of you. I believe after you've had time to think about all this, you'll agree that selling MSI to me is the best option for everyone."

"The best option for everyone? You mean the best option for *you*! The best option for everyone else is to keep things the way they are!" Roger Cunningham's face was reddening with every word, except right around his mouth, where there appeared to be a white ring.

Dana took a deep breath and continued with her now well-rehearsed speech. "Then yes, Mr. Cunningham. I suppose I mean the best option for me. As I said, after nine years, I feel I've worked hard enough for someone else. I want to work this hard for my own company. I was hoping you'd understand, since you have *your* own company. I'm sorry you feel the way you do, but I won't change my mind about what I want and my plan to get there. Believe me, I've been thinking about this for years. I'm talking to several banks about obtaining a loan, and soon I should be able to tell you what I can pay each of you. As I told Mr. Redmond and Mr. Higgins, I hoped that by talking to the three of you now, we could agree on how to proceed." Dana sat back in her chair and waited for the explosion.

Roger's jaw set and his eyes narrowed. "And just how do you think you're going to *take* the company from us?" he asked in a sarcastic voice.

"I hope it doesn't come to that, Mr. Cunningham. Instead, I hope you acknowledge you made quite a lot of money with no initial financial investment by anyone, since the $100,000 start-up money was from a signature loan, which we paid back in a few months. No one has had to make any further investment in MSI, nor perform any of the work — except me. So, now I hope you'll understand why I feel the situation is unfair and why I want to receive the benefits of my long hours and hard work." Dana hesitated, and then reluctantly finished the speech she'd rehearsed for many weeks. "But to answer your question, Mr. Cunningham, if you decide not to sell MSI to me, I am prepared to force a sale legally."

Roger leaned forward in his chair and stuck his face closer to Dana's. "You can't be serious! Force a sale legally? How on earth do you think you could do that?" He abruptly stood up, glaring down at her.

Dana pushed back in her chair, trying to put space between them. "I asked an attorney to look at the paperwork I had from the startup. He believes that in order to have a legal corporation, the owners must file an application with the Commonwealth of Kentucky. Once the Commonwealth has approved the application, then the owners must issue shares in the company and hold annual meetings, plus meet other legal requirements. But in our case, we never filed paperwork and we didn't issue shares, so MSI is not a legally registered company in the Commonwealth of Kentucky. The fact is, there's no actual corporation for me to buy. So, I could just quit my job at MSI, file the paperwork, and start my own company. That would be the easiest thing to do. However, rather than take away all of MSI's clients in the process, I want to do the right thing and make an offer to buy the business of MSI. And as I said, I'll soon be talking to banks about a loan, so I don't want to make a monetary offer at this point because it might be incorrect." Dana stared up at Roger and refused to look away.

He returned the steely glare. "I seriously doubt there's a price you can offer that will make up for your actions. I would be very careful if I were you, Mrs. Smolenski. You may come to regret this move of yours." He turned on his heel and stormed out of her office, slamming the door behind him.

Dana sprang up and ran to open her office door. She caught a glimpse of him turning the corner at the end of the hallway and heading for the front door. Good Lord! Could that have gone any worse? Her stomach felt sick and for a moment she thought she might throw up. Dana leaned against the wall for balance. Her head felt too heavy to lift, and she stared at the ground. No longer able to contain weeks of pent-up worry and frustration, tears rolled down her cheeks and onto the floor. She knew this was going to be hard, but she didn't think she'd feel so terribly alone. It didn't seem appropriate to seek out Brenda for comfort. Joey was working. Marie was in the middle of her annual sojourn to London. Of all times to go, Marie had to pick now, when Dana probably needed her support the most. What Dana really wanted at this moment was to run away to London and join Marie, leaving all this heartache behind.

Walking back to her office, she closed the door behind her and slumped down in her chair, swiveling to face the open window. It was a beautiful Summer day outside, though she'd hardly noticed before. A slight breeze rustled the leaves of the two red maple trees just outside her window. She could hear a lawn mower somewhere in the distance. Wiping the tears away with the back of her hand, she looked up at the fluorescent light on the ceiling and blinked several times to clear her eyes. She'd be so glad when all this was over and her life got back to some semblance of normalcy.

The telephone on Dana's desk rang loudly. She grabbed the receiver and placed it to her ear. "MSI, Dana Smolenski," she said, her voice quivering.

"Ah, good morning, Mrs. Smolenski. This is Henry Townsend from Liberty National Bank and Trust. I received a call yesterday from one of my clients — Mr. Jim Fugitte — who gave me your name and phone number, and asked if I might help you. Mr. Fugitte said you're considering purchasing a small business and our bank could be a suitable match for your financial needs. I thought I'd reach out to you and see if that is indeed the case, and if you'd like to set up a time to talk?"

Dana blinked several times and frowned. "I'm sorry, did you say Jim Fugitte asked you to call me? What did he tell you?" She was having trouble shifting her mind from what just happened in her office.

"Yes, Mrs. Smolenski. Jim Fugitte has been a client of Liberty National Bank and Trust for a number of years." Mr. Townsend's voice was deep and polished. "He provided me a little information about you, your history working for him, and said you're considering purchasing a small business located in Elizabethtown. He said you're starting to look around at financing options and thought our bank might be able to help you. I don't know what your timeline is, but if you're starting your search for financing soon, I'd be happy to talk to you, learn a little more about your needs, and see what Liberty Bank can do for you."

"I'm sorry, when you called I was concentrating on something else and I'm having a little trouble shifting gears." Dana figured she might as well be honest. "Did you say your name is Mr. Townsend?"

"Yes, Henry Townsend. And it's quite all right, Mrs. Smolenski." Mr. Townsend's voice adopted a friendly tone. "I've had similar mornings myself. Is this a bad time? Would you prefer I called back another day?"

"No, no, not at all," Dana replied hastily. "Your call was just a surprise, Mr. Townsend. I do remember Jim mentioning he had a banker friend who might be able to help me with financing, but that was some time ago and I'd forgotten about the conversation until you mentioned it. Actually, your timing is good, as a matter of fact. The financing issue is at the top of my 'To Do' list."

"Great!" Henry Townsend's velvety baritones were comforting to Dana's ears. "I'll make myself available to suit your schedule."

"How about tomorrow morning at 10AM, Mr. Townsend? I'm assuming you're at the Elizabethtown branch?" Dana figured it would be better to know sooner rather than later if she could get a loan based on her and Joey's measly assets. Despite what Jim Fugitte and Dave Lockwood seemed to think, Dana couldn't believe any bank would give her the large loan she needed to purchase MSI. She'd taken another look at their finances recently, and she and Joey's net worth consisted primarily of a small amount of equity in their home — maybe $10,000. Their two cars weren't worth very much, and they owned nothing else, other than the furniture in their home and their personal belongings. The balance in their bank accounts would barely cover living expenses for two months. Childcare for two small children was hugely expensive, so they'd never saved much.

"10AM is perfect, Mrs. Smolenski. And yes, my office is in the Elizabethtown branch. We can meet there, unless you'd rather I come to your office — your preference."

"No, I'll come to your office," Dana blurted. She didn't want to risk a confrontation or an awkward encounter between Townsend and one of the three men. Roger Cunningham was so mad he might look for a reason to fire her and keep her 10% equity.

"Then you've made it easy for me," Henry Townsend said, as if on cue. "I look forward to meeting you tomorrow, Mrs. Smolenski. Until then, have a good day."

Dana heard the phone line click as she held onto the receiver, unwilling to hang it up just yet. Things were happening much too fast this morning! She was emotionally spent after the disastrous meeting with Roger Cunningham, which couldn't have lasted 15 minutes. Then came the phone call from Mr. Townsend, giving her a glimmer of hope again. This morning's emotional roller coaster was too much for her to process.

"Dana!" Brenda Sheppard appeared in Dana's doorway and was shifting her weight from one foot to the other. "Marie's on the phone for you! She called my number because yours was busy."

Dana dropped the phone into the receiver. "Marie's on the phone? I thought she was in England." She jumped up from her chair and ran down the hallway behind Brenda.

"She *is* in England! She's calling from England, or ringing from England, as she put it. Then she told me I needed to find you bloody well quick because this was costing a bloomin' fortune!" Brenda was sprinting down the hallway now.

"Gosh, wonder if something's wrong." Dana's voice trailed off as she entered Brenda's office and snatched the phone off her desk. "Marie?"

"Well, she lives!" The British accent was crisp and in full throttle. "I'm not sure you're worth all the trouble I went through to get you on the wire today!"

"Marie? Is everything OK?"

"Of course, Darling; everything is fine!" The accent was topped with attitude. "But I couldn't manage another day without hearing how things were going on your end. I'm assuming by now you've jolly well tamed the three beasts and have them heeling to your demands, yes?"

"Lord, no! You have no idea how awful this has been! The timing is perfect because I just finished a meeting with Roger Cunningham, who showed up a couple hours before our actual appointment, mad as hell I might add. So that went as expected. It was truly disastrous and may be the end of me and this company! But you and I must have telepathy, Marie, because I was just thinking not 15 minutes ago that you picked a fine time to leave me!" Dana's words spilled out before she remembered Brenda might still be in the office. Normally, she didn't share her doubts and worries with subordinates whose livelihoods depended on her. She spun around to look, but thankfully Brenda was nowhere in sight.

"Yes, I regret this minor infraction of mine, Darling; but it couldn't be helped. When Daddy rings, I must go. Family wedding and all. Attendance required for all family members to show the flag or family crest or whatever it is these days, and demonstrate that we remain tightly bonded, even if a handful of us have quietly defected to greener pastures."

Dana smiled. "How is Daddy?" Marie's father was a brilliant, mannered, quick-witted, and silver-tongued English gentleman, through and through. Not to mention, he was quite wealthy and apparently happy to subsidize Marie's 'American Experiment,' as he dubbed it. Understandably, Marie adored him.

"Couldn't be better, I'm afraid. I fear he will live forever and I will never be free of his endless diatribes regarding my husband-less life." Marie sighed heavily into the phone. "He doesn't seem to believe me when I say I'm a free spirit who needs to fly solo."

"Well, if that's the most you have to put up with, you've got little to complain about," Dana said unsympathetically. "I'm glad he's doing well. He's a sweet man with a big heart. But right now, I need my dear friend back on this side of the pond. Please tell me you're coming home soon."

"Eventually, I suppose," Marie said lackadaisically. "I do have another week of holiday approved by the bank, but I believe it might be best for me to mosey back to my life in America. I'm finding it increasingly difficult to come up with excuses to avoid John. Remember him — my former beau from university?"

"Ah yes," Dana said in a teasing tone, "or as your father calls him, 'Pining John.' Well, I can assure you *I* need your advice and help much more than he needs you." Dana's voice took on a more serious tone. "The first two meetings were hard sells, as you know, but at least at the end I think I had them convinced their best move would be to sell MSI to me. The meeting this morning with Cunningham was a disaster. One or maybe both of the others tipped him off, and he showed up here this morning about as angry as I've seen anyone lately. He literally screamed at me! I tried not to get emotional and to present my points logically, but he kept yelling and then stormed out of the office. I have no idea what to do at this point."

Marie took little time to answer. "Call your lawyer chum, the colonel, and explain to him what happened. I suspect he'll not be at all surprised, and already will have the next steps laid out in his head."

"I was thinking that too. Sometimes he seems like a father, giving advice to a child in trouble. I always feel like I'm doing something not quite right, and I need his approval to proceed. Considering the things he has been through, I feel like my problems are miniscule. He's a comfort more than anything. It's odd. I can't explain it." Suddenly, Dana felt foolish confiding this to Marie.

"I understand, Darling, I do!" Marie's voice had a distinct lilt that was discernible even across the long-distance airways. "As I've often said, it's lonely at the top and no one can do this for you. It's got to be nerve-wracking, taking on these three men who gave you your start. You're young and they're terribly frightening, especially if they band together to take you on. But they haven't done that, have they? It seems they talk every so often, but they don't really work together, do they?"

"No, they don't, and that has been my saving grace so far," Dana said wearily. "I just hope they continue to operate in this disconnected way, because if they *do* band together against me, I'm done."

"Then let's cross our fingers and hope they'll continue to operate as short-sighted, money-driven businessmen! I'll be eager to hear what the colonel proposes. Now, I must run, Luv. Daddy is paying for this call, and I very well could see you in a few days, anyway. We shall catch up completely then. Cheerio and behave yourself! Give the kiddies a hug from Auntie Marie."

Dana heard the phone click, followed by a dial tone. Marie was gone. She looked down at Brenda's desk and shook her head. She couldn't help but smile. Marie blew into your life like a hurricane. The effect was immediate and overwhelming, and then it would disappear as soon as she was gone. Dana doubted there ever would be a man Marie wouldn't tire of after a few months. She certainly felt sorry for Pining John — whoever he was.

19

One day later, late June 1995

Henry Townsend was younger than Dana imagined. Impeccably dressed in a light grey suit, crisp white shirt, and grey-blue patterned tie, he strode toward Dana with his hand outstretched. "Good morning to you, Ms. Smolenski, and welcome to Liberty National Bank and Trust."

"Good morning, Mr. Townsend," Dana said, returning the handshake. "Nice to meet you." She'd woken up this morning feeling chipper, and for no discernible reason. Maybe it was last night's phone call to Colonel Lockwood that provided calmness to an otherwise maniacal day. Maybe it was the sense of moving forward this morning with loan possibilities at Liberty Bank. Or maybe it was her lunch meeting today with the colonel to discuss the next steps. Whatever the reason, Dana smiled brightly and genuinely at Henry Townsend and shook his hand firmly.

"I'm assuming you've not previously engaged in any business with our bank?" he asked, looking inquiringly at Dana.

"No, I haven't. Quite a few years ago, I worked at First Citizens and so my personal accounts were there as well. When I started with MSI, I moved my accounts to Fort Knox National Bank since that's where we had MSI's business account. Made it easier for me to deal with just one bank."

He nodded in agreement. "Is that where you met Jim Fugitte, at First Citizens?"

"Yes, Mr. Fugitte was my boss at the Radcliff branch for about three

170

years. He was the bank president. I worked in the allotments department when the bank first began setting them up for military service members stationed at Fort Knox. Mr. Fugitte was very interested in seeing the allotment program become successful. We traveled together some. I got to know him fairly well." Dana was hesitant to say too much. She had no idea what Jim Fugitte had said about her.

"Apparently, he thought a lot of you," Mr. Townsend said. "He provided a glowing endorsement of your character and work ethic."

"Oh! That's good to hear!" Dana said, relieved. Jim Fugitte had a friendly, outgoing personality and was widely known for chatting up people easily. It crossed her mind he might have confided to Mr. Townsend that she was fired from the bank and went crying to him, hoping he would hire her. She didn't want Mr. Townsend to think she was the stereotypical semi-competent, emotional, working woman.

"My office is just down this hallway." Mr. Townsend led the way to a sizable, plush corner office with floor to ceiling windows next to his desk. There was a small round table in the corner and he gestured for her to sit in the chair facing the windows. "Can I offer you a cup of coffee or water?"

"No, thank you, Mr. Townsend; I'm fine." Dana sat down in the chair and gazed out the window while Mr. Townsend picked up a pen and legal pad from his desk and joined her at the table.

"Please, call me Hank. And if it's OK with you, I'll call you Dana. We'll keep this as informal as possible," he said, smiling. "Now, why don't you start by telling me about your business idea."

"Sure." Dana reached into her briefcase and retrieved a folder. She handed it to Mr. Townsend. "This is a three-page document that describes the company as it exists now, a little of the history, and a page summarizing the financials for the past five years."

"Great! You came prepared. Just give me a minute or two to read over this and then I'll no doubt have some questions." Mr. Townsend placed the paper on the table in front of him and donned a pair of reading glasses.

Dana settled back into her chair, feeling surprisingly tranquil. Mr. Townsend had a warm and comfortable aura about him. She could work with him, she decided.

After a few minutes had passed, he looked up. "This is pretty impressive, Dana."

"Thank you. As I'm sure you know, those couple pages are the result of many years of hard work and long hours." She reached into her briefcase again and pulled out another folder. "This is a brief business plan that builds on the paper you just read. I have a longer version of it, which I'm sure you'll need later, but I just brought this one today."

He took the folder from Dana's hand. "Thank you. Yes, later on I'll need the long version for documentation; but for our purposes today, this'll be fine."

As Mr. Townsend scanned the documents, Dana studied his face. Only a few slight lines around his eyes and some across his forehead. He had dark, thick eyebrows, a nicely shaped nose, clean-shaven, and surprisingly delicate skin for a man. All in all, Henry Townsend was a well-dressed, well-spoken man, who Dana found easy to like.

"You've put a lot of thought into this business plan. It's a pretty aggressive timeline too." Mr. Townsend looked up at Dana.

"It is, but I've been doing this for nine years, and longer if you count my time at the bank. I believe it's realistic."

Mr. Townsend leaned back in his chair and stretched out his long legs. He picked up the documents again and shuffled through them. "I'll need approval from upstairs before I can give you an answer. But from what I'm seeing here, I believe we can work with you. You're still requesting a loan amount of $750,000 over a term of five years, is that correct?"

"Yes, that's correct." Dana thought how absurd that enormous amount sounded when he said it out loud. She couldn't believe the bank was even considering loaning her that much money. Certainly when they discovered she had a mortgage payment, very little equity in her home, hardly any savings in the bank, and two car loan payments, they'd never loan her a nickel! Henry Townsend probably was being optimistic, because anyone in their right mind who would ask for a $750,000 loan certainly would have a lot more assets than did she and Joey. Why would a bank loan three quarters of a million dollars to someone in their mid-thirties who'd never owned a business before? Maybe they'd approve a loan for something much less, but she needed the entire amount simply to pay off her three bosses. Their meeting this morning was probably a waste of time, for both her and for Mr. Townsend. She suddenly felt embarrassed, and now just wanted to get out of there and go home.

Mr. Townsend stood up and walked over toward his desk. He picked up a glossy white folder and then returned to the table where he and Dana were sitting. "This is our loan application package, and my business card is in there as well." He placed the folder on the table in front of her. "Why don't you complete the forms and return them to me at your earliest convenience. I'll submit your package to the loan approval board, and will get back with you once they make a decision. It shouldn't take too long. I believe the board's weekly meeting is in a couple days."

Dana picked up the white folder from the table and looked up at him. "Thank you. I should be able to get this back to you by tomorrow so you can get it to the board before their meeting."

Mr. Townsend sat back down in his chair. He had a relaxed look about his face — like he had all the time in the world. "Is there anything else I can do for you? Answer any questions?"

"If I'm approved, how soon would it be until I saw the money?" Dana didn't want to seem presumptuous when she hadn't yet submitted a loan application, but she needed to know. She still had to arrange that final meeting with all three men together.

Mr. Townsend smiled. "Usually everything is ready within a day or two. It won't take long."

"Oh, OK," Dana said. "I'm just trying to plan."

"The bank will make every effort to work with your schedule and meet your needs. As a local bank, we have more flexibility, as you probably know."

Dana nodded her head. That's why she was here. Not only did local banks have more flexibility, they were quicker to make decisions and rarely required as much paperwork. However, they often had more stringent loan requirements. There were pros and cons.

Dana stood up and extended her hand. "Thank you very much, Mr. Townsend, for making time on your schedule to meet with me so quickly, and for trying to work with me. As I said, I'll complete the loan package probably tonight and try to get it back to you either tomorrow or the next day. I'm anxious to see if we can make things work."

Mr. Townsend smiled back at Dana and gave her a hearty handshake. "I hope we can make things work too, Dana. I suspect we can. By the way, how is Jim these days? When he called the other day to tell me about you, I started thinking about how long it has been since I've seen him — close to a year, maybe."

"I believe he's doing quite well actually, which might be why you've not heard from him. He's extremely busy these days with his own bill paying business. We stay in touch and have lunch together occasionally. We've remained friendly competitors, which has been good for both of us, I believe."

"Staying friendly with your competitors is a good way to remain a leader in your business, I agree." Mr. Townsend walked over to his desk and placed Dana's documents in the center. He then escorted her out of his office and down the hallway toward the front entrance to the bank. He turned to shake her hand again. "It was a pleasure meeting you, Ms. Smolenski. I look forward to receiving your paperwork and doing business with you."

"Thank you for everything, Mr. Townsend." Dana beamed up at him. "I hope my loan application will be acceptable. I'm very much looking forward to working with you as well. Have a great day!"

"Same to you." Mr. Townsend held open the door with one hand and raised his other to wave goodbye.

Dana strolled out into the bright sunlight toward her car. What a nice man, she thought. Such a contrast from the one I dealt with yesterday, and what I'm going to have to deal with again soon. She got in her car and decided although it was a little early, she'd drive to the restaurant where she and the colonel were having lunch. She could sit down before he arrived and digest the morning's events.

174

* * *

The colonel's spotless gold Mercedes sedan was already in the parking lot when Dana arrived. She'd wanted some time alone to think. Apparently, the colonel did too. She could sit in her car and strategize, but he probably had spotted her already. Reaching across the seat, she grabbed her purse and swung open the car door. She didn't need to think; it was time to act. She'd been thinking about this for too many years.

Ascending the three concrete steps, she swung open the cafe door with renewed purpose. The colonel spotted her instantly and waved her over. "Dana, good morning!" He stood up and extended his hand. "I was just having some coffee and writing down a few ideas, so we have some specifics to bounce around over lunch." The colonel wore his trademark starched and pressed khaki slacks, matching khaki socks, and dark-blue polo shirt. His hair was expertly trimmed around his ears and neatly combed into place. She couldn't see his shoes, but Dana knew they'd be wine-colored penny loafers, and they would be spit-shined.

She shook the colonel's hand with a firm grip. "Good morning to you, Colonel! I had the same idea to get here early and draft some talking points after my meeting with the bank this morning, but obviously you're already here," she said, laughing.

"I take it the morning went well?" Colonel Lockwood asked, with raised eyebrows and a knowing smile.

"I don't want to be prematurely optimistic, but I have a good feeling about this bank, and especially about Henry Townsend, the loan officer — actually Hank, he told me to call him Hank. He was a nice, helpful man, and we had a productive meeting — such a contrast from my session yesterday with Cunningham." Dana hung her bag on the back of her chair and settled into her seat. "Thank you again for meeting with me today. I'm nervous about this final meeting with all three. I'm hoping your advice today helps build my confidence."

175

Dave Lockwood smiled and momentarily looked down at his hands, clasped together in front of him and resting on the table. "It's something you learn, Dana. Right now you have a lot of confidence regarding your knowledge of how to do your job and your ability to manage the business. You have confidence in those areas because you've been doing them for a long time and doing them well. You don't have a lot of self-confidence regarding your ability to take a company and purchase it from an unwilling seller because you've not done anything like that before. We're going to develop a strategy and you're going to practice delivering it, so that you'll develop more confidence every time you practice. You'll still be nervous; I'm not suggesting anything to the contrary. But if you practice your pitch over and over, and consider every probable scenario or outcome, then you can plan what your response will be to whatever they might say. This will help you become as prepared as possible. This is similar to what we do in the military. We conduct exercises where the bad guys do various unacceptable things, and then we plan our reaction and practice it. It's how we do war planning. Basically, this is what *you're* doing. You're going into battle to win the company that is rightfully yours."

"I never thought of it that way. You're right; it's the same thing. This is going to be a battle, and I've got a lot of preparation to do to win. I'm certain I want this company more than they do — at least more than two of them do — so I hope that gives me an edge. But I completely agree with what you said and I'll certainly practice," she said, with a grin. "Of course, the most reassuring part is you'll be at the meeting this time. Even though you won't be doing any of the talking, just being in the same room will keep it from appearing like it's three against one. I know I've said this at least 50 times, but I appreciate your being there more than you know." Dana looked the colonel directly in the eyes and smiled sheepishly.

The colonel settled into his seat and smiled. "Actually, I'm looking forward to it. I've been hearing about these three characters for the better part of a year, and I'm ready to get this show on the road. I *know* you are." He reached down and picked up a steno pad from the seat next to him. "How about we move on to discussing a tentative plan for the meeting?"

"That would be great." Dana reached around and grabbed her bag from the back of her chair. "Do you want me to start?"

"Sure, whenever you're ready." The colonel laid down his pen and shifted back in his seat.

Dana pulled out a briefing packet from her bag and passed it across the table to the colonel. Then she retrieved a second briefing, with the pages covered in yellow highlighting and hand-written notes in red. "This briefing is a more streamlined version of the one I provided the three of them when I talked to them individually. On the first page, I compiled the information from each of my annual financial reports. It shows the number of original clients I brought in from their respective companies; the number of clients I added each year, grouped by their physical locations; and of course, overall costs and earnings, all on an annual basis. At the far right is a column with my annual salary, both in dollars and percentage increase from the previous year. Totals are at the bottom. So immediately you see the vast difference in annual percentage increases in company earnings and annual percentage increases in my salary. I intend to point out this difference as my primary reason for wanting to purchase the company. I don't want to place too much emphasis on the annual increases in profit because I don't want them to focus on how much money they're going to lose annually, but I want to show in black and white the growth rate of the company compared to my salary growth rate, and why I deserve to own the company."

Glancing up to gauge the colonel's reaction, Dana continued when she saw he was looking down and flipping to the next page. "Next, I'll talk about the legal paperwork that should have been filed with the Commonwealth of Kentucky nine years ago in order to either incorporate MSI, or register it as a limited liability company. Also on this page is the list of annual requirements in order to operate the company legally. Then I have a couple bullets that basically say since they didn't take these steps, MSI is not a legal entity in the eyes of the Commonwealth. Therefore, there are two options. I can either leave and start up my own corporation and probably take away most of MSI's clients, or I can pay them a sum of money and they sign over to me any perceived rights pertaining to MSI. All of this information is on the second and third pages of the briefing. Finally, the fourth page is my offer to them — their pay-off, so to speak — followed by the accompanying document that legally transfers ownership of the business and the company name to me. As you know, I'm hoping the bank will loan me the seven hundred fifty-thousand dollars so I can pay them each two hundred fifty-thousand. That's where I left it for now. I wasn't sure what else I needed to add. In fact, I wasn't sure I needed to talk at all about the annual financial reports and the clients."

The colonel continued to study the pages of the briefing for a while after Dana stopped talking. She watched him nod his head up and down occasionally. Finally, he closed the briefing, laid it on the table, and placed his hands on top. "Dana, I think you've included all the key points we've discussed over the past few months. There's some word-smithing you could do here and there to tighten it up, but if you feel more comfortable including your rationale for why you deserve the company, that's up to you. From what you've told me, I'm not sure any of them will give a damn about that aspect. This is all about money, and the only thing they'll take note of is that monthly flow of income into their coffers that will now cease. That's the bottom line for them. Therefore, I recommend you focus your discussion on the information you have on pages two, three, and four."

"OK, I understand your point," Dana replied, sighing. "I guess I just feel better about laying out the rationale on the first page. It ties it all together for me and provides the basis for why I'm doing this."

"Oh, I completely understand why *you* want it included," the colonel said, smiling at Dana. "I just don't think any of them will give a damn. Now, let's talk about room set-up and some moves we can take to make it harder for them to say no."

"Sure," Dana said, instantly curious to hear what the colonel might believe would make any of these men more likely to accept her offer. Maybe a small handgun on the seat next to her would do the trick.

The colonel centered the briefing on the table in front of him and stared at it for several moments before speaking. "Place yourself at the head of the table. Put me to your right. Put the briefing packages for the three of them to your left and in this order - Redmond closest to you, then Higgins, then Cunningham. You'll want the one most likely to agree with you sitting next to you. The one least likely to accept your deal should sit as far away as possible. That'll diminish his stature in front of the other two." The colonel picked up his steno pad from the table and opened it to the page where he'd laid his pen. "Hopefully, you'll receive confirmation from the bank in a week or so that they have approved you for the signature loan. Even if you've not yet received the written confirmation, but you've gotten verbal approval from Hank Townsend, I suggest we place three cashier's checks for $250,000 each, on the table underneath the three briefing packages. So, when they get to page four of your brief, the next thing they'll see is a check for $250,000 with their name on it. That's a powerful incentive for accepting your offer."

"That's a great idea!" Dana said excitedly. "It'll be hard to walk away and literally leave $250,000 on the table when their future profits are uncertain!"

"You might have to remind them of that if they start to whine and then balk at your offer." The smile had left the colonel's face.

Dana's excitement promptly faded too. "Is that what you think is going to happen?"

Colonel Lockwood placed both hands on the table and looked Dana squarely in the eyes. "I have no idea what their reaction will be, and I wouldn't fathom a guess. You know these three gents much better than I do, or Joey does, or I would imagine anyone else who has seen them in action at MSI. You've witnessed a sample of their reactions during your initial meetings with them. Since then, they could've thought it over and mellowed into acceptance. Or, they could've gotten together and are ready to oppose you as a group, or oppose you individually and legally. Who knows what they're thinking and planning to do? We won't know what we're up against until we get in the room with them and witness their reactions. All you can do is present your briefing with accurate data and with confidence. Then, you hope for the best."

"You're right, of course. I've thought about this so much my head hurts.

I can't tell you how much sleep I've lost over this, thinking about every conceivable reaction they might have, and then what options I'll have in response. At this point, I almost feel like I'll just be happy when it's over, no matter what the outcome. I don't think I can take much more worrying about it. It's affecting my relationships with family members; I know it is." An image of Joey flashed through her mind. She had had little patience lately.

"I'm sure it's a strain on everyone," the colonel said sympathetically. "But hopefully it'll be over soon. You've got your sweat and blood in this company and anytime that happens there's an emotional cost. So you need to use that emotion to your advantage. Let it fuel your passion and drive to finally get what you've worked for so hard and for so long. But you have to control that emotion and not let it control your actions. Your opponents will come to admire you for it. Always remember, calm under stress."

Dana nodded her head. "That's a great piece of advice, Colonel. Easier said than done, too. But I'm going to try like heck not to let them get to me. Or, I'll be kicking myself for the rest of my days!"

The colonel smiled. "Based on what I've witnessed, I'm fairly confident in predicting that's not going to happen. Now, how about getting that waitress over here and ordering some lunch? I've worked up an appetite with all this thinking."

"Absolutely! It definitely has been a long morning." A long, but productive one, Dana thought. The long-awaited day was nearly here.

20

One week later, July 1995

"I do believe they've grown since I last saw them, Dana! Well, it can't be but a month ago, maybe a month and a half." Grandma Adkins shook her head in disbelief. "What are you feeding them?"

Dana glanced over at Ryan and Liz, and her face eased into a wide grin. Ryan and Liz laughed at Grandma Adkins. "I can't feed them enough anymore," Dana said, setting down her purse on the kitchen counter. "They come home from school and eat everything they can get their hands on before I walk in the door. I usually catch them in the act when I get home from work, or maybe they're on round two by then. So I chase them outside until dinnertime."

"What's for dinner, Grandma?" Ryan gazed at the stove, topped with three metal pots emanating some delightful, savory aromas.

Grandma leaned over and rubbed the boy's back. "Some of your favorites, my dear! Homemade macaroni and cheese, of course, chili for the hotdogs, and cinnamon apples, which I happen to know you two love. And there's vanilla ice cream in the freezer to put on top of the apples." Grandma Adkins kissed Ryan on the top of his head and then sat down at her normal place at the table. "Does that sound good?"

"Yes! Can we eat now?" Ryan was looking intently at his great-grandmother.

"Soon, my dear," Grandma Adkins said with a chuckle. "We just need to wait a little longer for your Dad to get here from work."

"Oh, I'm sorry, Grandma, I forgot to tell you," Dana said. "Just as we were leaving the house, he called to say he's going to be late and not to wait for him. If he's really late, I'll take a plate home for him, if you don't mind."

"Of course, Dear." Grandma Adkins stood up. "I planned to give you all the leftovers, anyway. It'll be a good snack for the kids tomorrow and maybe hold them until dinnertime."

"We certainly won't ever turn down Grandma's leftovers, will we?" Dana grinned at Ryan and Liz. "Why don't you both set the table and we can eat whenever everything's ready."

"Dinner is ready to eat," Grandma announced. "So after you set the table, grab a plate and we'll serve from the stove. We'll make this nice and easy tonight."

"OK, guys, you heard Grandma. Put the silverware, napkins, and salt and pepper on the table, and the plates next to the stove, including one for your dad." Dana walked over and took her grandmother's arm, steering her back to her place at the table. "You look tired, Grandma. Have a seat and I'll fix you a plate."

"Thank you, Dear." Grandma Adkins collapsed into her seat at the end of the table. "It seems I tire out easily these days. This growing old stuff is not for sissies."

Dana looked down at her grandmother's face as she settled into her seat. Her skin appeared translucent now, except under her eyes, which some years ago had taken on a blueish-grey hue. Her eyebrows had disappeared long ago, and the color of her lips was barely distinguishable from that of her skin. Dana's smile faded, and she felt a twinge in her chest. "What would you like, Grandma? Mac and cheese, and apples?" Watching her grandmother grow old was heart-wrenching. Dana couldn't imagine her life without Grandma.

"Yes, but not too much, Dear." She looked up with a faint smile. "I don't have the appetite I used to."

Dana walked back to the stove and retrieved a plate from the stack Ryan had just set on the counter. She spooned small helpings onto the plate and set it in front of her grandmother. Next, she filled her plate and took the seat at the opposite end of the table. "I've got a big day tomorrow, Grandma, and you're my good luck charm."

"Mom's going to buy out her bosses and take over MSI!" Ryan blurted excitedly.

Grandma Adkins' fork stopped in mid-air. She looked up at Dana.

"I'm going to *try* to buy them out," Dana said. "I've got a meeting tomorrow with all three to present them an offer to buy the company. Colonel Lockwood will be with me at this one. I'll be doing all the talking, but he'll be there to keep everything legal, and as a witness in case an issue crops up later. If you remember, I've been talking about this for a long time, but the colonel finally figured out a way we might make it happen. I didn't want to tell you before in case it didn't work out."

Grandma Adkins' face broke into a wide grin and she put down her fork. "That is the best news I've heard in a long time!" She leaned across the table and grabbed Dana's hand, squeezing it tightly. "You deserve to have that company, my dear. You worked hard enough for all those years, slaving away while those three took all the profit, paying you a pittance. How did you finally get them to agree? The last I remember, you thought it was a long-shot."

Dana let out a long sigh. "They haven't agreed yet."

"Mom's going to give them a lot of money if they give her the company," Liz said.

Grandma Adkins looked at Dana. Her empty fork resting on her plate.

Dana put down her spoon. "Last week Liberty National Bank and Trust approved me for a loan to buy off my three bosses. I'm going to present them with a briefing tomorrow morning explaining why legally MSI is not a company in the eyes of Kentucky, like they think it is, because they never filed the required paperwork. And if they don't agree to accept my offer, basically I'll have the company anyway by bringing every MSI customer I can with me to the new company I'll be starting."

Grandma Adkins was silent for a moment. Her face gave no indication of her thoughts. "That sounds pretty risky. What does the colonel think?

I suppose he must believe there's a good chance it'll work or he wouldn't have recommended this approach. From what you've told me, he sounds like a reasonable man and a careful attorney."

"Yes, he is both those things. I know it's risky, but I decided some time ago if the three of them say no and fire me, I'll do just what I said. I'll start up my own MSI. Nearly all our customers are companies I brought in, and I believe they'd stay with me. I've developed good relationships with all of them over the years. And if they don't want to come with me, I'll just continue to branch out and get new customers. I'll make it work, regardless. It'll take longer, but I know I can do it." Dana's voice sounded confident. She hoped Grandma didn't see through it.

Grandma stared at Dana, and then nodded her head. "I believe in you, my dear. I'm sure you've given this a lot of thought, and if you think it will work and you can buy them off, then trying seems the right thing to do. After all, you're not happy now and being happy in your work is vital, as you well know. You spend a good part of your life working, so it should be something you enjoy. How much you're willing to pay for MSI is between you and the bank. But I don't believe they would've loaned you the money if they didn't think you could make this work." She smiled at Dana, then picked up her fork and poked at her macaroni and cheese.

"That's what I think too." Dana was grateful Grandma didn't ask the loan amount. Knowing she'd incurred a debt of three-quarters of a million dollars would no doubt cause Grandma to lose sleep for months. "You'll be one of the first people I call after the meeting tomorrow, which can't come soon enough!"

"I'm sure," Grandma said sympathetically. "I'm glad you and the kids came over for dinner tonight. Hopefully, being here helped you relax and not worry so much about what tomorrow will bring."

Dana smiled across the table at her and then looked at Ryan and Liz. "It did, Grandma; it did. You've always supported me no matter what, and you can't imagine how much that has meant to me over the years. I don't know what I'd do without your love and support — and your help."

"You'll never have to worry about that, my dear." Grandma smiled back at her. "You can always count on my love and my help, and I'll be waiting with bated breath to hear from you tomorrow."

"You will," Dana said, hoping it would be a joyous call and not another disappointing one. "By the way, your mac and cheese is as delicious as ever. I can never get mine to turn this crusty on top. If I manage to get it a golden-brown color, it'll also get too hard and dried out. You have that magic touch, Grandma."

"I think it's my many years of experience." Grandma chuckled and then looked over at Ryan and then at Liz. "You two love macaroni and cheese as much as your mom did many years ago. For a while it was the only thing she would eat. I had no choice but to become a macaroni and cheese connoisseur!"

"That's hilarious! Mom, you never told us that!" Ryan said accusingly.

"Yeah, well, that's because I never wanted you two to be the same way. Macaroni and cheese is OK now and then. Every so often a little green in your diet is a good thing." Dana smiled at Ryan.

Just then the door to the carport opened, and Joey's head emerged through the opening. "Any food left for a hungry working man?"

"Of course, my dear! Come on in." Grandma was up and out of her chair before Dana could swallow and answer him.

"Dad!" Liz and Ryan said, turning in their chairs to greet their dad. "You made it!" Ryan added, his mouth still half-full of food.

"Grandma made her delicious macaroni and cheese," Liz said. "We left you some on the stove."

"You better have," Joey said, smiling at Liz. "Or I'll eat yours off your plate."

"I don't think so," Liz replied as she downed the last bite. "All gone!"

Joey walked around the table to where Dana was sitting, squeezed her shoulders, and kissed the top of her head. "How's everybody this evening?" He reached over and rubbed Liz's back, then he moved to the stove and retrieved the plate Grandma had just fixed for him. "Thank you. Looks and smells as wonderful as ever. We appreciate your having us for dinner tonight. I'm sure Dana has filled you in on the exciting events of tomorrow."

185

Joey sat down next to Dana and dove straight into his dinner.

"Yes, we were just talking about that as you came in the door," Grandma said, as she cautiously settled into her chair. "I'm sure you've put a lot of thought into this plan and know what you're doing. I'll be praying things work out the way you want them to."

Dana thought she spotted a glimpse of worry in her grandmother's eyes, but it vanished as quickly as it had appeared. "Guys, while Dad's eating, let's start to cleanup so we get home at a decent hour and get things ready for tomorrow."

Grandma started to stand, but Dana leaned over and patted her arm. "Not you, Grandma. You did all the cooking; we'll do the cleanup."

"Then I'll just sit here and keep Joey company." Grandma smiled at Joey. "How are things with you these days? Everything at work going OK?"

"Everything is fine. Just my normal complaints — too many hours and not enough pay!" Joey took the last bite of his hotdog and washed it down with milk. "That was perfect. Just what I wanted for dinner — comfort food."

"Glad you enjoyed it. Seeing you all eat makes my heart warm."

"We know, Grandma!" Liz said. "You're always trying to feed us, every time we visit."

"That's how grandmas show their love," Dana said. "They cook you delicious meals. Plus, I don't recall you ever turning down Grandma's food!"

Joey picked up his plate from the table and handed it to Ryan. "Grandma can feed us anytime!"

"Yeah," Ryan said, taking the plate to the sink.

Grandma stood and walked around to hug Joey and the kids. Then she turned to Dana and gave her a long, firm hug. "Best of luck tomorrow, my dear. You know I'll be thinking of you all day. Remember, you're very good at what you do and already a success. So if this doesn't work out tomorrow, you'll find something else, or you'll start your own company. I have no doubt about that."

"Thanks for always supporting me, Grandma, no matter what crazy thing I want to do. And thanks for fixing my favorite dinner tonight. I'm leaving feeling much better than I did when we got here. Now, I just want tomorrow to be over. It seems like all this preparation and thinking about it has been going on forever."

"I'm with you there!" Joey said. "Kids, you can ride home with me or your mom. Pick a car and hop in. Thanks again, Grandma," and with a wave of his hand, he was out the door to the carport, kids in tow.

Dana hugged her grandmother again and gazed over her shoulder, soaking in one last look. The familiar kitchen felt like the center of her being. It was the place that gave her solace and taught her about unconditional love. Even when Grandma wasn't there, Dana felt a blanket of security envelop her when she stepped into her kitchen. Maybe that was the reason — the kitchen exuded Grandma's steadfast determination and love. Dana tried to hold that feeling in her chest as she turned and followed Joey and the kids to the car. She'd try to remember it tomorrow too, when she'd need it the most.

21

The next morning

Joey stood in the kitchen doorway, one hand on his hip and the other propped against the wooden door frame. "You're up early. Didn't sleep well, or too excited about today?"

Dana had heard him padding down the hallway, but had hoped he was going to the bathroom and not coming to look for her. She wanted to be alone. "I slept OK," she lied. "I just felt like getting up and getting started with the day. Lots to think about."

"I'm glad you got some sleep. I worried you wouldn't. You'll think better when you're not jacked-up on coffee."

She didn't look up, continuing to stare at the notes in front of her. "I'm just practicing my briefing and trying to think of all the questions or arguments they might come up with, so I can think of a suitable response now. I don't want to be surprised and not have a good answer or counterpoint."

"I thought you and the colonel had gone over all that already, no?" Joey cocked his head sideways.

"We did. But I know them better than he does, and I'm trying to think of anything Cunningham might come up with, because he's going to be the hardest one to convince and the most troublesome one, as you know." Dana rubbed her forehead and sat back in her chair. She was feeling a little queasy, and her head had begun throbbing.

Joey sat down in the chair next to Dana. "You'll be just fine today, Dana.

You've thought about this literally for years. No one knows the business like you do; that's what you need to remember. They can ask anything and everything they can think of, but you'll always know more, because you work with the information day in and day out. They can get as angry as they want, but the fact is the required paperwork wasn't filed and a legal company doesn't exist. I have a feeling they'll be mad as hell too. But after they've had some time to think about it, they'll realize if they take you to court, it'll be a long, drawn-out process and you have as good or better chance of winning as they do. In the meantime, no one will be doing the allotments or taking care of business, because you won't be at your desk tomorrow — or ever again, for that matter — and they'll have lost the $750K you're offering them today. So, it may take some time before they come to this conclusion, but I can't help but believe they will eventually. You just have an ugly day to get through, and then it's over. You need to hang in there a little longer. The end is in sight."

Dana's solemn face nodded slowly in agreement. "Yeah, that's what I keep thinking too. They'll huff and puff, but in the end, there's not much they can do. But I know myself too. The more prepared I am with answers to all their inane questions, the more confidence I'll have, and then I'll project a stronger image, which will help. I can tell they think I'm just a woman who doesn't know the first thing about actually *owning* a business, nor do they think I *deserve* to own it — that's certainly clear."

"Marie said the same thing when she called last night. Before you picked up the extension, she said all three were acting like spoiled, entitled businessmen. I think those were her words, along with a few others I couldn't repeat in front of the kids. You know Marie — never one to hold back her true feelings." Joey sat back in his chair and laughed.

Dana grinned. "No, she's never been afraid to say what she thinks. I like that about her, actually. Wish I were more that way. I'd like to have half her gumption. It would help on a day like today. I'm going to finish getting dressed and then head to the office to get things set up. I'm sure I'll feel better once I get there. Thanks for getting the kids off to school today. Give them a hug from me, and tell them I hope we'll be going out to dinner

189

tonight to celebrate."

"Absolutely we'll be celebrating! And all this will be behind us." Joey smiled up at Dana.

She managed a weak smile back and turned to walk down the hallway to the bedroom. She was eager to get dressed and into the office, where solitude would prevail for a couple hours, anyway. That should be enough time to review her briefing a few times and then set up the conference room for the most important day of her professional life. Geez, she just wanted this day over, one way or the other. The stress was almost too much to bear.

* * *

The sun had barely risen above the horizon, casting a long shadow across the dingy, grey parking lot. How many times had she parked in this decrepit asphalt rectangle, situated on the right side of the building that had been home to her work life for so many years? When she parked tomorrow morning, would she be heading to her office for her first day as the new owner, or would she be toting cardboard boxes to pack up her belongings? It was an all-or-nothing gamble she would make in a few hours. She still couldn't quite believe what she was willing to risk today. This could be the most incredibly stupid move she'd ever make in her life. The thought caused Dana to feel a sudden pinching in her chest, like someone had grabbed her heart and squeezed tightly. She'd felt this before — the tangible effect of stress, the feeling of self-doubt, inadequacy, and dread of a contentious encounter. Next she would feel the sensation of her throat tightening and she'd have trouble breathing. Then she'd worry that people sitting close to her could see her heart pounding in her neck and chest. And if she were really scared, she'd have trouble getting her words out of her tightened throat. God! She hated feeling this way!

She hastily gathered the manila files splayed across the front passenger seat, threw open the door, and swung her legs out of the car. It felt good to stand up and stretch. She took in a deep breath, trying to calm her frazzled nerves. There was a smattering of clouds on the horizon, but it looked like a beautiful, sunny day was in store, and that was a good sign. Dana liked signs. She liked to believe it was her guardian signaling that luck was on her side today. If it had been raining or even cloudy, she would have interpreted the greyness as an ominous sign. Thank goodness she didn't have *that* to deal with right off the bat.

As she walked across the parking lot, several dozen thoughts blew through her mind. She tried breathing calmly and steadily, like she'd learned during Lamaze class. Lamaze — what a bunch of baloney, she thought. It didn't work then, and she wasn't having much luck with it now. Does concentrating on your breathing really enable you to forget the unfathomable pain wracking your body? Pain that feels as if your womb is being shredded from the inside out? The cleaning crew was still in the building when Dana walked down the hallway to her office. Coffee was her next thought. Then, she'd shut her door and review her notes before anyone else arrived for work. One hour of quiet probably would be enough. Two hours would be perfect.

Dana dropped her files and purse on the top of her desk and made her way down the old linoleum hallway to get the coffeepot started. Before she could turn on the pot, the phone in her office rang. Dana stopped in her tracks. Was that really *her* phone ringing? Who would call this time of morning? She hesitated, trying to decide if she should answer it or let it ring and hope no one knew she was there. But she had kids; she had to answer the phone. Someone could be sick. Running down the hallway, she grabbed the phone, "MSI, Dana Smolenski."

"Top of the morning to you, Dana," the deep, gruff, and familiar voice resounded through the phone.

"Good morning, Colonel," Dana said. Her heart quickened. "You're calling awfully early. Is everything OK? Please don't tell me you're not able to come today," she blurted before she could stop herself.

The colonel laughed. "Wouldn't miss it for the world! In fact, I'm looking forward to putting the faces with the stories I've heard over the past year. It'll be most interesting, to say the least. No, I had a hunch you might be in early this morning, so I was calling to let you know I'm planning to be there around zero nine-thirty, which will give us 30 minutes to run over any last-minute items. Sound good? How are you doing, by the way?"

Now it was Dana's turn to laugh. "You know me; I'm nervous and anxious and will be happy when it's over."

"I know you will." The colonel's deep, steady voice was soothing to Dana's ears. "Here's what I want you to think about when you look across the table at your opponents this morning. This is not the first time we've talked about this, but it warrants repeating. *You* are the brains behind this company — the sweat *and* the brains. I can't think of a question any of them could ask that you won't be able to answer. That should give you a tremendous amount of confidence."

Dana sighed. "Yes, you've told me that before and I've been reminding myself of it over the last couple days. I've told you this before too, but I have to say it again — particularly today. You just don't know how much all your help and support has meant to me over the past year, and especially, being at the meeting today. If it weren't for you, I'd still be sitting here, working my tail off, and going nowhere. If I'm able to make this work, I *will* somehow pay you back." Dana felt exhausted already, and could barely contain her emotions and not cry. She hoped the colonel didn't hear her voice quiver.

The colonel laughed — a calming, reassuring tone to Dana's ears. "I'll tell you what, Dana; if we're able to make this work today, and your new company becomes a raging success like I think it will, you can carve out some minuscule percentage of profit for me. If that were to happen, I'd be golden for the remainder of my days. That's how much faith I have in you."

"You've got a deal! And that's the least I can do, since I seriously doubt I would ever have made it to step one if I hadn't met you."

"Oh, I don't know if I agree with you there. I have a feeling sooner or later you'd have figured out a way to make this happen." The colonel cleared his throat. "I didn't intend to consume more than a few minutes of your morning because I want you to have time to review your notes a few times. But I did want to call and check in with you and ask if there's anything you need from me before the meeting."

"No, I think I'm fine," Dana said, glancing toward her desk and the pile of folders. "I did just walk in the building and was making the coffee when you called, so I've not had a chance to look over anything yet. But I think I'm all set. I know you don't plan to do any of the talking today, but I sure am grateful for your presence on my side of the table."

"Yes, and that's one of the primary reasons I'm coming. I believe having a lawyer next to you will ensure these gents understand we've done our legal homework and are prepared to take this to the next level, whether or not you ultimately decide to do so. We want them to believe there's the potential for a long and drawn out court fight if they don't take the money and run."

"And with any luck, they'll come to that conclusion sooner rather than later." Dana didn't know how long she could hold up this morning if it turned into a long, confrontational meeting. Cunningham's verbal attacks could be brutal, which she remembered well from their last meeting.

"That's the hope. So, if there's nothing else for us to discuss, I'll see you around zero nine-thirty."

"Sounds good. Thanks, Colonel." Dana heard a click on the end of the line, so she placed her handset back on the cradle. She sat there for a moment, wondering how she'd ever be able to express her gratitude. She was 36 years old, yet she felt like a child getting emotional support and advice from a parent. He, the sage colonel, took great pains to explain things in layman's terms, and ensure she understood the implications. He encouraged her when she felt the situation was hopeless and she should give up. He put in hours of work and research without assurance of, or even hope for, any financial compensation. Individuals like the colonel were scarce these days. He reminded Dana of her own father, also retired from the military. Her dad's generation was full of men like the colonel —

honorable men who were used to looking out for each other for no purpose other than to help a fellow man. Marines, especially, were used to taking care of each other. Brethren for life. Once a Marine, always a Marine. The colonel would forever be this way, she figured. It was ingrained in his persona. This sense of duty to help someone in need. This time, she was that person. Dana hoped she was worthy of his effort.

Suddenly remembering the coffeepot in the kitchen was still empty, Dana turned around and hurried back down the hallway. She noticed her breathing had slowed and her heart wasn't pounding in her neck and chest as much as it had been earlier in the morning, before the colonel had called. The corners of her mouth curved upward at the realization, and a smile slowly engulfed her face. That's why the colonel called! He knew she'd be in her office early this morning, and likely in a state of near panic. He wanted to reassure her she'd have the upper hand during the meeting, and she just needed to get through her brief with the confidence of someone holding all the cards. The sole purpose of his presence this morning was to function as her support system, to add mass to her side of the table. How would she ever repay him? If she succeeded today, she owed it to him.

Pulling an ivory-colored ceramic cup off the shelf, Dana poured herself some coffee and returned quickly to her office. She picked up the stack of files she'd brought from the car and opened the one on top. Red ink and yellow highlighting covered her copy of the briefing. Underneath were five clean versions. She picked up the file and took it to the conference room, dropping three briefings on one side of the table and two on the opposite side. Then she sat down at the table and reviewed her notes for nearly two hours. She imagined three bodies on the other side of the table and read aloud her briefing to them, cutting herself off occasionally to answer questions she expected. She envisioned herself sitting up confidently in her seat, looking into their eyes, matching their gaze, and responding matter-of-factly to each question. At the end of her briefing, after she'd answered every question she could imagine they might ask, she pointed across the table to the imaginary three checks that would lie in plain view next to their briefings. The colonel's idea — placing each check next to the briefing so throughout the entire meeting, each of the men would stare at a check written out to them and signed by Dana in the amount of $250,000. If they didn't agree today to sign over the company to Dana, they would have to stand up and walk out, leaving that enormous amount of money lying on the table. Or today, they each could be $250,000 richer. Dana agreed with the colonel; they wouldn't be able to resist the dollar amount written on the checks.

"Top of the morning to you again!"

Dana instantly recognized the sound of the colonel's low, raspy voice. She swung around in her chair and stood up to greet him. He was wearing his signature outfit — crisply pressed khaki pants, a dark blue short-sleeved polo shirt ever so neatly tucked into his pants, and spit-polished brown loafers. By now, Dana realized this was the only style of clothes he wore. His light brown hair was trimmed so short, she doubted he ever needed to comb it. Yes, she was sure he woke up every morning looking exactly the same. "Good morning again to you!"

The colonel stepped into the room. "How are things progressing?"

"I've been going over everything for the past two hours and I hate to jinx anything by saying this, but I'm feeling pretty good about it all right now. I've been coming up with an answer for anything I can think of that they might ask me, or in Cunningham's case, accuse me of doing. I've got copies of all the paperwork from our first few months of operation, and my notes regarding how we started MSI versus Kentucky's requirements for starting a company, along with the mandatory forms. And finally, I've got the three $250,000 checks ready to put underneath their briefings," Dana added, pointing to the briefings across the table from her.

"It sounds like you're ready." The colonel placed his briefcase on the table next to her and pulled out the chair. "I think I'll find a cup of coffee before we get started."

"Sure." Dana turned around and pointed down the hallway. "Just around the corner to the left. Cups are in the cabinet above the coffeepot, sugar's on the counter, and cream is in the fridge."

The colonel walked briskly but silently down the hallway and returned

195

a few minutes later holding a cup of steaming black coffee. He sat down in the chair next to Dana and turned squarely in his seat to face her. "We have 30 minutes. Would you like to go over anything in particular, or do you want to practice your brief on me, or would you rather just sit and talk about something completely unrelated in order to get your mind off the obvious?"

Dana smiled and looked down at her papers, shaking her head. "I don't want to go over my brief anymore this morning. I've practiced so much I'm tired of listening to myself. And I definitely could use a distraction because I've been sitting here worrying about how I'll go back to working tomorrow — or go somewhere else — if things go badly today. I'm not sure what I'll do. It crosses my mind every so often and I hate to go down that path, but I guess I should think about it," she added, groaning loudly.

The colonel laughed, leaned over, and gently patted Dana's arm. "I'd be surprised if you hadn't been dwelling on it. But we're not going to talk about it now. If we need to do so after today, we'll regroup next week and come up with a different strategy for getting you the company you deserve. But today we're going to focus on winning, because more than anything else, a strong and uncompromising position on your part is what's needed to convince these three gents they're better off taking the money and running — before *you* change *your* mind. Just remember, you have the Commonwealth of Kentucky regulations on your side. You need to convince them that because they didn't follow the regulations when setting up MSI, they'll have no case to pursue in a court of law. And if they aren't entirely convinced of this after listening to you today, I'm hoping my presence puts them over the edge."

"I just hope they haven't gotten together and are planning to gang up on me. Although I really can't see them doing that because they don't get along all that well. But you never know what they've been doing since I had my last one-on-one meeting with them. Clearly one or both of them had talked to Cunningham before I had the chance to tell him anything myself."

Colonel Lockwood nodded in agreement, hesitated, and then spoke to

Dana in a solemn and deliberate tone. "There's no point in guessing or worrying about it now. The best thing you can do today is to look each of them in the eyes and demonstrate you've done your homework, you know the regulations, and you *will* pursue this legally, if necessary. This is all about your ability to be convincing and to call their bluff. I know deep down inside, there's a lady who's tired of being taken advantage of by men who don't know half as much as she does, and who aren't working nearly as hard. I know you have it in you to do what it'll take today to negotiate your company from them."

Dana sat silently for a moment, looking at the colonel, and slowly nodding her head. It was reassuring to have her feelings validated. "Thank you, Colonel. You're right; I'm tired of being taken advantage of. Once the meeting starts, I'll think about what you said. I've already had enough coffee to stay wired until dinnertime, so I'll have to work on not talking too fast," she added, grinning and rolling her eyes.

"Good morning, Dana . . . Colonel!" Brenda was leaning around the door frame and only her upper body was visible. "I don't want to disturb you, but I wanted you to know I'm here if you need anything. Just holler. When the first one shows up this morning, I'll be sure to let you know right away," she added, smiling at Dana.

"Thanks Brenda," Dana said.

"Top of the morning to you, Brenda," the colonel added amiably. "I see that sense of humor is intact even in the early morning."

"You know it!" Brenda's face broke into a wide grin. "Gotta have a sense of humor to work at MSI. It helps when the paycheck arrives." She chuckled at her own joke. "Let me know if you need anything. I'll leave you two alone so you can get back to working on my future. I have a big stake in today's outcome too, you know."

"How could I forget?" Dana said, laughing. "You remind me nearly every day!"

"Just don't want you to forget your first *and* your best employee, Boss!" Brenda was standing squarely in the doorway now, rubbing her hands together, as if she were preparing something delicious in the kitchen. Then she turned and left.

The colonel and Dana looked at each other and laughed. "Never a dull moment around here, that's for sure!" Dana said, and then her expression turned serious. "But she's right, and I'm aware of it every day. She's my best employee and has never let me down. She's here, day in and day out, and the last thing I want to do is have her end up with no job tomorrow. That's one of my biggest fears — to let everyone down who has trusted me with their financial future. It's one thing to screw up my own career, but I hate to think I might hurt the employees here." She slumped in her seat, looked down at the table, and sighed.

"Hey, I thought we weren't going down that path this morning," Colonel Lockwood said gently. "Now, let's assume everything goes as planned. If these three gents pick up the checks from the table this morning and then head directly to the bank to cash them, are the checks good, or is there a waiting period for cashing them?"

Dana perked up. "They should be able to cash them now. Yesterday morning I called the loan officer I'd been working with — Hank Townsend. I told you about him a while ago. He's with Liberty National Bank and Trust. He'd called me about a week ago to let me know they'd approved me for the loan, but as of yesterday, I still hadn't received any of the paperwork. So, I called him. He assured me I was good to go; the paperwork just takes a while. I'd feel better if I actually had it in hand, but I'm trusting he knows what he's talking about and everything is OK."

"Good, because I suspect at least one — if not all three — of your bosses will deposit the checks today, if all goes well. The other thing you'll want to do immediately is file the required paperwork with Kentucky to incorporate MSI."

Dana laughed. "I've already thought of that! I have all the paperwork, not filled out yet, because I didn't want to jinx anything, but that part's easy. Wouldn't want to make the same mistake twice. But if all goes well today, I'll be filing everything tomorrow."

"Sounds like an excellent idea." The colonel scooted back in his chair and stood up. "I think I'll get a refill on my coffee before the action starts."

"Sure," Dana said. "I'd better *not* drink any more or I'll be shaking from caffeine instead of fear!"

"Dana, Wayne Higgins just pulled into the parking lot!" Brenda announced excitedly from the hallway. "I thought I recognized his SUV, but he hasn't gotten out yet. He's still sitting in it."

Dana's heart jumped. "Really?" She checked her watch and tried to swallow. "If that's him, he's 20 minutes early."

"I'm sure it's his car," Brenda said. "Maybe he's going to sit out there for 20 minutes. I'll go sit at the desk in the lobby, just in case he comes in early."

"Thanks, Brenda. Let me know when you see him get out of the car. I'll finish setting up everything here." Dana stood up and began reconfiguring the table according to the plan she and the colonel had discussed. Her hands were slightly trembling, and she took a deep breath, trying to calm herself. She placed her things at the head of the table, the colonel to her right, and the briefings for the men neatly along the left side. Then, she picked up her briefcase and pulled out the envelope with the three checks. She carefully centered one check under each of the three briefings.

The colonel returned to the room with a full cup of coffee. He placed it at his seat to Dana's right and stood behind his chair, looking over at Dana. "I heard Brenda announce we've already got someone sitting out in the parking lot. Let me take one last opportunity to say you know your brief inside and out, so speak directly to them. Look each one in the eyes with the confidence of the one person who has been running this company for nearly nine years, and who knows infinitely more than they do. Remember, Dana, this is your company. You just need to take it."

Before Dana opened her mouth to respond, she heard Brenda yell down the hallway, "Dana, it's definitely Wayne Higgins and he just got out of his car!"

"I guess this is it," she said to the colonel in an uneasy voice.

The colonel nodded his head and smiled.

Dana walked over to the conference room door so she could greet Mr. Higgins as he came down the hallway.

* * *

It took Wayne Higgins a good ten minutes to get from his car and into the conference room. Dana listened to his curt greeting to Brenda, who was sitting at the front desk waiting for him. He seemed more interested in curtailing any pleasantries so he could down some coffee and a donut or two before the meeting began. The longer he took to make his way into the conference room, the more aware Dana became of her heart pounding away in her chest.

"Good morning, Dana," he said brusquely, finally rounding the corner and into view. He was holding a cup of coffee. Usually when Dana saw Wayne Higgins he was wearing brown polyester pants and a beige-colored shirt. But today he had on beige pants and a nondescript light green shirt. His paunch still flowed heavily over his belt.

"Good morning, Mr. Higgins. I was going to say there's coffee and pastries in the kitchen, but I see you found everything yourself." Dana worked hard to keep the tone of her voice calm, yet assertive, just as she'd practiced for weeks. She opened her mouth and took several discreet breaths. Her heart pounded a little less fervently. "I'd like to introduce you to my colleague, retired Marine Corps Colonel Dave Lockwood. Colonel Lockwood has been helping me navigate the ins and outs of the corporate legal world. I asked him to sit in our meeting this morning, purely in an advisory capacity, to ensure I keep things on solid legal footing."

The colonel stepped forward and held out his hand to Wayne Higgins. "Good morning, Wayne. Pleasure to meet you," he said, in his typical gruff fashion.

"Morning Colonel," he replied, without a smile.

Dana thought Wayne Higgins seemed caught off-guard, and he opened his mouth as if to say something else. Then he stepped back and closed his mouth, keeping his eyes locked onto the colonel.

"Nothing to worry about, Wayne." The colonel winked at him. "I'm a non-practicing attorney in the Commonwealth of Kentucky. As Dana said, I'm here to listen only and to make sure she follows Kentucky corporate law. She'll be doing all the talking," he added with a smile.

Wayne Higgins waved his hand in the air. "Sure, no problem. We all figured Dana had been getting legal advice somewhere."

Dana ignored his last comment and pointed toward the three seats to the left of her briefcase. "Mr. Higgins, I have you sitting in the middle of those three seats where I laid the briefings. I've got Mr. Redmond to your right and Mr. Cunningham to your left. I'll sit here at the end of the table and the colonel will be on my right side."

Wayne walked around the table and pulled out the chair next to the middle briefing. He tossed his briefcase on the table and dropped heavily into the chair, placing his pudgy palms on the table. "Dana, I'm not happy about the turn of events over the last few weeks. And I'm sure you're aware I'm not the only one who feels this way. You're going to have a hell of a time convincing Roger to go along with your plan, but I suspect you know that already."

Dana had been preparing for this discussion, but didn't think it would come this soon. "Yes, I am aware of all that, Mr. Higgins. I hope by the time I'm finished with what I plan to say today, you'll understand why I'm doing this and you won't be so opposed. I believe I'm offering you all a fair deal," she added, forcing herself to look Wayne straight in the eyes, and not look away when she finished speaking.

"Dana, Mr. Redmond and Mr. Cunningham are here." Brenda's voice broke the uncomfortable silence that followed.

Dana turned around to see George Redmond and Roger Cunningham follow Brenda through the doorway. As usual, George was in slacks and a short-sleeved polo, and appeared ready for 18 holes on the links. Roger donned his typical rumpled dark suit, white shirt, and plaid tie. "Good morning, Mr. Redmond, Mr. Cunningham" she said, trying to keep her voice strong and controlled. "Mr. Higgins just got here a few minutes ago too. I'd like to introduce you both to my colleague, Colonel Dave Lockwood. Dave is a retired Marine Corps attorney who has been assisting me."

Colonel Lockwood stepped forward and held out his hand. "Good morning, gentlemen, and as I was just saying to Wayne, not to worry. I'm a non-practicing attorney in Kentucky. Just here this morning to ensure things stay on track from a corporate legal perspective and answer any questions of that nature."

George reached out and shook the colonel's hand. "Morning, Dave. Didn't know we'd be treated to any legal arguments today," he said, soberly.

"And I don't think you will," the colonel shot back cheerfully. "I'm just here to keep Dana on the straight and narrow. Make sure she explains the corporate issue correctly, and as I said, in case anyone has questions of a legal nature she can't answer. Nothing more."

"Good." Roger stepped forward to shake the colonel's hand. He was rigid and straight-faced. "Otherwise, I'd have brought my lawyer. I'm Roger Cunningham."

"Morning, Roger. Pleasure to meet all of you." Colonel Lockwood shook Roger's hand as well and then pulled out his chair to sit down. "Gentlemen, I know you're busy and I believe this lady is ready to get started."

"Yes, I am," Dana said, exchanging looks with the colonel. "Mr. Redmond, I have you sitting next to me, and Mr. Cunningham, you're on the other side of Mr. Higgins." Dana motioned them toward their seats. "There's a brief on the table for each of you."

She took a deep breath, pulled out her chair, and sat ramrod straight on the edge. Her hands were trembling and her heart felt as if it were pounding through the wall of her chest. She glanced up to see if anyone was watching her, but the three men to her left appeared focused on settling in, and on the papers in front of them. Forcing her thoughts to the much-practiced briefing in front of her, she tried to clear her mind of the fear. "First, I want to thank you for coming here this morning. I want you to know I've enjoyed the past nine years of working with each of you, and I'm proud of what I've been able to accomplish with MSI. If you turn to the first page of the briefing in front of you, on the left side you'll see the number of original clients I signed up from each of your companies that first year, and the number of clients I added for the subsequent eight years we've been in business. Right below those figures you'll see annual total costs and earnings. A sub-category of cost is my annual salary, both in dollars and percentage increase from the previous year. If you look at the bottom of the page, you'll see the total percent increase in my salary over the past nine years and the total percent increase in MSI's earnings during this same timeframe. I hope you'll be as shocked as I was over the vast difference in these two figures. Not that I expected my salary to increase proportionally with the growth of MSI, but I expected something a little more representative of compensation for the head of a business who has worked days, many nights, and many weekends to enable the returns MSI has experienced. Over the past nine years, I've been sitting in a job with no upward mobility. I don't know anyone who would be happy with this arrangement indefinitely," she added, looking directly at Roger Cunningham. Dana hoped he might realize her last statement was meant for him, but he showed no signs of recognition. He sat halfway back in his chair, flipping through the briefing so quickly she wasn't sure if he was listening to her. "Mr. Cunningham, is there a problem or are you looking for something specific in the briefing?"

"What? No! There's no problem," he said irritably, as he looked up at Dana and then around the table at the others. "I'm waiting to hear why you think this company should be yours, and so far I've not seen anything concrete to support your claim!"

"I'm getting to that next, Mr. Cunningham," Dana said carefully. She kept her eyes focused on his face. "If you turn to the next page, I'll explain the legal issues." She glanced over at Colonel Lockwood to gauge his reaction, but he also has his eyes trained on Roger. Dana breathed deeply and tried to calm herself. She noted her heart wasn't pounding as wildly as it had been 10 minutes ago. Thank God, she thought. Don't let them get to me. Help me remain calm and get through this. She picked up her briefing from the table and flipped to the next page. "Gentlemen, when I met with each of you recently, I talked about the requirement to file paperwork with the Commonwealth of Kentucky whenever you're setting up a corporation or a limited liability company. If you turn to the next couple pages of your briefing, you'll see a copy of the required filings. This paperwork serves the purpose of registering the company or LLC with the Commonwealth and also documents the issuance of shares to each of the investors. Once the Commonwealth receives the paperwork, it certifies the corporation or the LLC as registered, and the Clerk of Courts enters the information into the court records. After the company is legally registered, there are certain things that must occur. An annual meeting must take place where minutes are taken and then filed with the Commonwealth. If you remember, none of this happened when we started MSI. I simply went to the bank and opened a line of credit in each of your names. Initially, I used this line of credit to fund the operations of the business. However, during the first year, we generated enough profit to fund our expenses and pay off the line of credit. At this point, I began depositing the monthly profits into a money market account and over the years I disbursed that money monthly to each of you. The point is, no one invested start-up money and received shares in the company, and no one ever filed the legally required paperwork. Therefore, in the eyes of the Commonwealth of Kentucky, MSI is not a legally registered company."

Roger's staccato voice boomed over top of Dana's last words. "Unless I'm missing something, we've been paying taxes on this company for nine years — some pretty hefty taxes! And Kentucky hasn't sent back that tax money with a letter telling us we forgot to register as a company!" His face and ears had turned bright red.

Wayne tossed his brief on the table and pushed back in his chair. "I'm in total agreement with Roger. The fact we paid taxes as a company every year has to mean something. As far as I know, the State never complained!" Wayne's typical mild-manner and unremarkable voice were replaced with hand-waving and accusing tones. "We set up this entire operation on the side because the whole intent was to re-create the allotments we had with your bank. Only now, we'd have the allotments under our control, and we wouldn't have to pay as much for every single transaction. We'd just have to pay your salary. I don't see the requirement to have made this minor operation a registered company!"

Dana laid down her briefing and clasped her hands together to keep them from trembling. "If you read the filing instructions on the form that's in your briefing, you'll see MSI meets the criteria for filing. And just to make sure I had interpreted everything correctly, I talked to the supervisor in the office responsible for the filing, and so did Colonel Lockwood. I can assure you, we've researched the issue thoroughly."

"I'm sure you have," Roger sneered, throwing his briefing on the table and looking out the window.

"Mr. Cunningham, if you'd filed the proper paperwork and MSI was a legal entity, this would be a lot easier and more clear-cut. I simply would offer to buy MSI. But since you didn't file the paperwork, all I can do is offer to buy the *business* of MSI. What I mean by buying the business of MSI is instead of leaving to start up my own legally registered company, potentially taking many MSI customers with me, I'm offering each of you what I feel is fair compensation for those customers. If you look at the last page of your briefing, you'll see my argument for this buyout. You'll also see a check made out to each of you for two hundred and fifty-thousand dollars." Dana scanned the faces of her three bosses, looking for a reaction as each one flipped to the last page of her briefing. "I believe seven hundred and fifty-thousand dollars is fair compensation for MSI's customer base," she added as she placed her pen down on the table, sat back in her seat, and waited for the reaction.

It took less than five seconds. Roger Cunningham's hand pounded the table loudly. "You think two hundred and fifty-thousand dollars is adequate compensation for MSI?" He spat out the words in his staccato fashion, as his face and ears turned a purplish shade. His torso stretched across the table toward Dana, and he looked as if he might come across it at any moment. "If I recall correctly, we've each been receiving about forty-thousand dollars every month for as long as I can remember! That means if things stayed the way they are now, we'd each make that much money in just over six months, anyway! So tell me again why this is a good deal for us?" His voice grew louder and more shrill with every sentence.

"Calm down, Roger," George said in a low voice. "I'm not happy about this either, but let's make sure we know all the details before we decide what to do."

Roger sat back into his chair, but his bulging eyes remained fixed on Dana. "I can't imagine what other details we're going to hear that'll make a difference. But sure, go ahead, Mrs. Smolenski! Tell us what other surprises you have in store for us!" He glared at her across the top of his glasses.

Immediately, Dana felt her throat tighten and she tried to swallow. She could feel the blood in her chest moving up her neck and her face flushing. This was exactly the reaction she'd been dreading — Roger Cunningham, irate and nearly out of control. And he was just getting warmed up! She had *so* hoped to avoid another of his combative outbursts, but the colonel was right when he predicted it would come to this. She took a deep breath and tried to relax her tight throat. "I've thought about this a lot, and I've talked to the colonel and others about my options. As I was explaining, I can see only two. The first option is the one I've just proposed to you on the last page of your briefing, which is I buy the business of MSI for seven hundred fifty-thousand dollars total, and each of you sign the attached page in your briefing stating you forgo any rights you might have for any future income from MSI. The second option is I leave MSI to start up my own similar company. Since I've worked hard for nine years to establish a successful client base, you can assume a majority of MSI's clients will follow me to my new company."

"We'll sue you for breach of contract!" Roger's fiery voice matched the flushed and enraged expression on his face.

Dana hated confrontation. Glancing toward the colonel, she tried to calm her pounding chest. "I was advised that might be your response. I also was advised the chance of a judge agreeing that we had a contract, and that contract had been breached, would be slim since I was never required to sign any sort of employee contract or agreement." Dana took a shaky breath and continued. "Gentlemen, I'd hoped you might understand I only want what each of you has — the ability to work hard for something and reap the rewards for myself and for my family. I want to own a company, just like you, Mr. Cunningham; and you, Mr. Higgins; and you, Mr. Redmond.

I want to use the monthly profits to grow the company in many directions. I want the responsibility to make the decisions *I* think are best. I feel the current situation is unfair, and after nine years of asking, I don't see the situation changing. So, it's back to the two options. You can accept the offer of two hundred and fifty-thousand dollars each by signing the accompanying document that legally transfers ownership of the business and the company name to me. Or, I will resign effective immediately to start up my own similar company." Dana paused for a moment and clasped her clammy hands together in her lap to keep them from shaking. "I hope you will choose the first option. I think in the long run it's the best option for everyone."

The room became eerily quiet — so quiet Dana wondered if anyone could hear her pounding heart. She wasn't sure what to say or do. She hadn't thought beyond this point. "Do you have any questions or is there anything else I can explain?" It was all she could think to say to break the terrifying silence.

Suddenly Roger Cunningham jumped up, pushing back his chair so forcefully it nearly tipped over sideways. "I don't know what Wayne and George intend to do, but I'm not signing a damn thing. You think this is the best option for everyone? Is that what you just said? *You* didn't take the risk when we started MSI, *we* did! Yes, you worked hard and got a lot of clients over the years, but the bottom line is the three of *us* came up with this idea and hired you to implement it! All the work you did over the past nine years was *your job* — what we hired you to do!"

Dana stared up at Roger Cunningham with her mouth wide open. Not sure what to say or do, she sat there momentarily stunned. Out of the corner of her eye, she saw the colonel slowly stand up.

George cleared his voice. He stood up halfway, leaned across the table and picked out a pen from the holder in the center of the table. "I'd certainly prefer the company continue as is, with Dana at the head, but since she has made it clear that's not likely to happen, Dana, I wish you the best of luck running your own company." He flipped to the last page of the briefing, signed his name midway down the page, picked up the check for two hundred and fifty-thousand dollars, and walked out of the room.

Shocked elation replaced Dana's terror as she watched the back of George Redmond walk out the door and down the hallway. She glanced at the colonel, who gave her a look of satisfaction.

"You've got to be kidding!" Roger hollered down the hallway after George. "You're going to let her do this?" He stood there for several moments staring at the doorway and then looked down at Wayne. "And what are *you* planning to do?" he asked, accusingly. "You know two hundred and fifty-thousand dollars doesn't begin to compensate us for what this company is worth!"

Wayne looked towards the window. After what seemed like an eternity to Dana, he turned toward Roger and replied, "I'm not happy about this turn of events either. But I have no intention of fighting this in court. I'm signing the release, taking the payoff she's offering, and calling an end to this ordeal."

Dana could hardly believe her ears. She watched as he unhurriedly took a pen from his shirt pocket and calmly signed his name. He picked up the briefing and the check, pushed back his chair and stood up, and slowly lumbered out of the room. Dana was tempted to thank him as he left, but decided he might come to his senses and change his mind. Silence seemed best.

"Well, you must be pretty pleased with yourself, young lady." Roger Cunningham glared at Dana as he leaned on the table with his fists. "Don't think you're getting off that easily with me, though. I certainly know what MSI is worth, and I have no intention of giving it away for two hundred and fifty-thousand dollars! You're going to have to make me a much better offer than that, or I'll see you in court!" His eyes bulged behind his glasses.

Stunned and frightened, Dana blinked several times and tried to compose herself. "Mr. Cunningham, there is no more money. Frankly, I was astounded I was able to secure a signature loan for seven hundred and fifty-thousand dollars! As I'm sure you can imagine, I don't own a lot of assets. It was a real stretch for me to get approval for that amount."

"Then you'd better think of something else because you need all three of our signatures, and there's no way I'm agreeing to this!" He turned around and stormed out of the room, leaving her briefing and the check on the table.

A moment later, Dana heard the front door slam as he left the building. Her heart pounded and tears flooded her eyes as she realized all was lost. Cunningham was right; she needed all three signatures before she would legally own MSI. She looked down at her lap and the tears dropped onto her navy-blue skirt. "Oh my God, I can't believe it! We were so close!" she blurted, while trying to contain her emotions.

The colonel sat back in his chair. "Don't give up yet. Let's sit here for a while and see what happens. Obviously, he's angry the nice little arrangement he enjoyed for a long time is not going to continue as he'd like. But he may go off and think about this and realize he could easily end up with nothing. He'll also be alone if he takes you to court, since the other two gents signed and took the money. So let's wait here for a while before we assume our plan didn't work." The colonel stood up and walked toward the doorway.

Dana stared down at her lap and blinked several times, trying to stop the tears and to absorb what the colonel had said. She sighed and looked up at the lights. Embarrassed, she glanced toward the colonel. "Sorry, Colonel. I've not slept well lately and I'm tired, and of course, stressed. Too much riding on this day."

Colonel Lockwood turned toward Dana. "Hey, that's perfectly understandable. Of course you're under pressure. You've got a tremendous amount riding on today's outcome, which is why we're not giving up hope that easily." He walked back over to the table and sat down gently in his seat. "The other thing Roger Cunningham should think about right now is what's going to happen Monday morning when no one is here running the business. His two partners have a lot of money in their hands, and he has the problem of a business to run and no one who knows how to run it. We can hope all these thoughts are running through his head right now."

Dana shook her head slowly and looked up at the colonel. "I've worked primarily with him over the years, and he's incredibly stingy. *He's* the primary reason I've been unable to grow the business to its full potential or take it in other directions that might be hugely profitable. He's not a risk-taker, and he wants all the profits disbursed to each of them every month. I just don't see him coming back now and having to humble himself, particularly to a woman, and when he's so livid."

"You may be right," the colonel said. "You certainly know him better than me. I just met the man. But let's sit here for a while, anyway. We can talk about next steps. That'll get your mind onto doing something. Taking action makes people feel better, like they've done everything they can, so they're ready to move on."

"OK," Dana said, sighing. "This certainly isn't the outcome I'd expected. I figured all three would do the same thing — they'd either all sign and take the checks, or none would. They rarely work together, and it's pretty clear they don't like each other very much. But in this case, I thought they'd get together and talk about what they were going to do. I can't believe they didn't."

"They may have, you don't know. They may have gotten together and decided to do exactly what happened this morning. The first two made their decisions pretty quickly, so one would assume they'd been thinking about it. Maybe Cunningham thought they'd change their minds if he said no. Who knows? We can speculate all day, but it doesn't change the facts about what happened. So let's do something positive and discuss some next steps you might consider."

"You're right." Dana tried to sit up straighter in her chair and garner the energy to think. She felt spent — as if a hundred-pound weight was on her and she couldn't move. Even trying to blink, her eyelids felt swollen and heavy. "I can't believe how tired I am!"

The colonel smiled. "I suspect you're physically and emotionally exhausted." He looked down at Dana, and then he stopped and looked toward the doorway.

Dana followed his eyes to the doorway. She heard something too — the sound of fast-moving footsteps — and soon, an unmistakable limp. She turned slightly in her chair so she could see the door, and held her breath, straining to listen.

Rounding the doorway, Roger Cunningham flew into the room. His face was flushed, his hair strewn across his forehead, and his eyes were glaring indignantly at the papers on the table where he'd been sitting only 15 minutes earlier. He swiftly limped to the table, picked up the pen next to his briefing, and scribbled his signature on the last page. Without looking at her, he threw the papers in Dana's direction, reached down and picked up the check, and turned on his heels and left.

Dana was stunned. Her heart still pounding, she sat frozen in her chair, barely able to comprehend what had just occurred.

The colonel reached across the table and picked up the strewn papers. He looked down at the page where Roger Cunningham had signed his name. Slowly and methodically, he pulled the signature page from the rest of the briefing and placed it neatly in front of Dana. Then, he sat back in his chair, clasped his hands behind his head and laughed.

Dana looked down at the piece of paper in front of her with the scrawling signature toward the bottom. She was quite familiar with the handwriting. It was a signature she'd seen many times over the past nine years. She looked over at the colonel, who had kicked back in his chair and was looking up at the ceiling, still laughing. A sensation of overwhelming joy, gratitude, and relief began sweeping through her body. What an unbelievable incident had just occurred right before her eyes! She still could hardly believe it! Her heart was pounding and her throat felt so tight it was hard to breathe normally.

Finally, Dana found her voice. "I can't *believe* what just happened!" She started slowly. "Except, you said it would." She turned toward the colonel. "Just what you thought might happen, actually did, and exactly as you predicted! How did you know?" She shook her head. "I can't believe he came back and signed the paper and took the check! Finally, this is over! All the months of worry, and preparation, and fear of losing my job and ending up with nothing — it's all over." Tears formed again in Dana's eyes as the realization of what happened sank in. "You know, I never let myself think this far ahead because I knew I'd get my hopes up and then feel devastated if it didn't work out. I'm sorry I'm rambling. I'm completely stunned!"

"It's OK, you're entitled!" The colonel was grinning from ear to ear. "I could not be happier for you! If anyone deserves this, it's you. I just had a feeling he'd be back after he had some time to think about it." The colonel stood up and began gathering up his papers. "Now, Mrs. Smolenski, if you don't need me for anything else today, I think I'll get out of your hair and let you make a few happy phone calls, and then start celebrating. I'm sure that's your plan for the rest of the day, or at least it should be," he added, looking down at her with a broad grin.

Dana pushed back her chair and stood up. "I don't know what my plan is for the rest of the day because I never thought this far ahead! But yes, I want to call Joey, of course, and my folks, and Marie." Dana wiped at her eyes and then extended her hand to the colonel. "Colonel Lockwood, I'll never be able to thank you enough for everything you've done for me. If it weren't for you, today would be just another typical day at the office for me. Instead, my entire life has just taken off in a different direction, and one with enormous potential. For the first time, I feel in control of my work life. I can't wait for tomorrow to get here and to get started! And I promise, I'm going to allocate a percentage of the profits to you once my loan is satisfied."

"You're most welcome, Dana. You certainly deserve it. It'll be fun to watch your success," he added, as he clasped their handshake with his other hand. "Keep me clued in as things progress and enjoy your new company."

Dana watched as the colonel walked out of the room and disappeared from sight. She sat back down in her chair and stared at the signed piece of paper in front of her. It was the most beautiful thing she'd ever seen in her life.

II

Part Two

22

Two years later, Spring 1997

The annual increase in Elizabethtown's traffic was visible now and new stop lights sprung up along local route 31W like wildflowers across a hillside. Not too many years ago, when Dana drove back and forth from Radcliff to Elizabethtown on a near-daily basis, there were open fields all around her. The small businesses and local restaurants that dotted the roadway often had difficulty staying afloat. Then, developers built the mall in Elizabethtown, the hospital expanded, and fast-food chains scurried to gain a foothold along the busiest sections of 31W. Now, Dana grew increasingly frustrated as she waited through one stop light after another, just to go a half mile to O'Charley's restaurant. She hated being late, and it seemed to happen now more often than she wanted to admit.

Again, Dana glanced at her cell phone sitting on the seat next to her. She reminded herself it would be Fugitte who would be late. Time management had never been his forte. When he was president of First Citizens Bank and Dana worked for him, she was the one who made sure they weren't late for meetings. That seemed a lifetime ago. So much had happened since that day he walked into First Citizens over 11 years ago and quit, leaving her to fend for herself against his replacement, Bernard Johnson. It was such a torturous memory. She still placed part of the blame for her painful firing and six agonizing months of unemployment and emotional devastation on Fugitte for not bringing her along when he left to start his new allotment business. By now, he had to know it was Dana — not her partner — who had done the lion's share of work that made First Citizen's allotment business so successful.

Dana was suspicious when Jim Fugitte had called last week to invite her to lunch. Although, it was Fugitte who'd connected her with the loan officer and bank that had given her the signature loan when she wanted to buy MSI, they'd kept in touch only occasionally over the past 11 years. She'd gone out of her way to thank him for helping with her loan. Another bank might have given her the loan too, but who knows, it might have been his reference that secured the deal. Banking was still a man's world, and she was a young woman with few assets and no track record of owning a company. She didn't know what to think about Fugitte's invitation to lunch today, except it was taking so long to get through all the stop lights on 31W, she might never get to O'Charley's and find out.

Propping her head on her arm, she leaned against the car window and gazed ahead. She suddenly realized that facing her on the opposite side of the intersection was Joey's patrol car. She rolled down the window and waved. A few seconds later, the driver's side window of the patrol car rolled down, and a hand waved back at her. The light changed and Dana looked over at the patrol car as it passed. Joey smiled and waved again. Dana forced a smile and continued ahead. She sighed deeply and suddenly felt tired. The spark she once felt when she saw Joey had gone. Maybe as the years went by, all marriages went down this path of apathy and detachment. They'd been through a lot of trials, but they used to talk through everything. Joey was her best friend, or he was for many years. Now Dana didn't have the energy or desire to explain her daily woes to Joey. It didn't seem important anymore to tell him all those things that happened during the course of her days. They confined their conversations to the kids and their activities, and to the family schedule. That seemed adequate now. Joey rarely asked about her days either. Maybe he sensed her apathy, or maybe he'd lost interest too. She had given little thought to his waning interest in her life. Perhaps that was a lot of the problem; after nearly twenty years of marriage, she didn't really care what he thought.

Finally, Dana spied the neon green sign and pulled into the parking lot. Scouring the lot for Fugitte's car, she decided he probably hadn't yet arrived. She gathered up her things on the seat and got out the car, locking the door behind her. As she entered O'Charley's, a hand rested on her shoulder.

"I worried I was late," Jim Fugitte said, breathlessly. "But it looks like I'm right on time."

Dana turned around to see her old boss breathing heavily from his jaunt across the parking lot. He was wearing a light grey suit and white shirt, and at 6'7" and around 260 pounds, he was an imposing figure. "Hello Jim, great to see you! I was hoping I wouldn't be the one late today. The traffic in Elizabethtown is terrible. I swear it gets worse by the month!"

"Yes, it does; but that's good news for us, actually. That means more vehicles on the road, and more vehicles means more loans, and more loans means more allotments."

Dana shook her head and laughed. "Always thinking like a businessman, but I guess you've got a point. Are you ready to get in line for a table? This place is always crowded over the lunch hour."

Jim nodded and then walked over to the hostess, who immediately escorted them to a table. "I made a reservation," he said, with a wink. "I knew it would be busy."

Ten minutes later, after ordering lunch and partaking in the requisite small talk, Jim pushed aside the condiments centered between them and placed his hands on top of the table. "Dana, I've been thinking. You know I spent several years at the FDIC and still have a lot of contacts there and friends in that community."

Dana stopped smiling at the tone of Jim's voice. "Yes, I remember. Your years at the FDIC were a great learning experience for you, and I've personally benefited from them as well. Also, I know I've thanked you several times now, but your help with securing my loan to buy MSI will always be much appreciated, which I've paid off, by the way."

Jim's eyes widened. "You're serious? You've paid off the loan already? It's less than two years, right?"

"Just over two years," Dana said. "And yes, it's paid off entirely and we've been turning a nice little profit. I couldn't be happier with the way things are going, and I love being in charge and not reporting to anyone. My goal is to never have to report to anyone like that again, especially to someone who knows less about the business than I do."

Jim leaned back in his seat and smiled. "That's terrific news, Dana! I couldn't be happier for you. If anyone deserves this, it's you. I believe you work harder than nearly anyone I know."

"Thank you, Jim. And the one thing the experience at First Citizens taught me is you don't make mistakes with someone else's money. Attention to detail is critical. If you make a mistake, they won't trust you and they'll take their business elsewhere. It's really as simple as that. So, Brenda trains all our employees to pay close attention and to not make mistakes with someone's allotment, or that person won't be employed very long with MSI."

"And in a nutshell, that's why you do so well, Dana." Jim nodded his head. "Anyone can set up an allotment business and find a few clients. But you get and keep your clients because of personal oversight within MSI and also good customer relationships. You just can't underestimate the value of the relationships you have with your customers."

"Well, I like that part," Dana acknowledged with a grin. "I enjoy getting out of the office and pitching what we do because I truly believe it makes their lives easier. They don't have to worry about forgetting a payment and then suffering the consequences. And really, two bucks per payment is not much for all that peace of mind — I don't think, anyway."

The waitress approached their table and placed two steaming plates in front of them. "Fish and Chips for you, ma'am, and Tuna Melt for you, sir. Can I get you anything else right now?"

Jim looked up at Dana, who shook her head. "Then I think we're all set," he said to the waitress. "Thanks." He picked up half of the Tuna Melt and took a large bite.

Popping a French fry in her mouth, Dana scooted forward in her seat and studied Jim Fugitte's face. "And how are you doing? How's business at your end?" She was still wondering if he had another purpose in inviting her to lunch.

"Things are going well," he replied, nodding his head thoughtfully. "We're busy as ever, just like you. But lately I've been thinking a lot about what the future holds for the allotment business. I mentioned previously I've been talking to several colleagues — you know, bankers and others in related businesses — about how paying bills by phone, and maybe later over the internet, is looking to be the next big thing." He took another substantial bite of his sandwich, then placed the rest on his plate, wiping his mouth and hands on the napkin from his lap.

Dana searched his face, surprised at the sudden turn of conversation. "Are you considering moving into bill pay by phone?"

"You and I deal mainly with community banking, in small town America. Maybe you're not yet aware of this, but larger banks are moving into some transactional phone capability. For example, you can imagine that being able to move money yourself between your own checking and savings accounts, or paying a recurring bill, by phone would be very attractive to customers. The consensus of my colleagues seems to be this is where banking is going in the future — calling up your bank and being directed to a series of automated prompts that would allow you to conduct transactions yourself." He stopped talking and took a drink of his water.

Dana frowned. "I've heard this sort of thing is being implemented as a pilot at some larger banks, but I didn't think it was going mainstream any time soon. What else have you heard?"

"I've heard exactly what you just said — the big banks are implementing pilot programs for customers to conduct simple transactions themselves over the phone. Right now, it's on a customer-requested basis. Customers sign up to get added to the pilot program, which is free while it's still a pilot program, but of course there will be a cost associated with this service eventually." Jim casually picked up his Tuna Melt and finished the first half in one bite.

Dana sat quietly for a moment, still holding a French fry between her fingers and studying Jim's face. "Are you considering trying to add this capability to your business?"

He paused for several moments and then nodded his head slowly. "I think if we want to stay relevant in this market, we'll have to move in this direction, and the sooner the better. You might remember that GMAC, the company that provides financing to automotive customers, is one of my bigger clients. They've already asked me about biller direct payments, which I'm working on now. But last week they asked about my plans for adding capability such as customer-initiated direct payments, which is what they call it."

"What did you tell them?" Dana had lost all interest in her fish and chips.

"I told them I was looking into it and would get back with them." Jim looked down at his plate and then slowly pushed it aside. "The fact is, I wanted to discuss all of this with you. I see a business opportunity for us. I think if you and I want to stay relevant in this business, we need to expand our allotment services to enable bill pay by phone. I think it's only a matter of time before our clients demand this service, so we need to get ahead of the game now and acquire the capability or we'll lose our clients to someone who can provide the service."

Dana felt a sudden rush of blood to her neck and face, and a tightening in her chest. She sat upright in her chair and stared at Jim. "You and I? What do you mean by that exactly?"

"What I mean is, I think you and I should join forces. I think we could both benefit by working together to develop the software and the interface that would allow us to offer the phone bill pay service to our customers." He looked intently at Dana, but showed no emotion.

"You and I? I remember a similar discussion about 11 years ago, but apparently you didn't remember it, or you chose not to." The words were out of her mouth before Dana could stop herself. Instantly she regretted it.

Jim looked down at the table and took a slow, deep breath. He shook his head and then looked up at Dana. "I honestly don't remember it the way you apparently do. I remember a notional discussion among you, me, and your partner that took place when we were at a conference in Hilton Head about the three of us starting our own allotment business. Maybe other discussions took place between you and your partner, but I don't remember any more between you and me. From the beginning, the plan was for me to resign as president of First Citizens once the holding company that hired me sold the bank. That's why the very day they sold the bank, I resigned. Your partner resigned too because he was willing to work without a salary until we got the software developed, found a bank, and got some customers. You had a family and two kids to support. I didn't think you'd have any interest in working with a company that couldn't pay you a salary indefinitely. But the day Johnson fired you and you came to see me, I realized you were deeply hurt and what I did was wrong. I should have told you what we were planning and let you make your own decision. It was wrong and I apologize."

Dana looked down in an effort to not show the pain she'd harbored for all those years. She'd needed that explanation from him 11 years ago! Just thinking about that time in her life made her chest tighten and her breathing difficult. She placed her elbows on the table and rubbed her forehead. "Thank you for the apology, Jim. After 11 years, I obviously still needed it because I've never understood how you could do that to me. I thought we had an agreement, and when you and my partner resigned, I was crushed. I felt like you'd left me there to fend for myself against that jerk, Johnson."

"Yes, and as I said, I realized that when you came to see me after being fired. But there wasn't a darn thing I could do at that point. There was no job for you with us; we had no money coming in." He paused. "There's nothing I can do about any of that now other than to repeat how truly sorry I am, and that I hope you can put it behind you now and see the benefits of our working together on this. I think the opportunity is in front of us right now."

Dana looked up, noting Jim's sincere and resolute expression, but she said nothing.

He quickly continued. "I've put a lot of thought lately into how to make this happen, and I think the simplest way is for us to combine our two allotment companies, and then start a new company that would focus solely on bill pay by phone."

"What about capital?" Dana asked. "Most of my profits over the past two years have gone to loan repayment. If I were to agree to this joint venture, I may have a problem coming up with the cash to fund software development, which I know would be the immediate priority."

"I suspected that might be the case," Jim replied, with a wave of his hand. "I don't see that as a problem. We can each own half of the company, but make the cash input at 60/40 or whatever that number needs to be." He gazed thoughtfully out the window and pursed his lips. "Regarding the business model, we would sell the software and the servicing of bill payments by phone to the community banks. We'd outsource the software development like we each did with our own companies. I'd envision your role as marketing to the banks, and later, generating customers. That was always your forte. I'd probably be best suited for taking over management of both our current allotment businesses." He stopped talking but continued to stare thoughtfully out the window.

Dana was silent, taking in Jim's expressions and demeanor and trying to comprehend his obviously well-considered ideas and his possible motives. "I can tell you've been thinking about this for a while, haven't you?"

"Yes, I have," he said without hesitation. "I've been watching what's happening with the big banks and it's clear to me the smaller banks and credit unions need to get onboard now and offer the same phone banking services, or pretty soon they'll start losing customers to the big guys." He reached over to pick up his leather attaché on the seat. "I brought you some information that'll help fill the gaps in my explanation. After you've had a chance to digest everything and give it some thought, give me a call and let's talk."

Dana took the manila folder from his hand and laid it next to her purse. "I certainly had no idea what you wanted to talk about today, but a new business venture never crossed my mind," she said, with a strained laugh.

A smile formed slowly across Jim's face. He picked up the second half of his sandwich and inspected it thoroughly. "I think this is a great opportunity in front of us and I look forward to hearing your views on it soon." He finished the second half of his sandwich in three large bites. After a quick drink, he put down his water glass and scooted to the edge of the bench. "I hate to eat and run, but I've got a meeting at 1PM."

Dana, surprised at his quick finish, started to stand.

"No, you sit here and eat. You haven't taken a bite of your lunch yet. We'll talk soon." Jim patted her shoulder, then reached down and picked up his attaché and left.

Dana looked down at her plate. He was right; she'd eaten one French fry. She took a bite of her fish. It was cold, just like the fries. Smiling to herself, she settled into her seat and decided to relax and finish her lunch. She thought about the new trajectory her life would take if she accepted Jim's offer to work together to create another company. How was she going to explain this to Joey? Life was just settling down after paying off her enormous loan when she purchased MSI. Maybe she should be happy with where things were now. After all, she had a good business with a reliable income, and she didn't owe anyone a single thing. Wasn't *that* the American dream? But maybe Jim was right; it was only a matter of time before the business model changed and she'd have to adapt or risk becoming irrelevant. He had his ear to the ground and access to information she didn't. He'd been right before, and what he said today made sense. She knew a little about phone banking and what the big banks were doing. What intrigued her more was *why* he wanted to partner with her? Why not her old co-worker, who was his current partner? Maybe that relationship had run its course. Or maybe Jim finally figured out her old co-worker wasn't nearly as resourceful and hard-working as he thought. But did it matter? Jim Fugitte had laid an interesting offer in her lap, and she'd talk it over tonight with Joey. She was pretty sure what would be her position. Now, she just needed to see if Joey could live with it.

23

That evening

The moon had risen, casting a long shadow across the driveway when Joey finally pulled in and parked. Dana watched through the window as he gathered his things from the passenger seat and opened the car door, slowly getting out and shutting the door behind him. He stood there for a moment, stretching his back. He moved like an old man.

Dana walked over and opened the kitchen door for him. "Hi Hon, long day?"

"Thanks," he said, as he walked through the doorway and over to the counter to set down his bag, keys, and coffee cup. "Yes, long day. How was yours?"

"Interesting," Dana replied with a light chuckle. "The kids are hungry. You ready to eat?"

"Sure." Joey walked over to the sink and washed his hands. "What was interesting?"

"I'll get the kids and tell you all at dinner." Dana disappeared down the hallway, returning momentarily with Liz and Ryan in tow.

"Hi Dad!" Ryan pulled out a chair from the table and flopped into it.

Liz walked over and kissed her dad on the cheek. "Hey Dad! You look tired."

"I am." Joey pulled out the chair at the end of the table and sat down slowly. "We're short-handed as usual, so I had to take another shift. I guess one day we'll have enough qualified people, but I could be retired by then," he added, with a sigh. "But your mom had an interesting day she's going to tell us about. Maybe she won the lottery?"

Liz and Ryan looked up at Dana as she placed a Dutch oven onto a hot pad and sat down across the table from Joey.

"Don't get too excited," Dana said. "I didn't win the lottery. I had lunch with Jim Fugitte."

Joey stopped smiling and looked up at Dana. "What?"

"I had lunch with Jim Fugitte," she repeated. "He called a couple days ago and said he wanted to talk, so we agreed to meet at O'Charley's for lunch today. That's where I was going when I passed you on the road."

"I'm surprised." Joey frowned. "As hurt as you were for all those years, I figured you'd written him off for good."

"I thought I had too," Dana admitted. "But who knows, I might not have gotten the loan for MSI without his reference. And I was curious to hear what he wanted to talk about. Anyway, I'm glad I went. The bottom line of our meeting was he and his colleagues in the banking world believe bill pay — like I'm doing — will be replaced soon by the customer making payments themselves over the telephone."

Joey paused, fork in hand, and stared at Dana. "Seriously?"

"It's already happening at the larger banks. Most of them now have pilot programs where customers can call their bank and request a customer service rep move money between the customer's savings and checking accounts. You also can use this procedure to pay your bills. Pretty soon you'll be able to call up and use the phone prompts to do it yourself without the customer service rep."

"Wow! I had no idea." Joey's face turned serious. "What does this mean for MSI? Please don't tell me just as things are going well, with the loan retired and steady money coming in, the business is going to become obsolete!"

"Well, yes, that was his point." Dana put down her fork and looked up at Joey. "Jim's colleagues in the banking community are fairly senior. They know a lot more than those of us in small towns about where the technology is moving and how fast things are happening. Their opinion is that in the not too distant future, our type of bill pay will become obsolete as the technology enables customer-originated transactions."

Joey was silent as he fixed his eyes on Dana. "Unless I'm misunderstanding something, I believe what you just said will sound the death knell for MSI."

"Eventually it will, if things proceed in the direction Jim described." Dana chose her words cautiously. She wasn't sure how much Joey could take tonight in his exhausted condition. "But clearly he'd been thinking about this for a long time, and his answer is for he and I to combine our two bill pay companies, and then start a new company that would provide the smaller bank and credit union customer the ability to make their own money transfers and bill payments over the phone. He asked me to go away and think about it."

It was Joey's turn to put down his knife and fork. "And what are you thinking at this point?" he asked in an accusing tone.

Liz was staring at Joey. "You don't look so good, Dad. Are you OK?"

Joey continued to glare at Dana. "I'm fine, Honey. Just waiting to hear what your mom has in store for us now."

Dana sighed loudly and looked down at her plate. "As with all the big decisions we've made regarding MSI, we'll make any future decisions together, Joey. I think you know that."

Joey looked down at his plate, smoothed the napkin in his lap, and began eating again. "I hope so. But this is a shock to hear the business could be obsolete soon. I'm not sure what to think about any of it."

"Believe me, I know how you feel," Dana said. "I was shocked to hear what Jim had to say too. First, I was shocked at the direction bill pay is moving, and the speed at which all this is happening; and second, that he wants to combine our companies, and he and I work together to create a new company. When he said he wanted to get together and have lunch, I thought it was just to get back on friendlier terms. It never crossed my mind he wanted to work together again."

Ryan stopped eating and looked up at his mom. "Are you going to take him up on his offer?"

Dana shrugged. "I have no idea what to do. Mr. Fugitte gave me a package of information and asked me to take a look at it, think about it, and let him know. So I'll do that, maybe try to do some research on my own, and then talk it over with your dad." She picked up her fork and tried to change the subject. It appeared they all had had enough uncertainty about their future this evening. Dana reminded herself it had been only a couple years ago that she'd taken a huge risk for her family with the $750,000 loan, only recently paid off. Now, she couldn't decide if it would be a bigger risk to start a new company with Jim Fugitte, or do nothing and potentially watch MSI become obsolete. This decision could end up being as tough as the one to buy MSI. Dana's head felt heavy. Why couldn't her major life decisions ever be cut-and-dried, where she knew exactly the best path to take? Her decisions seemed to be all-or-nothing, affecting not just her but everyone else in her family, and all the people who worked for her.

Liz reached over and rubbed her Mom's arm. "Don't worry, mom. You'll figure out what to do. It'll all be fine."

"Yeah, it'll be OK," Ryan agreed. "Maybe you and Mr. Fugitte will start up another company and it'll be a huge success!"

Dana placed her hand on top of Liz's and gave it a reassuring pat. "I guess we'll see. It's a lot to think about. Anyway, thanks for believing in me." She reached over and grabbed the salt and pepper. It *was* a lot to consider, and she'd need to make a decision fairly soon. Jim Fugitte would move forward with or without her, that much she knew. He wasn't one to sit around and watch a business opportunity pass him by. He was an entrepreneur. She was more of an opportunist. But she wanted to be more like him. Maybe one day she'd feel free enough to take her own ideas and develop them into something tangible. Right now she just didn't want to lose the financial security she'd worked so hard to get, and she didn't want to let down any of the people who depended on her for their livelihood. She needed to figure out the right thing to do for everyone.

* * *

Dana moved quietly from the small bathroom adjacent to her and Joey's bedroom to the closet to hang up her robe and kick off her slippers. She hadn't planned to stay up this late. But it took her longer than expected to digest all the material Jim Fugitte had handed her earlier that day. She was having a hard time accepting the undeniable conclusion. Bill pay was moving quickly to being customer-generated — there was no doubt about it. And the implications for MSI were crystal clear. Get onboard or be eliminated.

She pulled back the covers and deftly slipped into the bed. Lying there motionless, Dana wondered if everyday life for most people was this complicated, this unsure. Did other people struggle with such heavy decisions in the normal course of their lives? Or did most people get up in the morning, get dressed, have breakfast, and be happy about leaving for a job they expected to have for years to come? Was there something about her that craved the excitement and uncertainty of change and turmoil? Maybe Jim was right; she instinctively knew what customers needed and could demonstrate those requirements to a computer programmer and thus create an effective user interface. She *did* like doing that, but she also liked stress-free days, shorter working hours, being with her kids, and relaxing. In her experience, you couldn't have both. You had an easy, relaxing job, or you had one with lots of change and uncertainty. You couldn't have both. It wasn't possible.

Dana opened her eyes and looked over at the outline of Joey's body next to her. The last couple years of MSI's prosperity brought relative calmness and complacency to their relationship. She wondered if boredom in their marriage might be a good part of the reason she found Jim's proposal today enticing. Perhaps she needed something to get excited about these days. The love she once felt for Joey had faded, and Ryan and Liz didn't need her as much anymore. Marie was busier than ever with her work and many admirers, and Dana hadn't seen her nearly as much lately. But Jim's offer gave Dana something new to tackle, and maybe even greater financial security, once they combined their two current bill pay companies. That should ameliorate Joey's financial fears. Jim would be an excellent manager of the combined bill pay company, and she would be free to draft the technical requirements and guide the development of the user interface for telephone bill pay, while finding new customers, something she enjoyed. This would play to her strengths too, which Jim often mentioned.

Dana was pretty sure she knew what her decision was going to be well before she'd left the restaurant this afternoon. Closing her eyes, she rolled onto her side and settled into the cushy mattress. Maybe sleep would be forthcoming soon. That would be a welcome change.

24

August 1997

Marie was late, but Dana didn't mind. She was too excited to see her friend and catch up. She missed the good old days before Bernard Johnson was president, and when they both worked at the bank and saw each other every day of the work week. So much had happened since then. Those days seemed so simple and carefree compared to now. Dana rubbed her fingers slowly up and down her forehead and temples. It felt good. She sighed deeply and forced herself to relax. The sun's rays were streaming in her office windows and onto her back, making her feel lazy and her eyelids heavy. Sleep was elusive these days. She glanced at the coffee-stained cup on her desk, trying to remember how many cups she'd had this morning.

"Marie is here to see you," the receptionist announced, standing in the office doorway.

"Thank you, Loretta. I'll come get her and bring her back here." Dana jumped up from her chair and followed Loretta down the hallway. She spotted her friend in the foyer. "Marie! It's so great to see you!" Dana hugged her tightly.

"You too, Darling!" Marie said cheerily, returning the hug. "I rather thought you'd fallen off the planet."

"I know, I feel terrible. Just too busy to take time and catch up. I'll do better, I promise." Dana led Marie down the hallway to her office. "You look great, by the way. Of course, I'd expect nothing less," Dana added, admiring Marie's sleek blue dress and matching pumps.

"Well, you know, Luv, I don't have kids to take all my money, so I'm forced to spend it on myself." She dropped her purse aimlessly on Dana's desk and lowered herself into one of the two chairs facing the desk.

Dana pulled out the other chair and sat down facing Marie, still smiling at her. "It's *great* to see you," Dana repeated. "The kids keep asking about you. You've got to come over for dinner some night."

"How are the two darlings?" Marie scooted back in her chair and crossed her long, slender legs.

"They're fine. Doing their various activities at school and keeping busy. They seem to need me less and less. I guess that's good. That's what Joey says, anyway."

"He's correct. And how is Joey?" Marie asked, in a concerned tone.

"Why do you ask that way?" Dana frowned.

Marie leaned forward in her chair and looked intently at Dana. "Because the last time we all were together, I could tell things between you two weren't well. For the most part, you ignored each other. There seemed to be a lot of tension."

Dana sat back and looked out the window. "You're right. Things are not great. We get along OK; that's not the issue. I just don't feel close to him anymore, and we certainly don't talk as much. We're both so busy, and with Joey's crazy schedule, we don't see each other that much. He's home for dinner maybe two nights a week now."

"I'm sorry to hear that. I always liked Joey. He seemed a bit wonky the last couple times I was around him — preoccupied, perhaps. He said little and didn't seem as cheery. I assumed he was tired, that's all."

"Yes, he *is* tired, most of the time it seems. He works crazy hours and neither of us is sleeping well, so we both end up exhausted a lot." Dana pursed her lips and hesitated, "I don't know if I ever told you this, but Joey and I separated once. It was a long time ago. I think Liz was around two."

Marie cocked her head and raised her eyebrows. "No, Darling, you never once mentioned anything of the sort."

"Obviously we worked it out and got back together. We'll get through this trouble spot too, I'm sure," Dana said, instantly sorry she'd confided such a personal and painful experience. She wanted to change the subject. "How are things with you and the bank?"

Marie stared at Dana for a long moment, then shrugged. "All is grand again since the bank fired Johnson. Pleasant and quiet, just as it used to be before he took over as president. It's just a bloody shame no one filed suit against him long ago. It was completely obvious and well-known he despised working with women — a true misogynist. I don't know if you'd heard, but he fired every single female executive who worked for him in the main office *and* in all the bank branches. You simply were the first."

"Yes, I did hear. It's sickening," Dana said, bitterly. "I *tried* to do something. I went to see an attorney, remember? The only thing they said I might be able to do legally was get my job back. Who in their right mind would want to get their job back after being fired and then have to face that person again? Can you imagine how horrible it would've been to have to work for Johnson after that?" Dana shuddered at the thought and rolled her eyes in disgust.

"Of course I remember," Marie replied. "It was a low point in your life and mine too. I remember having to ring you whilst you were on maternity leave to tell you they were packing up your office. It took me the entire morning to get the courage to break that bit of news to you."

"I'll never forget it either," Dana looked down and shook her head. A hint of satisfaction slowly spread over her face. "But you know, I've thought a lot about it since then and I've concluded that if he hadn't fired me, I'd never have gone to work for Cunningham, Higgins, and Redmond, I wouldn't have bought the company from them nine years later, and I'd not be in the enviable situation I'm in right now. So maybe I should call him up and thank him! What do you think?"

"I think you've gone bonkers," Marie said dryly. "Besides, you'd have a difficult time finding him. He must have moved far away because no one has seen him since *he* packed up his things and left. Poetic justice, I believe."

Dana laughed. "Absolutely! But I hope he didn't leave before someone told him how well I'm doing. I want him to know he may have fired me, but I got the last laugh."

"It would be difficult for him *not* to have heard about you and MSI's success in this small town." Marie repositioned herself in the chair, smoothing her satiny dress beneath her. "Word gets around, you know."

"Living in a small town has some benefits," Dana agreed.

"Tell me, how are things with the new company? It's always thrilling to hear about your new ventures, and I'm curious how things are going with Fugitte too. I still can't believe you two are working together now, or again, I should say."

"Sometimes I can't believe it either," Dana said, laughing. "But we'd stayed in contact, you know. Anyway, it's an adventure, as you would expect. Jim has these great ideas and so far he seems to have been right about the direction bill pay is taking and where the technology is going." Dana sat back in her chair, stretched out her legs and crossed her ankles. "Last month we completed the merging of our two allotment processing companies — my MSI and his Fort Knox National Company. Jim's managing that part and we're splitting the revenue. He's on the board of directors for the merged company, has oversight of the entire operation, and takes care of the finances. When we merged the two companies, we became the largest processor of automatic payroll deductions for the US military and civil servants. And we're the only private company with direct access to the Defense Finance and Accounting System. Not bad for little old Elizabethtown, huh?"

"Not bad at all! You two should be pleased with yourselves! Now, what is your role? What do you do each day?"

"My role is to set up the new company, which currently has no customers, little money, and the software is a long way from complete," Dana said, in a skeptical tone. "I'll be out recruiting community banks and credit unions as clients, and offering to provide their customers the capability to pay their bills over the telephone. Basically, their customers will be able to call a telephone number that is branded to a particular bank or credit union. The software we develop will enable the bank or credit union customer service rep to access a portal and allow us to pay the bill. Later, we'll automate this entire process and won't need the customer service rep."

Marie sat back in her chair and crossed her arms. "I know the big banks started this a year or so ago, but I thought it was still in the pilot stage. By the by, I think it's a brilliant idea — ring someone and pay your bills — I adore the concept!"

"Yes, it *sounds* good, doesn't it? Jim is funding the new company, at least initially. I still need a salary, of course, but as soon as things settle out and our cash flow improves, I'll share in the funding for the new company. But right now I spend a good part of my time cold-calling potential clients. Jim calls this my forte — shaking trees and then raking up the leaves. I've hired Barbie Steck again to build the software. She's amazing. I describe to her what I want to happen, and she builds it. By the way, we've named the new company, 'Call Me Bill.' What do you think? Catchy title, right? Just rolls off your tongue!" Dana grinned from ear to ear.

Marie laughed out loud. "It's brilliant, Darling!"

"I thought it was perfect since it's all about the consumer using the telephone to call the bank themselves and pay their bills." Dana frowned and bit the side of her lip. "The only trouble I'm having is raking up new clients, as Jim calls it. We might be late to market. Most of the big banks have been doing this for a while, and even some smaller banks and credit unions have signed contracts already with companies like ours. Even more concerning, I've had a couple clients tell me their customers are asking when they'll be able to pay their bills over the internet. Jim said he's hearing the same."

"I've heard a bit about internet banking," Marie said. "But I understood it's still a few years away."

"I hope you're right. As I said, we don't even have the software and services figured out for the phone bill pay."

"You'll make it happen soon enough," Marie said. "You two made a great team all those years ago at First Citizens. Jim has his ear to the ground with lots of colleagues and friends in the examiner business. He'll know what the future of bill pay holds before most community bankers."

"That's what I think too," Dana said. "So, I'm out shaking the trees for new clients, and Barbie will keep building the software for phone bill pay until Jim tells us to stop. It's always a little nerve-wracking though."

"How's the cold-calling going? I imagine that's not a simple thing to do."

"No, it's definitely not!" Dana shook her head. "But you learn to take rejection and move on. I've been doing this on a smaller scale for years now, so I've had lots of practice. Do you remember the gigantic directory we had at the bank that lists the names of all the banks and credit unions in the country, along with their addresses and phone numbers? I use that and it helps a lot."

"Yes, I remember that book. I'm sure it's especially useful for cold-calling." Marie raised her eyebrows. "And Joey is OK with you and Jim starting a new company? What has he said?"

"As long as the merged company is generating revenue and paying my salary and our bills, he doesn't care what I'm doing with the new company." Dana sighed and looked down. "I don't talk to him about this like I used to. He doesn't seem interested, and I'd rather not mention things he's just going to worry about or be mad about. Is that wrong?" Dana asked, sheepishly.

"You're the only one who can answer that question, Darling." Marie sat up and pitched forward in her chair. "If you're comfortable with that approach and don't feel guilty, then I suppose it's OK."

Dana pondered Marie's words. She'd realized a while ago she didn't feel the need to tell Joey much about her work life these days. He hadn't shown much interest in her or her work in some time, so why should she share her concerns or successes or failures any longer with him? Dana remembered when they used to come home from work each day excited to share the day's events. So much had changed over the last few years. Perhaps they both just became too busy to bother, or maybe by the time they got home from work, they were exhausted and didn't want to rehash the day's problems. Whatever had happened, their marriage had suffered. There was no mistake about that.

25

Summer 1998

"Come on in, Dana, and sit down," Jim Fugitte announced, holding the phone to his ear with one hand and a cup of coffee in the other. "I'll be with you in a minute. Just need to finish this call with the bank."

Dana walked into the bright corner office and took her normal seat at the large oblong table next to the far wall. She'd always liked Jim's office. He'd decorated it with sizable brown leather chairs and two antique oak lawyer bookcases, the kind with the glass doors. A red and blue kilim from Turkey lay on the floor in front of his desk, and scattered across the walls were photographs he'd taken while traveling across the Middle East, before she'd known him. As she waited for him to finish his phone call, Dana reflected on her initial encounters with Jim Fugitte after he'd become president of First Citizens bank in the early 1980s. In one of her first meetings with him, Jim told her about his other love — teaching business classes at the Fort Knox Community College on the nearby Army post. Before long, he'd talked her into signing up for one of his classes. She didn't know how much interest she'd have in business and finance, but agreed to take the class since he was her boss. Besides, Joey was taking classes in Police Administration at the same college, so she figured she might as well go along and take a class too. It surprised her how much she enjoyed Fugitte's class, so she signed up for more. Eventually, she pursued a degree in business, finishing in two-and-a-half years, and while working at the bank during the day.

Sometimes she wondered if she'd ever have found her way into the banking world without Jim talking her into taking that first class.

"Sorry about that, Dana." Jim's booming voice jolted her back to the present. "I needed to get that call in before we had our weekly update this morning."

"No problem," Dana said, turning around in her chair to face her business partner. It still seemed a little unreal to think of Jim as her business partner and not her boss. "Everything OK?"

"Sure." Jim's voice was not convincing. "I was just telling Josh at the bank about my trip last week to San Francisco, which I was planning to tell you about this morning too." Jim picked up the papers from his desk and joined Dana at the table.

"That's right. You and Helen were in San Francisco last week. How'd it go?"

"Everything went well. It was quite enlightening too," Jim said, chuckling. "I have one interesting story for you. There were tons of vendors there from all over the country, and I met a lot of new folks. But the most interesting part happened during one session. The speaker started out by asking how many vendors were processing at least 200 electronic payments per month, and a portion of the vendors in the room raised their hands. Then he asked how many vendors were processing 400 payments per month, then 600 per month, and he kept increasing the number of payments processed per month until I was the only one in the room with my hand raised! Dana, I never realized how far ahead we are from everyone else in this business. We're not just processing a few hundred more electronic payments per month than nearly everyone at that conference, we're processing a few *thousand* more!"

Dana raised her eyebrows and stared at Jim. "Seriously? We live in this small town and *we* were the vendor at the conference processing the most payments?"

"Yes — and by far! Hard to believe, isn't it? You could've knocked me over with a feather! I kept looking around the room to gauge the number of raised hands, and I couldn't believe what I was seeing. I had no idea! Several

237

of the folks in the room came up to me during the break and wanted to know if we really processed that many payments per month. They thought I'd misunderstood the question, and that was how many electronic payments we processed in a year! I find it hard to believe we're that far ahead of our competitors." Jim picked up his papers and shuffled through them, pulling out a couple in the middle and placing them on top of the pile. "One other interesting item came out of the meeting. As you would expect, there was a lot of discussion about current electronic payments being replaced by phone bill pay. But I have to say, I was surprised how much focus there was on internet-based banking and how the big banks already are out there working on this, including paying bills over the internet."

Dana's head dropped and she hunched over resignedly, staring blankly at the floor in front of her. "I was hoping you *wouldn't* come back with that news. I've had a few of our customers ask about this already, but just here and there, no big ground swell. We've just gotten the phone bill pay nicely started, and now we find out we're behind the power curve on internet banking."

"We knew it was coming," Fugitte continued. "My colleagues at the FDIC and in the banking community have been talking about this for quite some time now. The technology is moving so fast, it's all about the internet now." He looked down at the piece of paper in his hand. "At the conference, they told us International Data Corporation estimates the number of internet users worldwide will increase from 142 million now to 502 million in 2003 — an annual growth rate of about 29%. We already know businesses are embracing the internet as a means of communication and to conduct transactions. They also estimate revenue from business-to-business e-commerce will increase from around $35 billion now to well over a trillion dollars by 2003, which equates to an annual growth rate of about 100%."

"Wow, that's crazy! But I don't think we should do anything about this right now, do you?" Dana was afraid to know what Jim thought. "We've barely had the phone bill pay up and running for six months and we're certainly not cash flowing yet, as you well know."

"Believe me, I understand your concerns," Jim said. "All that money, time, and effort we just put into creating the software for phone bill pay, and already the banking community is moving to the internet. But we have little choice except to move with it, or we'll become irrelevant. I suspect we can use a lot of the same software for internet bill pay that Barbie just developed for telephone bill pay. Should be the same back-end software anyway, I would think."

Dana lifted her head and stared at the ceiling. Her head felt heavy. She didn't know what to say. She could only think about all the work and long hours spent the past nine months cold-calling community banks and credit unions, trying to convince them of the benefits of using Call Me Bill as their new *phone* bill pay provider. Maybe they could transition some of those new clients to an internet-based bill pay service, but all that money spent developing the up-front part of the phone bill pay software might as well have been flushed down the toilet. "I can't believe we're going to have to start all over again so soon," she said, barely audible.

"Yeah, I knew you wouldn't be happy to hear this, Dana," Jim said, in a sympathetic tone. "You've done all the heavy lifting with Call Me Bill. Obviously there will be some financial loss with the software development for phone bill pay, but that's inherent in a technology-based business. Things move fast and we have to keep up, or we lose customers quickly."

"Yes, I know. I just didn't think it would happen this fast. I thought we'd get a few good years out of phone bill pay before we had to think about switching to internet bill pay."

"I did too," Jim said, shaking his head. "I did too."

Despite Jim's recent warnings about the eventual dominance of internet banking, she hadn't had time to give it much thought. She was too entrenched in the new phone bill pay service and keeping their error rate to a fraction of their competitors' rates. Dana looked up at Jim. "I imagine you've had several conversations about this with your bank colleagues. What are they saying?"

"Well, here's what I know so far." Jim settled back into his chair and crossed his long arms. "The big banks started looking into computer banking some time ago — I'd say mid-1980s. Most of those banks started by adding online banking through their existing systems using software called middleware. They use Netscape and other popular internet portals. One of the supposed incentives for banks to adopt online banking is a reduction in their operating costs, but who knows. Initially, they believed they could use their existing computer systems for internet banking. But recently I've heard that next year Citibank, considered a pioneer of consumer internet banking, is planning to abandon many of their decade-old computer systems and create a new entity called e-Citi, which will be a new retail bank on the internet."

"Internet banking is moving ahead much faster than I thought," Dana said. "It makes sense from a financial viewpoint. Banks should see reduced costs, as you said, and conceivably customers should see increased interest rates and reduced fees. But I thought customers would be slow to adopt a system where eventually they wouldn't be able to talk to a person at their bank, or deposit checks and cash without having to go through the US Postal Service. I hear they're supposed to put ATMs at places like Kinko's and Blockbuster Video, but I still don't see people rushing to this sort of limited-service banking. I do see people liking the ease of internet banking, once you can be sure of the security of it, which I understand is also a big problem."

"That's right." Jim nodded his head. "Regarding security, the big banks invited a few of the larger internet service providers to speak with them and provide information concerning how they would ensure internet banking services would be secure. One of the biggest concerns among the large banks is how to ensure the bad guys don't gain access to customers' accounts through the internet. The computer folks call this information assurance. Supposedly, the big banks have been losing millions to their computer systems being hacked. They've been keeping this quiet and don't want to disclose how much money they've lost for fear customers will withdraw all their money and move it to small, community banks or somewhere they think it'll be safer."

Dana frowned. "I hope they have this hacking problem solved by the time we're up and running. Community banks and credit unions won't be able to absorb losses like the big banks. Not to mention, this might even have repercussions for us."

"I'm sure it will." Jim pursed his lips and then stared out the window.

"Scary stuff, and too much to dwell on right now." Dana decided it was a good time to change the subject. All this talk about internet banking made her head hurt. "How about we get back to discussing where we are now with phone bill pay?"

"Yes, good idea," Jim said, turning back around to face Dana. "First, let me say I know you've put in a lot of hours getting us up and running in the phone bill pay business. Cold-calling is a hard way to drum up clients, but you seem to have a real knack for it. Also, you're meticulous about processing electronic payments correctly the first time, which is what sets us apart from all the other players in this field. I want you to know we all recognize that and appreciate all the effort you're putting into this. I don't know anyone else who could do as good a job."

"Thanks, Jim," Dana said, surprised by his praise. "And yes, I know internet bill pay is coming and we'll have to adapt. In the meantime, I'll keep plugging away with signing up new clients, and maybe Barbie won't have to write an entirely new software package for us. Next time I meet with her, I'll start the conversation and see what she thinks. She'll probably be happy to have the work. We've already put one of her kids through college; why not the other one too?"

Jim laughed and then looked toward the window. "Why not, indeed! At least we know it's going to a good cause."

"Hopefully, when we're finished developing the new software, we'll be able to follow Citibank's business model of having new clients move right into internet bill pay, and at some point we'll transition our existing clients as well. Then eventually, we'll be able to turn off phone bill pay."

"That's what I envision happening as well," Jim said.

Dana turned to her yellow legal pad and picked up her pen. "OK, regarding Call Me Bill, we now have 140 customers, which is about 40 more than I figured we'd have by now. I have a few former customers I'm still pursuing, but now I'm mainly cold-calling. Mostly, I use the Bankers

241

Directory for cold-calling, but I'm also getting a few referrals from current customers. I'm focusing first on the smaller community banks and credit unions in Kentucky. Usually I get straight through to the president and that person can make the decision, as opposed to the larger community banks and credit unions that'll have a board of directors. I'll work on them later. Right now, I'm going after the low hanging fruit to get our numbers up faster and hopefully have us cash flowing quicker. We're also having some luck with our fairly recent partnering with a couple small financial service providers who want to add phone bill pay to their offerings. So things are moving along nicely, and as I said earlier, much better than I projected just a few months ago."

"That's terrific news, Dana!" Jim sat back in his chair and grinned from ear to ear. "I know you've been putting in a lot of hours lately. That kind of growth is all because of your tenacity and sales skills. You should feel proud! You started Call Me Bill with no budget, no customers, and no software. And in a short amount of time, you've built a thriving new company with significant growth potential. You have a real knack for product development — seeing a problem and figuring out the best solution — and then getting customers to believe in it, too. Not a day goes by I don't congratulate myself for talking you into joining me in this venture."

"Thank you, Jim," Dana said, even more surprised. "I have to admit, those first few months when the reality of all the necessary work hit me square in the face, I wasn't sure I'd made the right decision. But I'm enjoying the challenge and I really want to see this thing succeed. There's such an obvious need for community banks and credit unions to have the capability for phone bill pay. Despite the long hours and all the cold-calling, which is never fun, I'm enjoying building a new company. Creating something from scratch is exciting, as you know."

"Yes, it is. And I'm extremely grateful you feel that way, Dana, because you're essential to the success of Call Me Bill. I've been fortunate in my career to be swept along with fabulous women — women like you who are way more capable than the glass ceiling allows them to be. Through the years, I've learned I prefer working with women managers because, in general, I've found they're more effective and produce more because they work harder. That's certainly true in your case, and Brenda Sheppard too. I can rely on you and Brenda to make sure there are no errors in our transactions, and that's what creates value in our company and gives us the edge over our competitors. We've got a couple competitors out there with a 10% error rate. The GMAC treasurer once told me right after we'd signed the contract to do their bill pay that I'd better never, ever tell him I put money in his account and not have it there. He said, 'do you have my message loud and clear?' I told him I got his message — no mistakes."

"And that has been our philosophy ever since." Dana smiled at the reminder from Jim. "I don't think that's something you *ever* need to worry about because, as I'm sure *you* remember, I learned that lesson in spades years ago when I was fired from the bank for incorrect amounts of money being taken from incorrect accounts. That was a hard lesson, and it's never far from my mind."

"I'm sure it isn't," Jim said, apologetically. "I guess I don't need to hound anyone about that issue."

"No, I don't think so!" Dana smiled and rolled her eyes. "Do you have questions or concerns about the progress we're making, or anything else?"

"No, everything sounds good. Keep doing what you're doing."

"Absolutely!" She picked up her papers and rose from the chair. Dana was eager to return to her office. She'd set a lofty goal for herself this week and wanted to see if she could beat her own record of new customers added per week. She'd given herself until 6 PM, Friday — her normal close of business. For her own personal satisfaction, she needed to beat her old record.

26

Christmas Eve 1998

"Come over here and sit down by the tree," Dana pleaded, motioning Grandma to the empty chair next to where she was wrapping Christmas presents on the floor. "You've done too much today, and it shows. You're tired, even though you wouldn't admit it for the world." Dana's eyebrows gathered and her forehead scrunched. Her gaze steadied on Grandma's pale face and thin mouth.

"I'm perfectly fine, Dana. I may be more tired than usual, but not enough to complain about." Grandma shuffled over to the chair next to Dana and sank her round frame into it. "And it *is* Christmas Eve — you're supposed to be tired!"

Dana's mom popped her head around the kitchen door. "Dana's right, Mother; you've been on your feet all day. You can keep her and Marie company while they finish wrapping presents."

"Yes, Grandma." Marie looked up at her and smiled. "Sit here with us. It's jollier next to the tree, and more fun playing with gifts than being responsible for Christmas Eve dinner."

Grandma giggled. "Truth be told, I'm happy to get off my feet for a while and sit in here with you girls. I think everything in the kitchen is good for now. Just need to have Joey carve the meat later. I still miss seeing your Dad do it, Dana." Grandma looked down and stared at her feet.

Dana sighed and nodded her head slowly. "I know what you mean,

244

Grandma. It has been 10 years and I still think about him all the time, but especially this time of year. I know Mom still misses him a lot too. But I think it helps when we can all be together over the holidays. Not everyone has that luxury."

Marie perked up. "That's right; I shan't see my family this year, but I have all of you!"

Grandma looked up at Marie and smiled. She stretched out her legs, settling deeper into her chair. "What time do you think Joey will be home, Dana?"

"I don't know if he *will* be home, Grandma. You know how the police force works. He's on duty for the rest of the night. He may be able to slip away and come home for dinner. It depends on what's going on and how busy they are."

"I don't understand how someone who has been in the force for so long would get stuck with duty on Christmas Eve," Grandma said. "Seems the new guys would have to work the holidays."

"I don't either, Grandma," Dana replied, then immediately regretted her tone.

Grandma glanced at Dana, but remained silent.

"It's OK that he's not here. We'll teach Ryan how to carve the meat." Dana flashed Grandma a quick smile and returned to her wrapping.

Grandma's gaze remained fixed on Dana's face. "Are you and Joey still not getting along? Is that why he's not home on Christmas Eve?"

Dana stopped wrapping presents but didn't look up. Her lips were drawn into a thin line. "I don't know, Grandma," she said in a soft voice. "Things are not great between us. We're both so busy with our work and our own lives. We don't seem to have much in common anymore — except the kids — and they're getting older and are off with their friends and activities most of the time. It's not that we argue all the time or anything like that; we just have little to talk about anymore."

Grandma hesitated and then spoke slowly. Her face was somber and her pale blue eyes never wavered from their target. "It makes me sad to hear that, Dana. You two dated in high school and you now have two children

245

nearly that old — or they will be in a few short years. You've been through so much together." Grandma's voice trailed away. "How does Joey feel?"

Reaching up and twisting her hair with her fingers, Dana sighed deeply. She glanced over at Marie and they exchanged looks. She rubbed her forehead slowly and deliberately with both hands and then looked squarely at Grandma. "I don't know how Joey feels because he rarely talks much anymore. By the time he comes home, he says he's too tired. He eats dinner and we exchange a few pleasantries, and he goes to bed. Sometimes he'll watch the 10PM news to help him relax before bedtime, but to be honest, I'm too tired to talk about anything substantive or important either. By that time of night, I don't have an emotional conversation in me. Then the weekends are here, and if Joey happens not to be working, we're off to sporting events or things with the kids, trying to relax and act like a normal family. I know that's no excuse; but it's the truth. I was hoping all this would blow over — like it normally does — but I don't think it's going to this time, Grandma. And I'm sorry I'm telling you this on Christmas Eve." Dana's voice was wavering, and by the time she finished talking, tears were welling in both eyes.

Grandma didn't say a word. She leaned forward in her chair and put her arms around Dana. She held her, patting her back gently.

"Aww, I'm coming in too," Marie announced. "I can't be left out of this hug fest." She wriggled forward on the floor until she could wrap her long arms around both Dana and Grandma.

Dana couldn't help herself. She laughed hardily at Marie's antics. Then Grandma was giggling too.

Soon Dana's mother was standing in the kitchen doorway, wiping her hands on her apron and grinning too. "What's so funny in here?"

"Come on in, Mummy! It's a group hug." Marie waved her adopted mother over to the beautifully decorated tree, where the three of them were wrapped in each other's arms, laughing noisily.

"I'm too old to get down on the floor," Dana's mother said. "But I'm happy to see you three having a good time. Are you nearly done wrapping presents, Dana? Dinner is about ready and I'm hungry. I just need someone to carve the meat."

Marie perked up. "If you don't mind what the meat looks like once it's carved, I'm your girl!" Marie turned around to Dana and said in a low voice, "And if you don't mind a good bit of it eaten while it's being carved, because I'm famished!"

"I'm sure you are," Dana said. "It must be two whole hours since you had your last meal."

Jumping up from the floor, Marie bolted into the kitchen ahead of Dana's mom. "Ta-ta, darlings! I'll leave you to carry on. Best to wash up soon, though. I'll have the meat ready in a snap."

"We should take her at her word, Grandma, and go wash up. She can move at the speed of light when there's food involved." Dana helped Grandma up from the chair and followed her down the hallway to the bathroom. "Dinner's almost ready, kids, so please wash up," she said, as she passed Liz and Ryan's bedrooms. "Oh, and Marie is carving the meat if you want to help. I suspect she could use it."

"I heard that!" Marie's lilting voice flowed down the hallway. "I'm not sure there's enough for the rest of you. But not to worry! Tomorrow you can make a tasty broth from the bones."

Ryan stuck his head in the bathroom door. "Don't pay any attention to her, Grandma; we don't. But I'll go help her so we have something to put on the table."

Ten minutes later, everyone was situated around the table. Dana raised her glass of iced tea. "A toast to Christmas Eve dinner. I wish all my dear family — and Marie is family too — a wonderful Christmas, and happy and healthy 1999."

"Hear, hear! And thank you for allowing me to join your brilliant family for this momentous occasion and meal!" Marie had a drink in her right hand and a fork in her left. "I want to say, from my perspective, 1998 has been an excellent year for the Smolenskis. Ryan and Liz are turning into two nearly-human beings," she said, grinning at Liz and nudging Ryan, who was sitting next to her. "Mummy and Grandma are healthy and doing well. And Dana, Call Me Bill is growing by leaps and bounds and looks to be yet

247

another successful venture!"

"It's a blessing to be healthy," Grandma chimed in. "Here we sit — four generations of my family. How truly blessed are we to still be together."

"Yes, that's the most important thing." Dana looked down at her plate and chuckled to herself. "I used to laugh when I heard people say, 'when you don't have your health, you don't have anything.' Now I get it. But it's good to have financial health too. I know in the past I've stressed a lot about not having a job and not being able to pay the bills. It's a great feeling to know all that's behind me, at least I hope it is," she added, looking up and smiling at everyone. "OK, let's eat! Although, I see some of you already started." She turned to glare at Marie.

"Can I help it if everything smells so delicious?" Marie loaded mashed potatoes and gravy onto her fork, and held a corn muffin dripping with honey in her other hand. "I'm looking forward to hearing all the latest regarding Call Me Bill. The last we talked, the software development for internet banking was going well, but you were having trouble getting many of the larger community banks and credit unions lined up. Any movement there?"

"Pass me the green bean casserole, Ryan, and then I'll be able to answer Marie." Dana grinned at Ryan and held out her hand. "I love this casserole so much; I don't know why I only make it on holidays."

Dana's mother poured herself a glass of iced tea and settled into her chair. "I'd like to know what you do at work too, Dana. You spend so much time in that office and on the phone, I can't imagine what you do in there all day. But I figure you must love it."

"I don't know about that — especially right now." Dana grimaced and rolled her eyes. "I spend most of my time on the phone, cold-calling banks and credit unions, trying to convince them their clients are going to love our new one-stop bill paying service, which the client can initiate themselves over the internet."

"I thought you were offering the banks bill paying services where their clients could call up a certain phone number and pay their bills that way. That sounds a lot easier to me," Grandma said. "I don't use the internet, and never plan to, so how would someone like me pay their bills?"

"You could stay with phone bill pay if you wanted, Grandma. I think there are many people like you who don't want to pay their bills over the internet. There also are many people who want to do so. Therefore, we need to offer the option to people or they'll find a bank that does offer it. That's what I'm selling to the banks and credit unions. I call and offer them the software we've developed to enable their clients to pay their bills online." Dana filled her empty fork and quickly took a bite. She enjoyed talking about Call Me Bill, but there was a table full of scrumptious holiday dishes sitting in front of her and they were still hot. She could talk anytime.

"What is cold-calling, Dana? You just pick up the phone and randomly call every bank in the phone book?" Dana's mother looked puzzled.

"Not exactly Mom, but you're not far off. There's a big bank directory I use that has all the information I need. For some time now, most of the big banks have had phone banking and now internet banking, which is what Call Me Bill is offering. But most of the small banks and credit unions, like the ones in Elizabethtown and Radcliff, don't have this yet. Some don't even have phone bill pay. So I started with the low hanging fruit — the smaller financial institutions and only those in Kentucky. I figured they'd be easier to deal with, especially if I have to drive to them to demonstrate our software."

"Wow, Mom. I had no idea that's what you were doing all day," Liz said, sympathetically. "That must be hard, calling people out of the blue and trying to sell them something. Sounds almost like telemarketing. Do you have people hang up on you?"

"Not usually," Dana said with a chuckle. "Financial Institutions often have vendors calling them, and I have a pretty tight spiel worked out now. I know what to say right up front to keep them listening. Plus, by now they all know about phone and internet banking, and they know their customers want it, which usually keeps them talking to me. Also, one major advantage of working with the small guys is it's usually one person — the bank president — who will make the decision. If it's a bigger bank or credit union, the person I talk to normally will have to present my proposal to a board of directors, and the board will vote whether to buy our product and service. This takes much more time and is a lot more trouble than if a single bank president can decide. So, I've found it's much easier to work with the smaller institutions, although we don't make as much money from them, obviously."

By now, Marie had put a sizable dent in the food on her plate. "I would think it's easier for you to work with the resellers. How are you making out with them?"

"What's a reseller?" Liz asked.

Dana managed to get in two bites before answering. "What has been working better so far, and has a lot more potential in the long term, is when I market our product to someone who's providing other internet banking services and is looking to only add bill pay. I've had several occasions where I talk to a group of salesmen and tell them about our software and services, and they add it to the marketing of their online banking products. Lately I've been working with a young guy who runs this sort of company, called Direct Access. They provide other online banking products, but not bill pay. So when they have a customer who also wants bill pay, he refers them to me. This has been working out great."

"I'm so happy for you, Darling!" Marie put down her fork and knife and folded her hands together. "As I've often said, you're such a hard worker, and I've watched you toil away day and night for many years. You deserve a grand success!"

"Yes, you do," Grandma said. "By the way, everything is just delicious, Dana."

"Thanks, Grandma. You and Mom helped a lot. But I hope no one is finished yet. I'm nowhere near done eating, and Marie's probably just now ready for seconds, along with Ryan." Dana looked over at her son. Sometimes she couldn't believe how much he ate now.

"You're right; I'm nowhere near finished!" Marie said indignantly. "Yes, please, I shall have seconds on meat, potatoes . . . and I'll have some veggies too. Suppose I must have something green on my plate. Then, I shall have a rather large piece of that apple pie on the counter, smothered in vanilla ice cream and maybe some cream poured over it as well."

Dana shook her head, and Liz giggled. "Cream on top of your pie and ice cream?" Liz asked. "Is that a British thing?"

"I don't know," Marie said, looking puzzled. "But it's a Marie thing — always has been. I've adored pie covered in sweet cream since I was in nappies."

"I know," Dana said, sighing loudly. "I know all your strange antics, so I bought some sweet cream yesterday."

"That is why you are my dearest friend!" Marie sat perched on the edge of her chair. As she stared at the pie sitting on the kitchen counter, her eyes lit up like the Christmas tree behind her.

"I love to see all you young people eat," Grandma said. "Makes me feel all the effort was worthwhile."

"Me too," Dana's mother added. "I also hate putting away leftovers, so eat up."

"Don't put away anything yet," a voice came from the kitchen. "I'm starving and I've been thinking about this meal all day."

"Dad, you made it home!" Ryan scooted his chair against the wall and stood up, squeezing behind Marie and Liz to get to the kitchen.

"I had two calls to check on today, and then it was pretty quiet. So I thought I'd slip out and was hoping you were still eating. I figured Marie was anyway."

"Lucky you got home now," Marie shot back.

Joey walked into the dining room and went straight to the empty chair at the head of the table. "Merry Christmas Eve!"

They all responded cheerily — except Dana. She couldn't remember when he stopped coming home, setting down his hat and keys, and giving her a kiss before he did anything else. One day she realized he didn't do it anymore. She wondered if he realized it. Joey dove into his plate and aimlessly chattered away with everyone at the table. He didn't seem to notice she was there too. "Are you still off tomorrow, Joey?" she asked, just to get his attention.

"As far as I know," he said nonchalantly. "Can you pass the green bean

251

casserole down here?"

"Sure." She kept her eyes fixed on his face. He didn't appear to notice anything was amiss. He's used to not asking me about my day anymore or much of anything else, she thought. I guess it happened so slowly, neither of us noticed. She pushed back her chair and stood up. "I think it's time to put dessert on the table."

"Oh, bloody yes!" Marie scooted back her chair as well and jumped up. "I shall help." She followed Dana into the kitchen.

"I sure wish I could eat like you, Marie. I swear I don't know how you do it." Dana shook her head in wonder.

"You have so many other adorable features and talents, Darling, such as your big brown puppy dog eyes." Marie turned around and gave Dana a quick hug. "You're really quite brilliant too, but you don't seem at all aware of it."

"Thank you. I'm not sure I agree, but thanks for saying it. I think I just work harder than most people." Dana picked up a large knife and sliced the pie.

"Yes, there is that. But you also see things others don't. You have a knack for identifying what people want in order to be comfortable paying their bills online and then designing the software and interface to do just that. Few people can do that, Dana, and that's why you're going to be incredibly successful soon — that's my prediction." Marie was standing next to Dana with a stack of small china plates. "Now, please put a rather sizable piece of that on this top plate and I'll be out of your way."

Dana's face broke into a slow, wide grin. "Here you go. The ice cream is on the bottom shelf in the freezer and the sweet cream is somewhere in the fridge. You'll have to search for it." She put down the knife and turned to Marie. "I don't know what I'll do when you decide to return to England. I may have to come with you."

"Not to worry, Darling," Marie said amiably. "I fancy the food here too much to leave any time soon. You know what they say about British food, and it's all true. It's horrid compared to American food — especially the sweets. I don't know why they even call them sweets, because they certainly are not!"

Dana watched expressionless as Marie picked up her plate and went in search of the sweet cream and the vanilla ice cream. She looked down at her reflection in the plate in front of her and thought about Marie. She'd always been nearby during the tougher times in her adult life. Dana had a feeling she soon would need her friend more than ever.

27

June 1999

The warm winds whipped Dana's hair across her face as she moved swiftly to cross the parking lot to Fugitte's office, trying to outrun the large rain drops pounding her head and back. She had a feeling she'd regret leaving her umbrella under the front seat of her car. The forecast for today had been erratic, like nearly everything else in her life lately.

She flung open the front door of the building and strode quickly down the hallway to Fugitte's office, her heels clicking loudly on the tiled floor. Today was going to be an interesting day, no matter how it turned out. At the least, today's meeting would be informative and useful, and she'd know much more about the future of the financial industry.

"Grab some coffee and come on in, Dana." Jim Fugitte's deep voice boomed down the long hallway.

"OK," Dana yelled. "Be right there." They had a lot to discuss in the next hour before the guy from NETZEE showed up. She quickly grabbed some coffee and a donut and hurried down the hall to Fugitte's office.

"Good morning," Jim said, as she appeared in the doorway. "Nice suit."

"Thank you. I figured it was a good time to drag one out of the closet." She went over to the table and placed her things at her usual seat. "I've been looking forward to this meeting, although I'm not sure why. Obviously, we don't intend to sell Call Me Bill. Guess I'm just curious about what he's going to say."

"Yeah, I feel the same way," Jim replied, getting up from his desk and joining her at the conference table. "It'll be interesting to hear what he thinks about the current situation, and where his advisors see banking moving in the near future. They may hear different things in Atlanta than we hear in Elizabethtown."

"Right," Dana said. "Maybe they get better projections than we do, or different ones anyway." She pulled out her chair and sat down, taking out a yellow legal pad and flipping over the pages until she came to the one with her notes for today's meeting. "I have a couple things I want to make sure you're aware of before he gets here, and I also want to make sure you have the latest info and numbers for Call Me Bill, so nothing I say to him is a surprise to you," she added, with a chuckle.

"Good, because you know how I dislike surprises." Jim settled back into his chair and crossed his arms. "Fire away."

Dana looked down at her notes. "First, we're having good results from our partnership with Direct Access, the company that turned NETZEE onto us. As you know, since their online banking products don't include bill pay, they're referring all customers to us. Second, I've been pitching our product to other resellers and sales folks, who then go out and talk to potential customers about lots of internet banking products, ours being just one of them. I'm surprised how this is taking off too. Although Call Me Bill still isn't cash flowing, we're getting more business lately and getting closer."

Jim nodded his head. "The numbers are definitely improving every month. Your new tactic of partnering with companies who are adding us to their product line is making the difference."

Dana nodded in agreement. "Yes, and I made one other change that's working out better. I'm getting some of these banks and companies — particularly the ones run by boards — to agree to get on our calendar now and set an installation date. While they're waiting, their boards or lawyers can work on getting the contract signed. I tell them if they're interested, fax me a copy of their check for the $1,500 installation fee, and let's get them scheduled now because the open dates may not last."

"That's a great idea!" Jim said. "Shows their commitment and probably pushes the board to make the go-ahead decision sooner."

"Yes, that was the plan, and it has benefited us several times now." Dana shifted in her seat, tucking her crisp linen skirt neatly beneath her. She picked up her coffee and took a drink, then pushed her notes aside. "Slowly, we're gaining traction."

"Agree," Jim said. "We're doing very well with Fort Knox National Company and MSI too. Our call center is up to 400 people — can you believe it? Our error rate is practically nil, and I'm having some success finding new markets for biller direct bill pay. It'd be nice to expand out of car loan and insurance payments. But after all these years, we still have a lock on Fort Knox military allotment payments. I still find that amazing!"

"What I find amazing is that Fort Knox National Company is the only private company in the country with direct access to the Defense Finance Accounting Service. In little old Elizabethtown, you own the only company allowed to access DFAS directly! I still think that's an incredible accomplishment, Jim." Dana smiled proudly at her partner. She'd always believed he was a real innovator in the world of finance and was glad others recognized this as well.

"Sometimes I can't believe myself that we're the largest processor of automatic payroll deductions for US military and civil servants. It's hard to believe it all started with a little bank in Radcliff that began providing life insurance allotments for the military at Fort Knox." Jim shook his head in wonder. "That seems like a lifetime ago, doesn't it, Dana?"

"It absolutely does." The smile faded from Dana's face. So much had happened since those days at the bank, some of it she preferred to forget. "That's all I wanted to update you on, Jim. Want to take a quick break before Alan Wingart arrives?" Dana glanced at her watch. "He should be here in about 15 minutes."

"Sure." Jim looked at his watch too. "By the way, were you able to find out any more about him?"

"Not really." Dana shrugged and raised her eyebrows. "Basically, Wingart and his partner are business owners already. One of them got the idea to put together a company that would provide services from all parts of the financial sector. They're looking for a bill pay provider and Direct Access told them about us."

"What's the connection between Direct Access, and Wingart and his partner? Do they have a formal business relationship?"

"I don't know." Dana stood up. "Guess we'll find out soon."

* * *

Alan Wingart cut a fine figure in his crisply pressed khaki pants and dark blue sport coat, as he walked smartly across Jim's office to join him and Dana at the conference table. His blue and white striped shirt and perfectly knotted tie stared her in the face when he chose a seat at the table opposite her. She couldn't see his shoes, but Dana presumed he wore polished tan loafers, the kind with the tassel. The shoes would be expensive, maybe Johnston and Murphy, or perhaps even Allen Edmonds. His cropped light brown hair parted at the side and hung lazily over his forehead. He was an elegant man; she figured he was a smart one too. "Good morning, Mr. Wingart," she said, standing up to greet him with her best smile. "It's nice to meet you."

"A pleasure to meet you too, Dana," Alan Wingart said, grasping Dana's hand with a firm shake. "And you as well, Jim," he added, turning to greet Jim. "I hope I'm not late. My plane was delayed this morning, but I had no problem driving here from the airport. Your directions were spot on, Dana."

"Good," Dana said. "Can I get you a cup of coffee?"

"No, thank you. I've had several already and breakfast on the plane."

"Please have a seat and tell us what we can do for you," Jim said, with a wave of his hand.

257

Alan Wingart sat down in the chair where he'd placed his briefcase. He took out some papers, snapped it shut, and set it on the floor beside him. "On behalf of my partner, Bill Harper, and myself, thank you for meeting with me today. I'm here because Bill and I are in the midst of creating an exciting new company for the financial sector, and we firmly believe there's an important role in our new company for Call Me Bill." He passed a neatly prepared briefing to both Jim and Dana. "There's a concept drawing on the first page of this briefing that will show you what we're creating. Our idea is to build a company that will be a leading provider of integrated internet banking products and services, and e-commerce solutions to community financial institutions. This company will provide cost-effective, outsourced, secure, and scalable banking and e-commerce products and services that we'll brand with the financial institution's own name and logo. This will allow customers to have the convenience of internet banking without losing the personal relationship they've established with their local community financial institution."

"What do you mean when you say e-commerce? Can you give an example?" Jim asked.

"Sure." Alan placed his briefing on the table and settled into his chair. "Recently, we added an e-commerce product into the concept design called Banking on Main Street. It will enable a community financial institution to place its business customers on the internet through the creation of individualized websites. We'll incorporate links to these websites into the financial institution's homepage, which makes this homepage a marketplace for consumers and businesses to conduct banking and e-commerce transactions. Local businesses can sell their products and services on this homepage, and vendors can access this entire group of customers — all under the trusted brand name of the community financial institution."

"Sounds interesting. How does Call Me Bill come into play?" Dana wanted to see how much Wingart knew about internet bill pay, and how much research he'd done on Call Me Bill's business model and customers.

Alan leaned forward slightly in his chair and alternated his focus between

Dana and Jim. "Call Me Bill could interface with the Banking on Main Street product I just mentioned. But primarily our company will offer community financial institutions all products and services of an internet banking system, such as account statements and balance inquiries, check imaging, fund transfer capabilities, loan application, and of course, telephone and internet bill pay. For the commercial customers of community financial institutions, our company will offer business banking and e-commerce services, including corporate cash management, custom web design, implementation, and marketing services. So you see, Dana, there are many diverse roles a business like Call Me Bill could play in our company, besides bill pay. I can easily envision broadening the scope of your company."

"What do you see as your primary revenue source?" Jim asked.

Alan smiled at him. "You're the economist."

"You did your homework," Jim said, then held up his hands and shrugged. "Someone had to ask about revenue! Dana's going to ask for details. She's the doer in the group."

Alan looked at Dana and smiled. "That's what I've been told." He turned back to Jim. "To answer your question, we expect to earn nearly all our revenue from recurring monthly service fees, which are based on flat monthly per user and per transaction charges paid by our community financial institution customers. We expect to derive little or no revenue from up-front software or implementation fees."

"Interesting," Jim said. "Do you plan to have a data center somewhere to support all of this?"

Alan nodded his head. "Yes, our data center will provide the web servers, computers, data storage, retrieval, security systems, and support personnel necessary to operate our systems, and allow community financial institutions to outsource their internet banking needs. And our network design and relationships with data processing vendors will enable us to interface our products and services with a financial institution's existing core banking and data processing systems."

"On paper anyway, correct?" Dana asked.

"We're confident in our analyses, Dana, and our initial test runs show we have reason to be confident." Alan shifted smoothly in his chair and folded his hands in his lap.

"Why Call Me Bill?" Dana asked, looking squarely at Alan.

"You, Dana," he said, without hesitation. "You're the reason we want Call Me Bill. For a while now we've been looking for a bill pay service to add to our portfolio and have been asking around to our contacts and doing some research. We're purchasing a company that often partners with Call Me Bill — Direct Access. They told us about Call Me Bill and they specifically touted your business acumen, Dana. They said you're absolutely trustworthy, very hard-working, and your company rarely — if ever — makes a payment processing error. Those attributes are scarce these days. We did our own research, which confirmed what we were told. So, we'd like to make an offer to buy your company and that's why I flew here today. We're prepared to start negotiations immediately with you and Jim."

Dana stared at Alan for several moments and then glanced at Jim, scanning his face for clues of his reaction. But she received no feedback from his countenance, except his furled eyebrows — a sign he was thinking. She turned back to Wingart. "Alan, we're flattered you've chosen Call Me Bill to supplement your portfolio, but unless there's something I don't know, our company is not for sale." Dana glanced back at Jim, but still couldn't discern any visible reaction one way or another to Alan's commentary. "As you probably know, Call Me Bill is a relatively new company and we're still ramping up business."

"Absolutely, I'm aware you've not been in business long," Alan said. "That can be a good thing when attempting to integrate the businesses of six varied companies."

Jim cleared his throat. "Alan, while we appreciate you flying here to discuss your proposal, Dana's correct when she says Call Me Bill is not for sale. There's a lot more we want to do with the company before we think about selling it."

Alan unfolded his arms and held out his hands. "I see no reason you wouldn't be able to do everything you have planned now for the company.

The beauty of this proposal is we'd like to keep Dana on the payroll as the head of the company indefinitely, and we'd be able to provide resources I suspect above what you're able to provide as a small company. Plus, you'd be able to leverage the assets of the other five companies." Alan leaned forward and spread his hands on the table. "Jim, Dana, we truly believe the time is now for community financial institutions to move to internet banking. Forecasters are predicting more personal computers in the home and workplace, improved communications infrastructure and security, greater ease of e-commerce, and easier, faster, and cheaper Internet access. People are now considering the Internet as a viable tool for paying their bills, brokerage services, insurance, payroll, monitoring financial accounts, and transacting business 24/7. And consumers don't have to load software onto their computers for this. But right now, only about 5% of community financial institutions offer Internet banking. That's a tremendous market opportunity for us, and we want Call Me Bill to be part of our success story. I'm leaving our proposal on the table." Alan laid his hand on top of a manila envelope. "I'm asking that you don't say Call Me Bill is not for sale, but that you take some time to talk this over and think about it. Then, call me and let me know your answer."

"Fair enough," Jim said, looking over at Dana.

"Sure," Dana replied. "But you know our going-in position, so please don't get your hopes up." She'd look at the proposal and talk it over with Jim, but she had no intention of selling Call Me Bill to him or to anyone else.

Alan Wingart gave Dana a quick smile and then rose from his chair. "I've taken up a good piece of your morning. It has been great to meet you both, and I hope to hear something positive from you soon." He picked up his papers, swiftly deposited them into his briefcase, shook hands with Dana and Jim, and was out the door.

Dana sat down in her chair. She picked up her coffee and took a drink, staring at the proposal left on the table. "That was interesting." She stuck her pen behind her ear and leaned back in her chair.

Jim reached across the table and picked up the manila envelope. He pulled out the folder and flipped over the cover to the first page. "They're offering $1 million in NETZEE stock. I have no idea if that's a decent offer or not."

"Does it matter?" Dana asked, surprised. "I thought you weren't interested in selling either."

Jim shrugged. "It's always interesting to see what someone else thinks your company is worth, especially if the company is not even cash flowing yet. I thought what he said about the imminent future of internet banking was interesting. It makes sense if you think about it."

Dana was silent for a moment, then looked over at Jim. "If only 5% of community financial institutions currently offer internet banking, and the rest no doubt are aware their products and services are inadequate and they risk losing customers to larger banks, you'd expect them to focus more resources on it. But I think the transition might happen slower than Alan Wingart is predicting. I think competition from other financial institutions has eroded the profit margins of community banks and they lack the capital to do it. You and I have talked about this before. I think it's a money issue. They *do* need a relatively inexpensive, out-sourced internet banking solution that'll interface with their own core-processing systems, and is secure and reliable. Maybe NETZEE can provide that service, I don't know. But I do know changes in the community banking world typically occur at a glacial pace."

"I agree with you there." Jim sat back in his chair and folded his arms. "Alan and crew have a good idea, but I expect it'll be harder to implement than they imagine. Not to mention taking six, already established companies, and trying to get them to work together. All those strong personalities! But who knows, maybe they'll pull it off."

"Well, I've got a full day's work on my desk and only half a day left." Dana gathered her things and stood up. "This morning was interesting, but now I'm going back to my office and deal with reality."

"Yep, me too." Jim stood up slowly and returned to his desk. "I've been setting up appointments to talk to boards of companies other than insurance and car dealerships. Trying to branch out to those other markets

I mentioned."

"Having any luck?"

"A little," Jim said. "We'll see."

Dana said goodbye and headed back to her car. It had stopped raining. The sun was out and steam was rising from the black pavement. She thought about Alan Wingart and NETZEE's proposal, then shook her head and smiled to herself. She couldn't imagine anything that would induce her to sell Call Me Bill.

28

One month later, July 1999

It was an unusually quiet morning in her office. No appointments were on the schedule until 2PM. This was a rare opportunity to get caught up, Dana thought. She felt like she was spinning her wheels lately. Lots of cold calls, meetings with potential clients, and presentations to sales folks. But there were few deals struck or contracts signed. Call Me Bill was doing OK, but they weren't moving as rapidly in the market as she felt they deserved, considering all the hours she clocked. The problem was Call Me Bill didn't seem to have any strategic advantage. And there was the other problem inherent in locating your company in a small town — it could be difficult to find the technical resources they needed.

"Dana, Alan Wingart is on the phone for you, line one." Her receptionist was standing in the doorway.

"Thanks, Loretta." Dana glanced at her phone and sighed. She took a deep breath and reluctantly picked it up. "Good morning, Alan."

"Good morning to you, Dana!" Alan Wingart's voice was solid and confident. "I'm sure you're very busy this Friday morning, and I won't take up much of your time. But I wanted to call and make sure you'd received our offer letter we mailed earlier in the week."

"Yes, I did receive it." Dana spoke slowly, choosing her words carefully. "In fact, I discussed it yesterday with Jim. But I'm afraid we're still not interested in selling Call Me Bill." She took a deep breath and continued.

"We appreciate that you doubled your original offer to $2 million in NETZEE stock, but we're not interested in owning NETZEE stock, and we're not ready to sell either. We feel even though Call Me Bill is not yet breaking even, we have a great company with vast potential. Jim and I plan to keep the ownership as it is now, a partnership between the two of us."

"What specifically don't you like about the offer?" Alan asked. "Is it the offer amount, that the offer is in the form of NETZEE stock, or that you don't want to sell? Maybe we can work through the issues and find a solution."

Dana chuckled. "You don't take no for an answer very well, do you, Alan?"

Alan returned a hardy laugh. "No, I've been told I do not. But in all honesty, Dana, my partner and I have our sights set on Call Me Bill. The company may not be cash flowing yet, but it has a great reputation — *you* have a great reputation — as a bill paying entity without errors. You do your due diligence and process payments accurately the first time. Your competitors can have error rates up to 20%. We don't want a company with a 20% error rate."

"I'm sure you don't." Dana smiled and her voice softened. "To answer your questions, Alan, we would never be interested in NETZEE stock as payment. Any deal would have to be cash. I don't know what offer amount we'd accept because, not being interested in selling, Jim and I have never discussed a price. And as we've said several times, currently we aren't interested in selling."

"Well, we're going to keep asking, Dana. I've always believed everything is for sale. You just need to offer the right price. What is your price, Dana?"

Dana thought about a cursory answer and getting off the phone, but she hesitated and tried to be patient. "I honestly have no idea, Alan. As I said, Jim and I haven't talked about it, except to agree we don't want to sell. But I'll tell Jim you called, asking about your offer letter."

"Tell him I asked for your price, Dana. What do you want for Call Me Bill? I'd like to ask that you take some time and talk about what you would ask for Call Me Bill if you were to sell it." Alan's voice was smooth, yet insistent.

265

Dana didn't answer for a moment. "I will, Alan; I'll talk to Jim about our phone call."

"Good! Then there's hope," he added, with a laugh. "You have a wonderful weekend, Dana."

"You too, Alan." Dana held the phone in her hand long after she heard Alan hang up. Then she put down the phone and immediately picked it up again, dialing Jim's number.

"Hello Dana. How are things going? Got a big weekend planned?" Jim's jovial voice resounded through the line.

She ignored his questions. "Jim, I just got off the phone with Alan Wingart. He called to ask if I got the offer letter I told you about yesterday. He said he and his partner have their minds set on Call Me Bill, and he refuses to take no for an answer. Basically, he wants to know what we want for Call Me Bill. He wants us to come up with a price."

Jim was silent for several moments. "That's an unusual position for a potential buyer to take. Normally they're more circumspect, trying to downplay the company's assets, hoping to negotiate a cheaper price. Did you tell him we would not be interested in owning NETZEE stock?"

"Yes, I did. It didn't faze him at all. He said to talk it over with you and decide what price we want. His view is everything is for sale if you offer the right price and he wants to know ours — and he was pretty insistent. So finally, I agreed I'd talk to you about it."

"Interesting," Jim muttered, more to himself. "After our phone call yesterday, I called an old mentor of mine — an attorney — with lots of experience buying and selling companies. I told him about our meeting with Alan Wingart and NETZEE's offer letter, and asked for his thoughts. He said we need to think about their offer as two different decisions. First, do we want to sell? And second, do we want to own NETZEE stock? We should not confuse the two things or allow them to merge into one decision."

Dana nodded her head and leaned back in her chair. "That's a good way to think about it, but how do *you* feel? I know we've said we're not ready to sell Call Me Bill, but we've never thought about selling either. Now we're faced with a potential buyer and have to decide if we're ready. So, have you thought about it since Alan Wingart and NETZEE came into our lives?"

"Sure, I've thought about it," Jim said. "I've thought about it a lot lately. I'm also trying to figure out why they're so persistent about buying Call Me Bill. Surely there are other good bill paying services out there they can easily purchase. Is their real motivation they're after *you*, because the error rate is so low? Or is there something else in this dot-com era we don't understand and will miss out on?"

"I've been wondering those same things," Dana said. "Maybe our low error rate does have something to do with it. Having a high error rate costs other bill paying services a lot of customers, and of course time and money trying to fix the errors."

"That's for sure." Jim said. "There was one other valuable piece of advice from my mentor friend. He said in this tech boom environment, a good offer would be ten times projected revenue. He didn't think we should accept anything less than that amount — and in cash."

"What? Seriously? Ten times projected revenue? That seems high! I'll have to sit down and figure out what that would be for Call Me Bill."

"It's three million dollars," Jim said slowly.

"Three million dollars? Geez!" Dana stared down at her desk. Her mouth hung open. After a long pause, she asked, "So, if we could get three million dollars right now for Call Me Bill, would you want to sell?"

Jim took a deep breath. "I've been thinking about variations of that question ever since we met with Alan Wingart. What *are* the growth prospects for Call Me Bill? You've been working the sales part hard, but as you've said, growth is steady but we have no strategic advantage, other than our low error rate. Maybe that's enough to continue to grow the company, I don't know." He hesitated, then his voice grew softer. "But I think I'd be agreeable to selling Call Me Bill if we could get three million in cash."

Dana was silent. She was unsure what to think. Call Me Bill was the first company she'd started from scratch, and from nothing — no money, software, employees, or customers the first day she stepped foot in her office. Now, less than two years later, they were discussing a three million

267

dollar price tag! That sounded like a genuine success story, but she didn't feel that way. She felt like Call Me Bill was unfinished, and someone else was trying to buy it and finish it themselves. If she and Jim sold Call Me Bill and she went to work for NETZEE, would she be sorry? Would she again regret not being her own boss and instead taking direction from someone who knew little about the business? She could end up unhappy again. On the other hand, she'd be a lot wealthier, and that could make up for any temporary unhappiness.

"Dana, did you hear me?" Jim asked.

"No, I'm sorry. I was thinking about whether I'd be happy working for NETZEE if we sold. The way I understand the offer letter, you could keep running my MSI and your Fort Knox National Company, and walk away with your share. I'd have my share of the money, but I'd have to stay and run Call Me Bill for some period of time — a company no longer half mine. What if I dislike working for NETZEE? At some point I'd be able to leave, but then what?"

Jim let out a hearty laugh. "Dana, after all these years of watching you grow into an astute, resourceful, and terrifically conscientious manager and entrepreneur, do you think I wouldn't find a place for you in my company if you wanted one? I can assure you, that's the last thing you need to worry about now. I think you should go home and think about what you want, talk it over with Joey, and let's talk again tomorrow."

"I can't believe we're actually having this discussion. I thought we'd have Call Me Bill for years."

"Who knows, maybe we will," Jim said. "Ten times projected revenue may be a pill too big for NETZEE to swallow. Anyway, let's wait for them to reach out to us again."

"That sounds reasonable. Have a good rest of the day, Jim."

"Thanks, you too."

Dana hung up the phone and stared at the desktop in front of her. Before the last couple weeks, it had never crossed her mind they might sell Call Me Bill any time soon. She thought about her bank account suddenly having a significant balance in it. That kind of money was nearly unimaginable. She would no longer have to worry about paying for Ryan's and Liz's college, or making her mortgage payment, or paying off her monthly credit card bill. She could afford to take care of her mom and grandmother. For that kind of money, she could work for most any jerk. And there was no reason to talk to Joey about a potential sale of the company. They no longer had the kind of relationship where she sought his permission or acceptance of her business decisions. She simply would tell him about her decision. Dana picked up the coffee cup from her desk, stood up, and walked into the kitchen to refill it. She felt an overwhelming sense of freedom and of being unencumbered, and she liked it.

29

One week later, August 1999

The late Summer sun poured through the car windows as Dana made the turn into the parking lot of her office building. Although it was still Summer, the mornings were already losing some of their humid haze, and the hues of the fields had assumed a bronzed glow. She quickly exited her car and made her way across the small lot toward her office building. Throughout the night, Dana pondered the phone call she'd received yesterday from Alan Wingart. Thankfully, Jim should arrive any time now to discuss what they were going to say to Alan when he called back this morning at 9AM.

Dana flung open the front door of the building and briskly strode down the hallway to her office. She was still settling in when she heard Jim's footsteps plodding down the hall in her direction.

The footsteps stopped, and a head appeared in the doorway. "I'm going to grab some coffee. I'll join you in a minute."

"Sure. Good morning, by the way," Dana shook her head and chuckled to herself. When Jim had something on his mind, he was all business.

"Good morning," he yelled loudly, halfway down the hallway. He returned shortly with his coffee in one hand, briefcase in the other, and a donut between his teeth.

"I'm glad to see you'll have some breakfast in you before our phone call," Dana said, rolling her eyes.

Jim set down his briefcase and coffee, and took the donut from between his teeth. "You know I've never been big on breakfast — not unless breakfast starts at 11AM. By the way, how did you sleep last night?"

"Fine," she lied.

"Hmm, that's surprising. I thought you'd be tossing and turning all night. This is a big decision we're making, and the outcome affects you more than me. Have you had any second thoughts or are we still on the same page as the last time we talked?" Jim pulled out a burgundy leather chair from the conference table and dropped into it.

Dana walked over to the conference table. "OK, I admit I'm a little nervous about all this. Obviously, it's a huge decision and I just want to make sure we've thought about all the pros and cons before we make our offer. They just might accept."

"Ten times projected revenue is a lot of money to pay for any company. If we can get it, I think we should take it. Honestly, I'll be quite surprised if they accept that price without trying to haggle for a better deal."

"If we *can't* get ten times projected revenue in cash for Call Me Bill, I don't want to sell," Dana said flatly. "I'm not totally convinced we should sell anyway, and I don't believe you are either. So unless we get exactly what we want, let's not have any further discussion about selling with Alan Wingart or anyone else, OK?"

"Absolutely. How did Joey take the news?"

"It surprised him," Dana replied, looking down at the table. "But he said if we could get a good price for it, why not?"

Jim raised his eyebrows. "That's all he had to say? I expected him to react unfavorably considering the risk involved in turning over the company to a couple of unknowns and your happiness up in the air."

Dana looked down at Jim with a thin smile. "It's hard to turn down that kind of money, don't you think?"

"I suppose it is. Now, would you like to do the talking when Alan calls or would you like me to present the offer?"

"How about you present the offer and I'll discuss my working arrangement. We both can chime in as needed." Dana placed her legal pad on the

271

conference table and sat down in the chair across from Jim.

The phone sitting in the center of the table rang loudly. Dana reached across the table, picked up the receiver, and pushed the flashing button. "Yes, Loretta?" Dana looked over at Jim. "Thank you." She pushed the 'speaker' button on the phone, and Alan Wingart's voice came through loud and clear.

"Good morning, Dana! It's Alan Wingart, and it's a beautiful morning here in Atlanta. I'm assuming Jim is in the room with you as well, is that correct?"

"Good morning to you, Alan, and you are correct. Jim is sitting right across the table from me."

Jim leaned closer to the phone. "Good morning, Alan."

"Morning, Jim," Alan said. "How are things in Elizabethtown? How's the weather there?"

"Things are good, Alan. Beautiful day in Elizabethtown today, and things at the office are going well too." Jim looked at Dana and winked. "If they got much better, I couldn't stand it."

Alan let out a hearty laugh. "That's great, Jim; glad to hear it. Dana told you I called last night, of course. We had a brief conversation, then she decided it would be best if you were in the room too." He paused for a moment and then got down to business. "The last time Dana and I spoke, I told her to talk with you and come up with a price you'd accept for Call Me Bill. I like to think everything has a price for which someone is willing to sell. We just need to find the price for Call Me Bill that makes you both comfortable. Were you able to talk and come up with a price?"

Dana looked at Jim and waited for him to speak. She felt no particular emotion, and her face reflected her noncommittal attitude. Since the plusses and minuses of the decision seemed equally balanced, she'd been unable to sort out her feelings on the issue. Even offering a price to Alan Wingart made her feel confused. It seemed like a betrayal to the company she was still building, but then she also was proud someone wanted it that badly. It was hard to rectify her emotions.

"Ten times projected revenue — three million dollars," Jim said. "And this would be a cash only deal. We would not be interested in trading Call Me Bill for stock in NETZEE."

There was no reply or hint of a reaction from the other end of the phone line. After several long moments, Alan Wingart cleared his throat. "All of our other company purchases have been in NETZEE stock, but I believe we could make an exception for Call Me Bill, given its strong financial prospects."

"If you want Call Me Bill as part of your portfolio, you'll have to pay cash, Alan," Dana said. "We would never trade for stock."

"I understand. I'll need to talk over your offer with my partner, Bill Harper, but I suspect we can reach a deal." Alan Wingart's voice was smooth and assured. "The other part of the deal, of course, is Dana. You'd continue as CEO of the company for probably two years, and at somewhere around your current salary level."

"Yes," Dana said. "That would be part of the deal."

"Then I'm fairly confident we'll come to a deal based on those terms. I'll give you a call tomorrow around this same time and confirm what we discussed today. If all goes well, we'll have the attorneys draw up the paperwork and get this deal consummated as soon as possible."

Jim looked over at Dana with a cunning smile. "Sounds good, Alan. We look forward to talking tomorrow."

"Great! Thanks again."

Dana heard the phone line click, and Alan Wingart was gone. She felt light-headed and realized she'd been holding her breath. Just like that, they made the deal. Soon, Call Me Bill would belong to someone else. It'd be just another dot-com company. She looked up at Jim. "Did that really happen? Did we just agree to sell Call Me Bill for three million dollars?"

Jim shook his head and laughed. "I think we did! How are you feeling? You look a little pale."

"I *feel* a little pale. I think I'm in shock. It all happened so fast."

"We'll see what his partner says." Jim stretched back in his chair and scratched his head. "But it sounded like Alan Wingart either had the authority to make the decision, or he and his partner already agreed to a price ceiling. He did sound confident the deal would go through, didn't he?"

"Yes, he did." Dana sat back in her chair too, her arms hung limply at her sides. "It sounded like he could make the decision, but still wants to get the deal blessed by his partner."

"We'll find out for sure in 24 hours." Jim stood up and placed his hands on his hips. He smiled and nodded his head slowly to no one in particular. "We won't bring out the champagne yet. Could be bad luck. But one thing is for certain — two years ago we had a great idea that you, Dana, through all your hard work and long hours, turned into fruition. And today, someone is willing to pay three million dollars for the result. That's a true entrepreneurial success story!"

Still numb with the speed at which things were happening, all Dana could do was stare at Jim. The words he spoke reverberated in her head and she could barely register their meaning. She was going to need time to process the events of the past couple days. Lots of time.

* * *

The restaurant was crowded, but it shouldn't have been a surprise. It was Friday night, and as usual, the small town's working class needed some release. "It's a good thing I called ahead and made a reservation," Jim said. "We'd be standing here for another hour."

"Or longer," Dana noted, looking around the crowded room. "There's not a single seat open at the bar."

A young girl with long blonde hair and wearing a black skirt and fitted black top waved some menus in the air to get their attention. "You can follow me to your table," she announced, in a high-pitched voice.

Dana threaded her way through the crowded tables, with Joey and Jim

274

Fugitte in tow. She was relieved to sit down at a table near the back corner where it was noticeably quieter. "This place is crazy!"

"Sure is loud," Joey said. "I hope we can hear each other talk."

The young girl who showed them to their table placed the menus in front of them. "Sara will be your waitress and will be with you shortly. In the meantime, can I get you some drinks?"

"Bourbon and water for me," Jim said. "Dana, Joey, tonight is on me. What would you like?"

"Thank you, Jim, that's very nice of you. I'll just take an iced tea," Dana said, picking up the menu and looking over at him. "You know I normally don't drink, but if we have champagne later, I may break down and have a glass too."

Joey looked up at the girl. "I'll take a bourbon and water too. There's cause for celebration, *and* it has been a long week!"

The girl smiled. "I'll put in the order and it should be just a few minutes." She turned and hurried away.

Jim leaned forward and clasped his hands on top of the table. He looked directly at Dana. "It seems like such a short time ago we were sitting around the table talking about starting up Call Me Bill. Now here we are, barely two years later, celebrating the pending sale of it. I can say with all sincerity I will miss working with you, Dana. I think you and I made a hell of a partnership."

Dana's face relaxed and she smiled back at Jim. "And I will miss your sage advice, your financial expertise, and your calm demeanor. But we still have our partnership with MSI and Fort Knox National Company — unless NETZEE says it's a conflict of interest and makes me sell. I hadn't thought about that until just now."

Joey nodded his head. "I can see where they might say it's a conflict of interest."

"We'll know more next week when we receive the contract," Jim said. "Alan didn't mention anything when he and Bill called this morning. But this morning's call was all pleasantries and congratulating each other. Next week when we see the contract's fine print, we'll find out the ugly details.

275

It wouldn't surprise me either if you're required to sell MSI."

"I really hadn't given any thought to details of the sale, other than my working for NETZEE," Dana said quietly, staring ahead.

"I wouldn't start worrying about it yet." Jim reached over and patted her arm. "But if that's the case and you have to sell, you and I can work out an arrangement for me to buy it from you over time — after the sale of Call Me Bill closes. We'll work out something. Right now we're here to celebrate."

"Yes, we are," Joey said. "And who knows, maybe you two will end up working together again. You have a long history — since before the kids were born, because I remember Liz was due when Dana was fired from the bank, which seems like an eternity ago. Dana, back then, did you ever think you'd end up here, selling your and Jim's company?" He shook his head and laughed.

Dana smiled and looked pointedly at Jim. She'd finally put that painful past behind her. "Not like this — no. After I finally got ownership of MSI, I thought I'd have that company for many years. But your idea to create a new company was too tempting, and now here we are, selling that company. We came full circle."

"We did indeed," Jim said, nodding his head and smiling at Dana. "You attained what you wanted with MSI and also with Call Me Bill, and you should feel immense gratification. It's a testament to what you can do when you put your mind to something. That's what I'm going to miss most about working with you, Dana. Your perseverance and determination to get things right the first time make you everyone's dream partner. And now you'll be NETZEE's partner. I wonder if they know how lucky they are."

"Or what's in store for them!" Dana laughed, then looked up to see a man standing at their table, holding a tray.

"I have your drinks for you folks," he said. "Bourbon and water for the gentlemen and an iced tea for the lady."

"Thank you," Dana said. "I think we'll order a plate of wings for an appetizer and order dinner later."

"Sounds good," the waiter replied. "I'll be back with the wings shortly."

As soon as he left, Jim raised his glass. "I'd like to propose a toast. To the partnership that created Call Me Bill — another successful business — and to its smooth sale and continued success as part of NETZEE. Dana, with you at the helm, I know it will be wildly successful."

"Here, here," Joey added, raising his drink.

Picking up her iced tea, Dana touched her glass to Jim's and then Joey's, and took a sip. "Thank you, Jim. We'll have to make a pact to have lunch together once a month and catch up. I may be calling you for help too," she added, flashing him a smile. "But in the meantime, I know we've got a lot of work to do to prepare for the sale. Alan said they want to get things finalized quickly, like in a few weeks. That seems a little too fast for all the due diligence work I know is involved. What do you think?"

"That's pretty fast," Jim said. "We'll certainly be busy during the next few weeks. NETZEE will send a letter letting us know what information they want. Getting all that together will be the tedious part."

"Don't let the thought of all that work put a damper on your celebration tonight." Joey was still holding up his glass. "I think you both deserve to be congratulated. You created Call Me Bill from the ground up. Not too many people can take an idea, turn it into a performing business, and within two years have someone buy it for three million dollars. That's pretty incredible, actually."

Dana looked at Joey and smiled. It was not like him to pour praise on her. Lately, they'd confined their discussions to home events and talked little about work. They seemed to disagree far more than they got along. She wasn't sure why she'd asked him along tonight; he was off duty and it seemed the right thing to do. Now, she was glad she did. It might buy her some good will during the next few weeks when she'd be too busy to take care of much at home.

277

30

3 September 1999

The morning sun was just peeking over the horizon, casting an orange glow through the bedroom window and across the comforter that covered Joey. Dana stared at the still body and thought of the time several years ago when he got up after a late night on patrol just to wish her good luck on closing day. Their lives certainly were on disparate paths now. She turned around and left the bedroom, eager to get on the road and into her office. It was going to be a long day.

There was a slight chill in the air as she got into the car and backed onto the street. Fall was showing. The air smelled different — crisper, somehow cleaner, and had an aura of tree bark and leaves. Fall turned Dana's thoughts to her high school days — football games, bonfires, building floats for the homecoming parade, and when she met Joey. They were together constantly then, and so in love. She wondered if they married too soon. But back then, it was common to get married after two years of dating, and she felt like she knew him well. Perhaps she was the one who changed. They'd made it twenty years now, but Dana was fairly sure there wouldn't be another twenty.

Few cars were on the road this time of morning, and in no time she pulled into the small parking lot adjacent to her office. Dana turned off the car and sat in the silence, looking up at the two-story red brick building she'd called her 'home away from home' since she bought MSI, four years ago.

With the growth in business expected following Call Me Bill's purchase by NETZEE today, she wondered how long it would remain her office building. Gathering her belongings and briefcase, she exited the car, walked up the stairs to the front entrance, and unlocked the door. The building had its own smell too — like that of an old school building from her childhood. She breathed in fully, savoring the scent of polished old oak. It was just one more thing she was going to miss.

Once she'd made the coffee, Dana walked down the hall to her office. It faced the main street. She opened one of several windows and then sat down, spreading the papers for today's closing on her desk. Today reminded her of a similar day four years ago when she was trying to purchase MSI from her three male bosses, only today would be more lucrative and significantly less stressful.

There was a knock at the front door of the building. Dana couldn't imagine who would want in the building this early in the morning. Jim Fugitte wasn't due for at least another hour, and neither was the staff. She stood and peered around the corner to the lobby. Marie's slender outline was discernible through the glass and wooden door. Dana smiled, hurried to the door, and unlocked the dead bolt. "Marie! What a surprise!"

"Good morning, Luv! I was on my way to the bank . . . well, to the Donut House and then to the bank . . . and spotted your car. Thought I'd pop in and wish you luck with the big closing today! How are you feeling?" Marie stepped inside and took off the long jacket that matched the sleek and tawny A-line dress underneath. Then she leaned down and gave Dana a quick squeeze.

"So far, so good; I just got here. Want a cup of coffee?" Dana turned toward the kitchen.

"No, thanks. Can't stay long. Just wanted to say cheers and good luck. Do you have any trepidation about working for someone again?" Marie followed Dana back to her office.

Dana shook her head. "That's supposed to be one benefit of this confederate-like arrangement; we continue to run our own companies. Of course, we're supposed to interface with the other companies that'll comprise NETZEE, so we'll have to wait and see how that's going to work out. NETZEE actually has three closings today — us, an internet banking division of TIB, and a company called Dyad Corporation, which does online mortgages and other loans. I think there are a few more planned acquisitions too before they're done. We've heard around six companies will make up NETZEE."

Marie took a seat next to Dana's desk. "That could be fun or it could be a challenge," she said, tilting her head.

"Exactly. I'm used to making decisions on my own, unless it's something major. We'll see how long it'll take me to step on someone's toes." Dana smoothed out her black linen skirt and sat down at her desk. "They've told me to expect to be very busy with a lot more customers directed at me from the other NETZEE companies. I hope we're not crazy busy. Things have been busy enough the past couple months getting ready for this sale. I could use a rest!"

Marie rolled her eyes and laughed. "So what else is new! Do you slow down ever? Between heading up your own company, raising two kids, watching out for a husband, a mother, and a grandmother, you never have a moment's peace or a good night's sleep."

Dana looked out the front window and chuckled. "You're right. Why would I ever think things will improve soon? I'm going to be tired for another five years — at least!"

"Speaking of husbands, how are things with you and Joey?"

Dana looked back at Marie and shook her head slowly. "Not any better, if that's what you're wondering. About the same, I guess. We just don't talk much anymore. Some of that is because we really don't see each other much. Between his patrols and odd hours, and my late nights and early mornings, there's not much opportunity to talk. When we *are* together, I don't feel like rehashing the workday, and he obviously doesn't either." Dana looked down at her feet. "To be honest, I've been wondering how much longer we're going to stay together. It has been this way for several years now."

Marie frowned. "Yes, but I thought you might find your way back to each other. I hate to see this happening. You two have been in my life for such a long time and I'm extremely fond of you both. I hate to see your little family breakup, which is why I shall never marry!"

"In your case, it's a good thing because I can't see you staying with one man longer than a few months at most!" Dana wanted to change the subject to something that didn't make her insides hurt. Selling Call Me Bill today was enough of a stomach-churning event.

"Good morning, ladies!"

Jim Fugitte's deep voice startled Dana. "You're here early!"

"Good morning, Jim!" Marie said. She stood up and stepped towards the doorway to shake his hand. "Congratulations on the big sale today! The only downside I see is you lose your brilliant partner."

"That I do," he said quietly, nodding his head and looking squarely at Dana. "Sadly, I lose her in this arrangement."

Dana looked up at Jim and smiled. "Good morning, Jim. Have a seat. I made the coffee if you want some. I didn't think you'd be here yet."

Jim placed his briefcase in a chair at the conference table in the corner. "I woke up early, and yes, I'd love some coffee. Can I get either of you ladies anything?"

"I'm good," Dana said.

"Sorry, but I really must crack on. Lots to do today." Marie retrieved her purse from the floor next to her chair and leaned over to hug Dana. "Good luck, Darling. Let me know how it goes."

"Thanks, I will."

Marie walked over to Jim and held out her hand. "Nice to see you, Jim. Congratulations again and best wishes to you as well." She donned her jacket and quickly left the office.

Jim went in the other direction toward the kitchen, returning shortly with coffee and a pastry. He stood quietly for a moment, eating his pastry and contemplating Dana. "How are you *really* doing?"

Dana chuckled. "I'm fine — really. Do we need to go over any of the paperwork before NETZEE arrives, or talk about anything in particular? And do you know who's coming from their side?"

"I understand they're sending just one lawyer since their two additional closings today have them spread pretty thin. But there's no reason to send more than one, anyway. The more lawyers who show up, the slower things will move along. They're paid by the word, you know." Jim took a seat next to the chair with his briefcase, and finished his coffee.

Dana flipped through the papers on her desk. "I'll be really surprised if we make it through closing without some problem related to our 'represents and warrants.' I still can't believe how little due diligence NETZEE has done. Maybe in the big scheme of things Call Me Bill is small potatoes, and it's no big deal to them if our numbers are a little off."

"True, or maybe they trust us to provide correct accounting figures," Jim added, then raised his eyebrows. "Maybe they don't believe a company in small town America would try to pass off inflated numbers to them, especially since you'll be working for them."

"I'm sure you're right. They could make my life miserable if we fudged the numbers, and later they found out. You'd be out of the picture and I'd suffer the consequences," she added, with a quick laugh.

"Then let me assure you the numbers are as accurate as we could get them, given the quick turnaround from contract to closing." Jim had a satisfied look on his face. "I sent you the updated package last night so you should have everything now."

"Yes, I got it." Dana looked up at Jim. "I think what's bothering me more than anything is having to sell MSI. I keep thinking about everything I went through to get that company and now I have to sell it. But I know it's the best thing to do, plus I know it'll continue to be well-managed. And since you were running it for the past two years anyway, nothing should change for the employees or for anyone else, right?"

Jim smiled at Dana and sighed. "That's right, you don't need to worry about MSI. Nothing will change. Besides, since I'll be purchasing it over a period of time, it still will be partly yours for another year or more."

Dana's receptionist, Loretta, appeared in the doorway. "Good morning, Dana, Jim. A Mr. Jason Bartel from NETZEE is here. He said he's a little early for your meeting this morning. Should I bring him down?"

"Oh," Dana said with surprise. She looked over at Jim. "Do you want to get started?"

"Sure, bring him down, Loretta." Jim stood up and ran his hand down the front of his shirt, smoothing out his tie.

Loretta reappeared shortly, followed by a short, stout man, wearing a grey suit and crisp, white shirt. "I'll bring in some coffee," she said to Dana.

"Good morning, Mr. Bartel." Dana stepped forward and offered her hand. "I'm Dana Smolenski, and this is my partner, Jim Fugitte."

"Please, call me Jason," he said, shaking hands with Dana and then Jim. "I hope my arriving a little early didn't cause a problem for you."

"Not at all," Jim said, directing Jason Bartel to his seat. "We were just talking about the closing today and about NETZEE's reliance on 'represents and warrants.' Obviously, the company is comfortable with that level of due diligence."

Mr. Bartel sat down at the table and took out several large, dark green portfolios from his briefcase. "Yes, in the fast-paced environment we're in now, that has been sufficient, and really is standard practice now for small companies in the tech world. I don't think either your side or ours has time for much more, or there are opportunity costs involved." He placed his briefcase next to his chair and settled in. "Shall we get started?"

"Sure," Dana replied. She was eager to get this over with, and Jason Bartel back on the plane to Chicago.

"Yep, launch it," Jim echoed.

Jason Bartel handed a green portfolio to both Dana and Jim. "We'll go through each page and I'll explain the contents and then show you where to sign. Stop me at any point where you have questions. This should take about an hour."

Dana glanced at her watch. An hour later she would be notably wealthier and hopefully less stressed. She wouldn't get to keep as much of the $3 million as she'd like; there were other entities getting their cut. But her share would mean a substantial supplement to her and Joey's retirement savings. Also, after today, funding Call Me Bill's operating account would be NETZEE's burden and no longer her and Jim's worry. Maybe this next chapter in her life wouldn't be nearly so frenetic. She could only hope.

* * *

Eight hours after Jason Bartel exited the parking lot on his way to the airport, Dana still sat in her office. The rest of the day had felt surreal, like she was watching her own body go about its daily tasks. Picking up the phone, she dialed Marie.

"Hello, Darling! How'd it go today? I've been anxious to chat."

Marie's dulcet tones calmed Dana's breathing. "I'm happy to hear your voice, Marie. It has been a long day."

"A long, but good day, I hope. Did things not go well?"

"Everything went great! We breezed through the closing today in about an hour and a half. No issues at all. I thought there might be questions regarding some of the numbers, but nothing. There was only one person representing NETZEE — an attorney. He was quick and thorough, and there was not much chitchat. The entire ordeal seemed like a dream. I guess I'm happy about it. All I have to worry about now is keeping NETZEE content. How we're going to pay the bills is no longer my concern."

"That's a big concern too," Marie said. "As I've said, you should feel quite pleased with yourself. Now, you should take a much-needed family holiday. You deserve it and it'll do all of you a world of good."

"I'd love to, but besides being busy getting things up and running with NETZEE, school just started for Ryan and Liz. Maybe we'll manage a quick trip over the Christmas holiday." Out of the corner of her eye, Dana glimpsed a flashing button on her phone. "Marie, I'd better go. The other line is ringing and I may be the only one left in the office."

"Of course! Ta-ta, Darling! Go home and drink some champagne."

"I just might do that!" Dana reached over and pushed the flashing button at the bottom of her phone. "Dana Smolenski, can I help you?"

"Good afternoon, Ms. Smolenski." A male voice with a southern drawl flowed through the phone line. "My name is Mike Bowers. I'm the Chief Operating Officer of NETZEE. First, I want to congratulate you on a successful closing today and welcome you to the NETZEE family. We're very pleased you'll be working with us now."

"Thank you, Mr. Bowers. Yes, everything went well today and I'm looking forward to being part of NETZEE." Dana wasn't sure the last part of her comment was true yet.

"Dana, as I'm sure you know, the vision of NETZEE's founders is to bring together a portfolio of innovative companies and have them work together to fulfill all the needed services of the financial sector. My role is to get you all to work together — not a minor feat, as you can imagine," he said, laughing. "You'll report directly to me. Any problems you have or things you need, I'm the one to call."

Dana had been wondering who would be her new boss. Mike Bowers has quite the job on his hands, she thought. It was never easy to get CEOs of companies to work together. They're used to making decisions in their own best interests, as opposed to the interests of the whole. She decided not to say any of that now.

Mike continued. "I've worked with Alan Wingart and Bill Harper in the financial tech sector for many years. Like you, I owned one of the companies that became part of NETZEE today. Anyway, I had a call from Alan this afternoon telling me to go to Elizabethtown and talk to Dana Smolenski. So that's why I'm calling, to see if you have some free time on your calendar next week."

"Sure!" Dana said. "You've got priority on my schedule now, so whatever day works for you, I'll make sure I'm free."

"Great! How about the 9th? My office is in Atlanta. I'll fly up that morning, we'll spend a few hours together, and then I'll catch the plane back to Atlanta late afternoon. Sound good?"

"Yes, and I'm looking forward to meeting you, Mr. Bowers."

"Good, but please call me Mike."

"Will do," Dana said.

"Congratulations again, and I look forward to meeting you next week."

Dana heard the line click and she hung up the receiver. He seemed nice enough. Let's see how he responds to my list of issues and requests I've been compiling for weeks. Dana smiled at the thought. That worry was someone else's now.

31

9 September 1999

It was an unusually hot September day. The amber sun blazed across the sky at lunchtime, as Dana glanced out the window again. She could sense the jitters in her stomach — just enough for her to notice. But she didn't understand why. There was no reason to be nervous about meeting her new boss today. He seemed pleasant on the phone last week, and the purpose of the meeting was purely to make introductions. Regardless, she'd done her homework and had prepared a list of things to discuss. Plus, she'd dressed in a navy-blue power suit today, which was unusual attire for her anymore. Her jitters were just her insecurities getting the better of her. She'd been busier than ever since the sale of Call Me Bill to NETZEE last week, and a new boss should interpret that as a positive sign. It was important that she compare favorably to the other sector heads at NETZEE. No matter how much time passed, she feared she would always be concerned about how the male-dominated banking industry viewed her and her work. Women were making inroads, but there was no question the leaders of the banking world remained overwhelmingly male.

Opening her bottom desk drawer, Dana retrieved a peanut butter and jelly sandwich and some chips. She popped the top of her soda, kicked back in her executive desk chair, and faced the street. In case Mike Bowers showed up early, she wanted to know before he came waltzing into her office.

As she munched away on her lunch, Dana stared out the window and watched the cars slowly navigate the residential street. Mike Bowers might think her office building was in a bizarre location for a thriving business. This was one peculiarity of working in a small town. Over the decades, and because of its location, the town government re-designated the street as mixed use, and businesses bought some homes and converted them to office space. Hopefully Mike Bowers wouldn't take her business less seriously because it was situated amongst family dwellings.

Dana quickly finished her lunch and wiped away the crumbs. Reaching across the desk for her yellow legal pad, she placed it in front of her and studied her notes until she heard Mike Bowers' smooth, southern tones emanating from the building's foyer. Soon she could hear two sets of footsteps coming down the hallway toward her office.

"Dana, Mike Bowers is here for your meeting," Loretta said, as she ushered in a slim man with smooth grey hair and bright green eyes.

"Thank you, Loretta," Mike Bowers said to her with a smile. "It was a pleasure to meet you, and I'm sure we'll be seeing each other again soon." He turned toward Dana and held out his hand. "Dana Smolenski, I've been looking forward to meeting you. I've heard a lot of good things about you and what you've been doing here in Elizabethtown."

"It's nice to meet you too and welcome to Elizabethtown," Dana said, returning the smile. "Can I get you something to drink?"

"Maybe later, I'm fine for now." He glanced around the office.

"Please, have a seat at the table and I'll join you." Dana retrieved the yellow legal pad from her desk and took a seat across the table from Mike Bowers.

"How was your trip?" Dana asked.

"Nice and quick," he said, with an easy laugh, "which is good because I suspect you and I will make frequent trips back and forth." He settled into his chair and glanced around her office. "I have to tell you Dana, I love this office building you have here. Old red brick and a red tile roof, it looks like it used to be a very nice old house. Did you have it renovated?"

"Thank you," Dana said, pleasantly surprised. She relaxed into her chair.

288

"One of the local banks previously bought the old house, had it renovated, and used it for their mortgage operation. I bought it from the bank about four years ago because I'd always liked this old building too. I love being able to open a window when the weather is nice. And often in the morning when the windows are open, I can hear the horse-driven buggies of the Amish going down the street. I'll bet you don't have that in Atlanta!" she added, with a grin.

"No kidding!" Mike Bowers leaned back in his chair and laughed. "No, I can honestly say I've not seen any Amish on the streets of Atlanta! Well, that's great. I guess that's one benefit of having an office in small town America." He stretched out his legs and settled in. "Dana, my purpose in coming here today is to meet you and anyone else on your staff you think I should meet, get to know your operation a little, and then tell you about some things we have planned for NETZEE and how you fit into the big picture."

"Great! And I've prepared a list of things to talk to you about when you're done — just some issues I've encountered," she added, pointing to her yellow legal pad.

"Oh, sure." Mike said, raising his eyebrows.

"Is that OK? You look surprised."

"Yes, absolutely. My other meet and greets didn't involve questions for me. But yes, if you're already seeing problem areas, I'm the one to talk to."

"OK," Dana said, sheepishly. Maybe she should've waited for another time to start asking for things.

Mike Bowers cleared his throat. "Let me start by saying we're thrilled to have an online bill payment company included in our portfolio of financial technical services we're offering to clients. As you know, Direct Access was the first company acquired, and it merged with NETZEE back in August. Their CEO spoke so highly of you and the way you ran your company, he convinced Alan that Call Me Bill had to become part of NETZEE, and here you are," he said, grinning. "Besides Direct Access and Call Me Bill, NETZEE purchased the Internet Banking Division of TIB, and they purchased my company, Dyad Corporation, which did online mortgages and loans. I'd partnered with Alan on other projects over the past 15 years, so we know each other well. I'm sure our long relationship is the primary reason they offered me the position of NETZEE's Chief Operations Officer. You probably knew most of that already," he added, with a smile.

"Some of it, but it's always nice to get the complete picture." Dana liked Mike Bowers already. He had a quick smile and was easy to talk to, which would be helpful as her boss. "I understand there are more acquisitions planned. Is that correct?"

"Yes, there are a couple more planned. Should be six when all is said and done. Alan and Bill are planning an Initial Public Offering — an IPO — in November to raise about $30 million. They'll use this money in part to purchase DPSC Software and Digital Visions. DPSC is a company that provides regulatory reporting and related software to community financial institutions, and Digital Visions provides Internet-based information and analytic tools to financial institutions. Those six companies will make up NETZEE." Mike leaned back and laced his fingers over his lap.

"There's a lot of capability in that mix," Dana said. "How do you see us learning about it and figuring out how we're going to work together?"

"That's a good question, Dana!" A broad grin covered his face. "In a nutshell, that's my job — to figure out how you'll work together." His face grew serious. "To be honest, or maybe I should say realistic, if you're the one running your company now, then you're the best person to understand your company's capabilities and how they might interface or add to the capabilities of other sectors of NETZEE. We'll be getting together regularly, so you'll have lots of opportunities to interface. And I'll be relying on each of you to give me your ideas and recommendations."

"Absolutely," Dana said, nodding her head. "But with us, it's pretty simple. We only do online bill pay. So I would envision the other sectors would refer their clients who want to add bill pay to their offerings to us — just like Direct Access used to do."

"You're right; it's easier with your company. We'll see how it goes with the others." Mike reached up and rubbed his head. "Basically, we want you to run your company as you did previously. That's the best way to ensure each of you has a smooth transition to NETZEE. We'll be working to interface where we can." He sat up in his chair, crossed his arms, and looked intently at Dana. "So tell me, how are things so far? What have you got for me on your list?"

Dana stared at Mike before answering. He wore a lopsided grin. She wasn't sure if he was teasing her or being serious. She reached down, picked up her pen, and repositioned the legal pad in front of her. "I'll email you the issues I've compiled over the past week, and maybe today we can limit our discussion to just the most immediate ones."

"Sure, whatever you'd like to do." Mike Bowers was still smiling.

Dana looked down at her ledger. She was feeling unnerved. "Although it has been only a week, already I can see the increase in business being directed to us. We have some room to increase capacity, but not a lot." She looked up and saw no reaction, so she continued. "Along those same lines, the servers we have weren't built to handle the amount of work we'll be throwing at them soon. They're nearly at capacity now. Most of my other issues are related to this same general problem." She put down her pen and hesitated. "In order to keep up with the expected demand, I'll need an infusion of capital fairly quickly."

"That seems to be the consensus of the other sectors too," he said, nodding his head slowly. "Most were at, or near, capacity when NETZEE purchased them. Now in order to grow, like you, they need capital. And that's one reason for the IPO — to raise the needed capital. If you can hang on until after November, there's help on the way."

"Sure, that should be fine. I just wanted to give you early warning it's going to be a problem soon." Dana was relieved he didn't seem surprised.

"Got it," he said. "Also, you'll be getting an email about this soon, but starting next month I'll have monthly meetings with all the sector heads together. I'm thinking we might rotate the meetings among the locations where the sectors are, at least initially. It would be a good way for all of you to get better acquainted with the various sectors and their capabilities. But the first meeting next month will be at NETZEE's headquarters in Atlanta."

"That would be helpful."

"Good." Mike uncrossed his arms and sat up in his chair. "If there's nothing else on your list you want to go over today while I'm here, how about you give me a tour of this beautiful building and introduce me to anyone I should meet."

"Of course, I was planning to show you around." Dana rose from her chair and made her way to the door. "I've told the directors you'd be here today, so they're expecting you."

"Great! Lead the way."

* * *

The sun was dipping toward the horizon when Dana tidied her desk and considering going home. She had to admit the day went pretty well and she actually enjoyed spending time with her new boss. So far anyway, Mike Bowers seemed to be a nice guy — smart, personable, easy to talk to, and funny. He hit it off with the others in her office too. Dana decided he should make a good boss.

Gathering up her purse and some papers, she left the building and got into her car. Driving home, she wondered how Joey and the kids would take her news that she would make frequent trips to Atlanta and to the other sector locations. They weren't used to her traveling, and the kids would have to fend for themselves at dinnertime. Joey often worked evenings.

When she turned the corner onto her street, Dana sighed when she saw Joey's car in the driveway. It had been a good but long day and she felt too mentally exhausted to rehash the details. She was surprised to see his car too. Lately it was rare he was home for dinner. After parking in the driveway, she gathered her belongings from the passenger seat and got out of the car.

"I'm home," she yelled as she entered the kitchen.

"Hey Mom," Liz said. "Ryan will be home soon. He's over at a friend's house."

"I just came home to grab some dinner and will leave again shortly," Joey yelled from the bedroom. "I've got to fill in for someone who called in sick."

"OK," Dana said, immediately feeling guilty that her initial reaction was relief.

Joey strolled into the kitchen and opened the microwave. "How'd everything go today?" he asked casually, retrieving a plate of last night's meatloaf from the microwave. He sat down at the table and started to eat.

"Everything went fine. My new boss seems nice." She decided not to elaborate unless asked. "Have the kids eaten?"

"They snacked as usual, but no dinner."

Dana went to the refrigerator and took out the remaining leftover meatloaf and the ingredients for a salad. She waited for Joey to offer some small talk, but he continued to eat and stare at the table in front of him.

10 minutes later, Joey picked up his plate, placed it in the dishwasher, and grabbed his hat. "You'll be asleep when I get home. Tell the kids goodnight and I'll see you all sometime tomorrow." He flung open the kitchen door, waved his hand, and was gone.

For nearly five minutes, Dana stared into the kitchen sink, mindlessly running the water over a head of lettuce. It was time to admit their marriage had run its course. Best to do something soon while things still were amiable. It would be hard enough to explain to the kids that their lives were about to be upended. Joey had been a wonderful dad; she'd give him that much. And they'd been married a long time. It would be tough on all of them.

32

Six months later, mid-March 2000

Dana raced up the stairs and threw open the door to the restaurant. She hated being late, especially for something fun, like lunch away from the office. Jim Fugitte wouldn't care, but Dana considered lateness disrespectful and rude. Spotting him in a sunny booth at the far side of the room, she adroitly weaved her way through the tables until she reached the booth. He was studying the menu, oblivious to her presence. "Jim, I'm so sorry! I was in a meeting that wouldn't end. Have you been waiting long?"

"Hi Dana!" he said, glancing up with a broad smile. "No, no, not long at all — about 10 minutes. It's no problem. I don't have a single meeting on my schedule this afternoon," he added cheerily.

"Oh, good." Dana took off her coat and tossed it to the far side of the booth across from Jim. "Anything interesting on the menu? I'm starving, and it smells like they're baking bread in the kitchen." She scooted in next to her coat and purse.

"Special of the day is grilled ham and cheese on freshly baked bread — your fav."

"Then I don't even need to look at the menu. Sounds good to me! You know my weakness." She crossed her arms on the table and her face broke into a wide grin. "It's good to see you! What have you been up to, and how's everything with MSI?"

Jim smiled and nodded his head thoughtfully. "Things are good, Dana.

Everything is going along well." He reached down and pulled a legal-sized envelope from his briefcase and passed it across the table to Dana. "Before I forget, here's the contract for the sale of the rest of MSI to me, merging it with my Fort Knox National Company. Thought I'd give it to you now and get the business part of our lunch over with."

Dana's smile faded and she sighed. "Wish I could hang onto MSI, but NETZEE will be happy *that* potential conflict of interest will be a non-issue soon."

A young girl dressed in black jeans, a white shirt, and apron appeared at the table. "Are you ready to order?"

"Yes, we are, and I'm confident I can order for us both," Jim said, grinning up at the waitress. "We'll take two of today's specials — the grilled ham and cheese sandwich — with fries and sweet tea."

"Sounds good." The waitress wrote the order on her pad and scurried away.

Jim placed his hands on the table in front of him. "Now, tell me how things are going with NETZEE? Since you were late for lunch, I'm assuming you're keeping busy."

Dana laughed. "That's an understatement! I've got misgivings about the way NETZEE does *some* things, but sending new clients our way is not one of them! Early mornings, late nights — it's all engines go, all the time."

Jim cocked his head to one side. "Lots of new clients is a good thing — if you can handle the increased capacity. Can you?"

"We could for a while. Now we need that capital they keep promising." Dana sat back on the bench and sighed. "Initially, we were told we'd get an infusion of capital following the Initial Public Offering last November. But now it's March, and nothing. I'm wondering if the Chief Financial Officer is qualified to do his job. I think the only reason he became the CFO is because he's long-time friends with Alan Wingart. But from what I've observed, financial management of the company does not appear to be his strong suit."

Jim sat quietly for a moment. "Hmm, I would think if they're ever going to provide you a capital infusion, it would follow the IPO. That's usually the purpose of an Initial Public Offering."

"Right. In the meantime, our servers are at capacity and we've actually gone down a couple times now, which is pretty scary for a business that provides a hosted service. I need to hire additional people, but I have no place to put them because we've outgrown our building. We desperately need more programmers and other technical types. We need another accountant. The list goes on."

"What do they say when you ask?"

Dana held up her hands. "They're working on it. That's what they've told me every time I've asked since last November. I'm sure you know how hard it is to operate like this."

Jim nodded his head, but was silent.

Dana looked down at the table and shook her head. "I feel sorry for the Chief Operations Officer — Mike Bowers — who is my immediate boss. We talk regularly, so he's well aware of the issues I'm having. Personally, I like him a lot and we see eye-to-eye on things. We've spent hours on the phone strategizing about this business, and he's trying to help. Mike used to be a consultant for banks, doing strategic planning and organizational design. He's an impressive man — definitely smart — so all I can assume is the CFO and Wingart don't listen to Mike's advice."

"Have you talked to Wingart yourself?"

"I have," Dana replied. "Right before the IPO last November, we had our first company meeting in Birmingham. The purpose of the meeting was to bring together all the sector heads — or operating entities, as they call them — so we could meet each other and the other key players from NETZEE, and tell us the plan for moving forward. The entire NETZEE Board of Directors was there, and I met them all at this first meeting. I already had some problems caused by lack of capital, and I mentioned this to Wingart then. From what I gathered, most of the other operating entities had the same needs. When Wingart gave his introductory speech, he mentioned the IPO and using some of the money raised for a capital infusion. But, like I said, that was a good five months ago and now it's just more promises. Actually, the only NETZEE Board Member at this meeting who said anything worthwhile was my boss — Mike Bowers. He was the only one who sounded like he'd prepared for the meeting and had something of value to say. I paid attention when he talked."

Jim Fugitte scratched his head. "At least your boss is a decent guy. That always helps."

"Yes, for sure."

A server delivered their lunches to the table and quickly disappeared.

"This looks delicious," Jim said. "I'm famished."

"Me too!" Dana reached for her grilled ham and cheese and took a big bite. "Man, this is so good. Nothing better than a grilled ham and cheese on fresh baked bread. Perfect comfort food." She put down her sandwich. "You know, I'm wondering if the only reason NETZEE bought these small companies is because they want to package them up and sell them. They seem to have no interest in actually running or managing them. There doesn't seem to be any long-term strategy for how the entities will work together or leverage each other's capabilities. Basically, we each run our own small companies the way we did before we were acquired. If we can interface on some level, then good. But if not, that's OK too. Reminds me of a confederacy."

"Rolling them up to sell them off sounds like a plausible theory in this hyper-growth environment. It would explain why you're not getting any capital too. They're hoping for a quick sale." Jim caught the waitress as she passed by the table. "Can I get more tea, please?"

Dana continued to eat her lunch, staring mindlessly at the table in front of her. "It would explain a lot. In the meantime, I've got a business to run and I have more problems than I can handle."

The waitress refilled Jim's glass as he finished his lunch. He sat back on the bench and laced his fingers together on his chest. "I don't know if you've heard anything about this yet, but the word from my FDIC buddies and contacts on the street is this tech bubble we've been experiencing could be near the end. There are definite signs the market could soon move south. So, if the intention of NETZEE's owners is to roll it up and sell it, they'll be wanting to do something soon. I suspect they hear the same rumors I do and know what's going on."

Dana looked up at Jim and frowned. "I've not heard anything about a potential fall-off in the market. Frankly, I don't know if that would be bad news or good news. If NETZEE sold and we got a new owner, maybe they'd manage the company better."

"Maybe, but in this fast-moving environment, you might experience a lot of turmoil before you get a buyer who's interested in running the company as opposed to making a quick buck."

"We're already going through a lot of turmoil." Dana pushed aside her empty plate. "I spent the morning looking at listings for a new building to purchase or lease. When I said I was out of space, I was serious. I'm desperate for more people, but I've got nowhere to put a single one. I hate to sell my building because I really like it there."

"Unfortunately, I can't offer you any space in mine. But I'll keep an ear open and let you know if I hear of anything suitable."

Dana smiled. "Thanks, Jim. Sorry to complain throughout our entire lunch. I should be happy we have so much business that our building is busting at the seams. I am, of course, but I'm also frustrated I have to fight for necessities. Everything seems to be a struggle because we have no capital."

"That's perfectly understandable." Jim clasped his hands behind his head. "How's everything else these days? The family OK? How's Joey?"

Dana winced at the sound of his name. "Joey and I separated, Jim — a couple months ago. It's hard to talk about, but I know it's time to tell people."

Jim raised his eyebrows. There was a heavy pause. "Dana, I'm . . . I'm so sorry. I don't know what to say. I'm shocked and saddened."

Dana looked down at her lap, and her shoulders slumped. "I know, but it has been a long time coming. Even so, it's hard for me to believe and we're all trying to adapt."

"How are the kids taking it?"

"They seem OK, but you never know. I'm worried about them, of course."

"You and Joey have been together a long time — ever since I've known you. Hell, I don't think Liz was born when we started working together at First Citizens." Jim was still staring at Dana, his eyebrows knitted together and lines etched into his face.

"No, she wasn't born yet. Joey and I got married in 1978 but we'd dated for a couple years before that, so yes, we were together about 24 years." Dana slumped further into the bench. She felt like someone was leaning on her back and shoulders.

Jim sighed visibly. "Well, I'm terribly sorry, Dana — for you and for Joey. I wish there was something I could do to help. I was thinking you looked beaten down, but I thought it was just work. This has been hard on you, I can tell."

"Yes, it has. And now I just want to get the divorce behind us and move on."

Jim nodded his head. "I'm sure you do. Let me know if there's anything I can do for you."

"Thanks, Jim. I appreciate that. I seem to be so busy at NETZEE now, I barely have time to process everything that's happening. But maybe that's a good thing. So far, Joey and I are getting along OK during the divorce process. A few bumps here and there, but it hasn't been ugly. I'm grateful for that because I know the kids suffer the most if things get ugly." Dana took a deep breath and tried to relieve the tightness in her chest. She glanced at her watch. "I probably should get back to the office. I'm sure someone is looking for me by now."

Jim laughed. "You're probably right. There's never any rest for the most capable person in the office. Why don't you go on and leave, and I'll get the check? You paid the last time."

"Are you sure?" Dana reached across the bench for her purse and coat.

"Absolutely. Don't forget to review the contract I gave you earlier. We should get that done as soon as possible so there are no more concerns about you owning a competing business."

"Will do. Thanks again for lunch, Jim. It was great to see you and catch up, as always. I hope I don't remember MSI and Call Me Bill as the good old days," she added, rolling her eyes. "NETZEE was supposed to be something new and exciting. We'll see if it turns out that way."

"Don't give up hope," Jim said. "It's early in the game. You never know what'll happen."

Dana stopped for a moment and smiled at the thought. There was one bright spot she'd discovered at NETZEE, and it had little to do with the business side of the company.

33

Summer 2000

"I've missed you, Grandma." Dana leaned across the kitchen table and squeezed Grandma Adkins's hand. "I'm sorry I've been so busy lately. You're the one person who makes me feel calm and normal after a long day at the office. I miss being able to spend time with you, like I used to do. And I especially miss our time baking or cooking up some of your old recipes in your kitchen."

Grandma Adkins placed her other hand on top of Dana's. "You're busy earning a living, my dear, taking care of two kids by yourself, and all the other things you have going on. I certainly understand. We'll just have to make the most of the time we have, that's all." She gave Dana one of her slow, gentle smiles and patted her hand softly.

Dana sighed and felt her whole insides relax. She didn't know if it was Grandma's delicate voice, the unbridled honesty she saw in her clear blue eyes, or her countless cheerful memories with Grandma that made Dana feel serene when she was near her. "You've always been a huge part of my life, and over the years you've helped me so much with the kids, I don't know what I'd do without you, Grandma."

"I don't think we have to worry about that for a long time, my dear." She gave Dana's hand another pat, slowly pushed back her chair, and shuffled over to the stove. "Our potato soup is ready to eat and the cornbread will be done shortly. Do you want to tell Ryan and Liz dinner is ready?"

"Sure, and thanks for being here and doing the heavy lifting with dinner, Grandma."

"It took no time at all. Anyway, you know I love to peel potatoes. Gives me a chance to relax and think about things."

Dana padded down the hallway and returned several minutes later with Ryan and Liz in tow. "I can smell the cornbread!" Ryan announced. "Mom, why can't you make cornbread like Grandma?"

Dana smiled. "Ryan, *no one* can make cornbread like Grandma. I use her recipe, but it just doesn't taste the same. I think it's the cast iron pan she bakes it in that's her secret weapon."

"Then I think you should make sure she leaves it here and we forget to give it back," he said.

"If it ever goes missing, Ryan Smolenski, I'll know where to look," Grandma said, wagging her finger at him.

"Get your drinks and let's sit down and eat. It's getting late and I'll need to take Grandma home soon." Dana took the cornbread out of the oven and placed it on the table next to the soup. She pulled out her chair at the end of the table, sat back, and kicked off her shoes. Her feet were hot and tired from being cooped up all day in leather shoes. She stretched out her legs and toes. It felt good. It had been another long, hot day.

Grandma took a few bites and then put down her spoon. "How are you two kids making out without your dad around? Are you getting adjusted?"

"It's OK." Liz's voice held no emotion, and she looked down at her bowl.

"Yeah, it's fine," Ryan said. "We're getting used to it. We stay here most of the time, but we see Dad a lot too."

"You'll be off to college next year anyway, right?" Grandma asked, looking at Ryan.

"Sure will. Can't wait." Ryan glanced at his mom, flashing her a devious look as he reached across the table and grabbed two corn muffins with one hand. "How was your trip to Atlanta, Mom?"

Dana sighed and shook her head. "That's what Grandma and I were just talking about before dinner. I don't know what to think. At our monthly meetings in Atlanta, we all talk about our issues, which for most of us boil down to the need for money. We're told our issues are being addressed and we should see some resolution soon. Then I fly back home and nothing happens. Or, the fix is not nearly adequate. For example, I keep telling them how desperate I am for more people, but I don't have the budget to pay them, and even if I did, I have no office space for them. The Fire Marshall showed up last week and said if I don't do something soon regarding the over-crowding, he'll shut us down. But without money to hire more people and buy more capable servers and other basic office equipment, I don't know how I'm going to continue to run the business."

"You'd think since your business is doing so well, they'd give you money to hire more people," Liz said.

"You'd think, wouldn't you?" Dana shook her head. "Or money to buy bigger servers or more printers. Our servers went down again the other day, and all hell broke loose. We couldn't answer all the calls. I told my boss you can't host a service for customers and then have that service go down — even for an hour. It's unacceptable. And lately it's happening more often. We're throwing too much at the servers too quickly. They weren't designed to operate at that capacity. But as much as I've explained this, I just get more promises. One day the servers will go down and stay down, and then we'll be in serious trouble."

Ryan looked at his mom with a puzzled expression. "Why don't you do what every other American does — charge new servers to the company credit card?"

Dana laughed. "That's a great idea, but it might get me fired."

"I don't see why," he said earnestly. "You'd just be doing what was necessary to keep the business operating."

"I'm not authorized to charge that much money to the company credit card, but I like the idea," Dana said with a chuckle, as she reached over and squeezed his arm. "I'll figure it out. Fortunately, I have one good boss — my immediate boss. He understands the problems and is trying to help. I think the real problem is NETZEE just doesn't have any money to give us. I heard they used all the money they raised from the IPO to pay for all the companies they acquired. At the time, they believed the companies would create enough revenue to sustain themselves and maybe even turn a profit until they sold NETZEE. The problem is, we're not. NETZEE is giving away our software as part of a larger package they provide to financial institutions and then charging those institutions monthly service fees, which are based on per user and per transaction charges. It's confusing, I know. The bottom line is we're not generating enough revenue to support our operations. I keep wondering how long it's going to be before NETZEE can't make payroll."

Grandma put down her spoon and look over at Dana. "Do you really think that could happen?"

"I don't know. But I keep wondering how long we can operate at a loss." Dana took another bite and then put down her spoon and sat back in her chair. "I wish there was some way I could buy back the part of my company I sold to them last year."

"Is that possible?" Grandma asked. "Have you asked? If they're having trouble paying the bills, maybe they'd be happy to sell it back to you."

"I haven't formally asked, but I mentioned to my boss that I hated the way things were going and I'd love to buy back my old piece of the company. I wouldn't want it all because there's too much that's not profitable. But I'd like to buy back my old customers — the ones who haven't taken on any additional business with NETZEE. I'd want to make a clean break from NETZEE and keep things simple." Dana picked up her glass and held it without taking a drink, as she stared at the center of the table.

"It sounds like you've been thinking about this a lot," Grandma said. "What did your boss have to say?"

"He said there's no incentive for NETZEE to sell such a small piece of a public company because it wouldn't be worth the cost and effort of putting together the legal paperwork. NETZEE is still hoping for a buyer for the whole thing."

"Oh, I see." Grandma nodded her head slowly. "Then what are you planning to do?"

"Keep asking them for money, I guess. Other than that, I don't know what else I can do. I can't leave. I'm legally obligated to work for NETZEE for two years following the sale of Call Me Bill. We're a long way from that, unfortunately."

"Don't worry, Mom," Liz said. "Two years will go by fast, and then you'll move on to something else. In the meantime, maybe you don't have to work so much every day. If they won't give you what you need, why should you be so dedicated?"

Dana smiled at her and hesitated. "I know what you mean, Liz. What they're doing doesn't seem right. But I couldn't go to work every day and not do the right thing for my employees and customers. I'd feel too guilty. I owe them my best effort because that's the way I'd want them to treat me. Besides, my reputation would be at stake if I slacked off and things went south. People need to trust me or they'll find another company to do their bill payments."

"I can't imagine you slacking off, Mom." Ryan looked over at his mom and then continued eating.

"Me either," Liz added.

"Nor I," Grandma said. "Your folks didn't raise you that way. As you said, treat others like you want them to treat you — the Golden Rule." She looked from Ryan to Liz. "I hope you'll both remember how hard your mom works, and to help her out more at home now that your dad is not living here. You should watch out for each other too."

"They do, Grandma, they help a lot. They help get dinner ready at night and do most of the clean-up. They do their own laundry, and Ryan drives Liz when she needs to go somewhere. Now, if I could just take them to work with me and get some free labor out of them . . ." Dana looked over and nudged Ryan.

"You can hire me after college," Ryan said. "I'm not missing out on four years away at school, on my own, doing what I want." He scooted back from the table and picked up his and Grandma's empty bowls and took them to the sink, still chewing his last bite of food.

"Oh, OK!" Dana said, with a sarcastic laugh. She got up from the table and placed her bowl in the sink. "If you two clean up, I'll take Grandma home."

Liz gave Grandma a hug. "Thanks for dinner and for being here, Grandma."

"Good night, Grandma," Ryan said, looking over his shoulder as he stood rinsing dishes at the sink.

"You're most welcome. I'll see you soon." Grandma walked over to the cabinet by the garage door and picked up her purse.

Dana grabbed her bag from the counter and followed Grandma out the door and to the car. It was a warm, humid evening and the air was still. A full moon glowed bright yellow in the night sky as Dana backed the car out of the driveway and started down the road toward Grandma's house.

After a while, Grandma broke the silence. "You seem preoccupied, my dear. Is everything OK? I know the divorce is hard on you and the kids, but it looks like everyone is handling it fine. Do you want to talk about anything?"

"I'm OK, Grandma. It's nothing in particular. Just trying to keep everything together at home and at the office." Dana glanced over at Grandma and could see the outline of her frown against the dark window. "Don't worry, Grandma, really. I've got lots of balls in the air, but that's nothing unusual. I'm certainly frustrated with the way things are at NETZEE because I know how to fix the problems, but I'm not allowed to make those decisions. I keep telling myself it's not my company anymore, and I shouldn't take it so personally. But that's not who I am, so it's hard to watch."

"I'm sure it is, my dear." Grandma reached over and patted Dana's leg. "But I have faith in you that there'll be a good outcome for everyone — eventually. You'll convince NETZEE to give you the money you need or something else will happen that'll solve the problem. One thing is certain — you're a good salesperson. You'll talk them into the right decision."

Dana laughed. "Thanks for the vote of confidence. I hope you're right."

"I can see you're at peace with your decision to separate from Joey. I thought after a few months apart, you two might work things out. But now I can see you intend to go through with the divorce. I just want you to be happy. I could tell you weren't for a while now, but I thought it was just work, or one of those troubled periods that happens in marriages."

"You're right, I haven't been happy in years. It's not because of any specific thing; we just grew apart. I know you're sad about us breaking up, and you're worried about me and the kids, but we're doing OK — really. It has been an adjustment for all of us, that's for sure. But I think when the parents aren't happy, in the long run it's the best thing for the whole family." Dana looked over at her grandmother and tried to smile.

"How's Joey doing?"

"I think he's doing fine. Honestly, this has been a long time coming. Joey agreed we had a strained marriage for several years, and we'd grown apart. He didn't seem surprised when I said I wanted to separate."

Grandma was silent until Dana pulled into her driveway and turned off the engine. Then she turned toward Dana and reached for her hand. "Life is too short, my dear, to live it and not be happy. I hate to see your family break up, but it's more important you don't live the rest of your life not content with it. And it looks like Ryan and Liz are handling all the change fairly well, which I'm relieved to see. If you need to talk, you know I'm here for you."

"I know, Grandma. You always have been. But, I'm doing fine. We'll get through this." Dana got out of the car and helped Grandma into her house. She kissed her goodnight and returned to her car. Driving home in the moonlit street, Dana ruminated on the past few years. NETZEE wasn't working out the way she'd envisioned, but she'd finally pushed the reset button on her personal life. Maybe at some point, she could do the same with her work life. It was a thrilling, yet terrifying, thought. Starting over takes a belief in oneself, and in the product or service. It takes dedicated employees and a capital investment — not to mention all the long work days. Dana wasn't sure she was up for all that again. Next time — if there were a next time — she'd want a partner who could help take the company beyond $2 million a year in revenue. She'd need someone with large company experience, who had a strategic planning background, and who — like Jim Fugitte — excelled at managing the logistics and finances of the business. Those were the two things she didn't want to spend her time doing. Unfortunately, she didn't know anyone — other than Fugitte — with those skills. But then, maybe she *did* know someone! Maybe she knew just the perfect person.

34

December 2000

Mike Bowers held open the door to the restaurant and ushered Dana into the crowded foyer. Dana searched for the maitre d' amidst the throng, finally locating the young girl. "I made a 7PM reservation for two under the name Smolenski."

"Sure, just give me a minute," the young girl said, as she glanced down at her chart. "Follow me."

Dana made her way behind the girl through the narrow aisle to a small table next to a window. She turned back to make sure Mike Bowers was behind her. "Thank you," she said to the girl.

Mike helped Dana remove her coat and he pulled out the chair as she carefully sat down. Earlier, she'd felt fatigued from another long and stressful day in the office. Now, she sensed anticipation in her stomach she hadn't felt in a long time. She relished her time talking to Mike Bowers, even when it was due to the maddening scenario that threw them together today. Over their many work-related phone calls during the past few months, she realized they could talk about most anything and she'd enjoy the discussion. She found him engaging, well-prepared, extremely bright about many varied subjects, and humorous and fun. He differed from the other people she knew or had worked with previously. He'd lived in different locations around the country, and his experiences brought a whole new level of insight to Dana. She found him fascinating. "After such a crazy day, I'm glad you could stay and eat dinner," she said.

"I am too. It's rare I have the opportunity to explore the big city of Elizabethtown and its culinary venues — not to mention having such an engaging dinner partner," he said, with a wink.

Dana laughed. "Oh yes, the big city of Elizabethtown! I'm sure it's a sleepy village compared to Atlanta."

"It is, but it's a pleasant change too — calmer, more relaxing. Actually, I've lived in several small towns during my adult life and liked them all. Every place has its gems."

"That's true." Dana sat back in her seat and turned serious. "Mike, I just want to say thanks again for jumping through the hoops today to get our servers back up and running. After those desperate phone calls I made the past two days, and then got no help from anyone, I don't know what we'd have done if you hadn't rounded up the company plane, flown to Birmingham to pick up the techs, and brought them here to fix our servers. I'd made numerous phone calls to every tech repair company I could find within driving distance, and literally no one could help. Since we'd been down for two entire days, I was desperate! So, I can't thank you enough."

Mike smiled and flagged down the waiter. "You did thank me, Dana, several times now. You're most welcome. To be honest, I feel NETZEE is responsible for your predicament. If they had given you the capital to purchase more capable servers, this would not have happened. Your workload is increasing weekly, but you're getting no additional operating funds. We're putting you in a tough spot and I don't see things changing anytime soon. We continue to operate at a loss."

The waiter appeared at the table and took their drink order. "I'll be back with those drinks shortly," he said, as he headed toward the bar.

"Do you know why we're operating at such a loss? Seems we enjoyed some success for a couple months and then things quickly went south."

Mike raised his eyebrows and held up his hands. "We're giving away the store. It's as simple as that. When a financial institution agrees to contract for our software and services, they get the software and installation essentially for free. We charge them for only the monthly transaction fee.

We have to charge those monthly fees for a long time to recover the cost of the software and installation. I'm not sure Alan Wingart and Bill Harper envisioned a long life for NETZEE. I believe they wanted to wrap it up and sell it fairly soon after putting it together. So, I don't see us at the break-even stage — let alone at the revenue-producing stage — before we simply run out of money."

Dana was silent for a moment, unsure how to respond to his candidness. She decided to push. "Are you worried? What do you think is going to happen?"

"I can't answer that question any better than you right now." He settled back in his seat. "We just need to keep plugging away, doing our jobs, and hoping for a sale. You know, the idea underlying NETZEE was to put together a portfolio of small, innovative companies, and if just *one* of those companies took off, that would draw in potential buyers. For one reason or another, that hasn't happened. Now, we have the problem of insufficient capital to grow the companies to their full potential. So it's hard to say what might happen."

"Are you worried?" Dana asked again.

"Well, like you, I sold my company to NETZEE, and therefore, don't have any skin in the game, so to speak. Since I'm not an investor, I don't have a sizable amount of money to lose. But as the Chief Operations Officer, I want to see NETZEE succeed, of course. I enjoy working with the board of directors. Plus, both Alan Wingart and Bill Harper are long-time friends and colleagues of mine, and I don't want to see them fail. And I enjoy my job and working with the heads of the operating entities that now make up NETZEE. I enjoy traveling to see them and learning about what they do and how they do it. And I enjoy coming here and working with you," he added, smiling at her.

Dana could feel her cheeks burning and she hoped in the restaurant's darkness he didn't notice. "That explains the lack of adequate funding, so I won't be expecting a capital infusion anytime soon."

Just then the waiter delivered their drinks to the table. Mike picked up his gin and tonic and proposed a toast to a successful day. Dana reached for her iced tea and clinked glasses with Mike. "Yes, here's to one of the most productive days I've had at NETZEE," she said with a chuckle. "By the way, what did you think of our new building? You drove to see it today, right?"

"Yes, I did." Mike took another slow drink of his gin and tonic and placed the glass on the table. "While you all were hunkered down in the server room, I decided it was a good time to get out of there, so I drove over to take a look. The building manager happened to be there when I showed up, and he gave me a nice tour of the place. It looks good. I admit I'll miss visiting you in your little red house with the red tile roof, but I know the Fire Marshall was about to put you out on the street. I have a feeling the girls who work for you will appreciate having more than one bathroom too," he added, with a mischievous grin.

Dana laughed. "You're right! Sometimes that was pretty inconvenient. I'll miss that place too, especially during Spring and Fall when I could open the windows and get some fresh air. I'll also miss hearing the Amish horses and buggies. By the way, I listed the building for sale last month and already have an offer from a local Title company."

"Great! That's always an enormous relief. Is it a decent offer?"

"Yes, I'm planning to take it and get that off my plate."

"That *is* good news. Congratulations!" Mike reached over, picked up a menu, and handed it to Dana. "Are you ready to look at a menu and order?"

"Sure."

A few minutes later, Mike flagged down their waiter, and they placed their order. He sat back in his seat again and glanced around the room. "This place was an excellent choice. Looks like a fun atmosphere, menu looked good, prices seem reasonable — especially compared to Atlanta." He laced his fingers together and placed his hands on the table. "Tell me about yourself, Dana. How did you get your start in banking, and maybe a more interesting question, considering how chauvinistic the banking world is, how did a lady like yourself move up the ladder to where you are today?"

Dana sat back in her seat and laughed. "That's a long story!" She felt self-conscious telling him such personal things, especially about being fired from her first banking job. She didn't want him to think she'd ever been an incompetent employee. There was no way anyone had ever fired Mike Bowers!

"We have all night and I'd like to know what drives Dana Smolenski," Mike said, as he settled into his seat. He took a drink, placed his glass on the table, and fixed his eyes squarely on Dana.

The attention made her laugh nervously. "My first job at a bank was a teller at First Citizens in Radcliff." She looked down at the table and shook her head as her cheeks grew warm. "I hate to admit this, but I was a terrible teller!"

"What? I don't believe it," Mike said. "You probably thought that at the time because it was your first job and maybe you were a little insecure."

"No, I really was terrible, as confirmed by my boss." Dana rolled her eyes and laughed.

Mike looked up at the ceiling and laughed. "Now that doesn't sound like the Dana I know! Did he move you to another position in the bank?"

"Yes, he made me his administrative assistant, and I learned lots of different aspects of banking over the next few years. But more relevant to your question, this was the mid-80s, and allotments were just getting started. My boss assigned me to our military allotment department, which at the time had one other person. With Fort Knox Army Post nearby, a lot of our customers were Army soldiers. They had regular monthly bill payments, like insurance and car payments, which they'd forget to make when they went on maneuvers for months at a time. So the military worked with us to set up automatic monthly allotments for these payments, which came directly out of their paychecks. These allotments were the precursor to bill pay."

"No kidding!" Mike sat up in his seat. "This is how you got into the bill pay business?"

"There's a little more to the story." Dana relayed the saga of the bank's use of paper ledgers to track the allotments, the two flawed attempts to implement electronic ledgers and the resulting account discrepancies, and her painful firing. Then she searched Mike's face for clues of his reaction.

His eyes narrowed. "Why would he want you fired? Seems to me it would've made more sense to work with you and fix the discrepancies."

"My prior boss had set up an incentive pay plan for this allotment program. I was about to receive my first incentive paycheck, which would have been somewhere around $100K. During the meeting when the new president fired me, he said no snotty-nosed kid was going to make more money than him."

Mike hesitated. His face had a blank stare, and he blinked several times. "You're serious? He actually said that?"

"He really said those exact words. He blamed me for the discrepancies and fired me as I was returning from maternity leave." She still could not talk about it without a tightness gripping her chest.

"Is he still around — the bank president who fired you?"

"I don't know where he is, but I doubt he's working in banking anymore. After he fired me, over the next several years he fired every woman who worked for him until he got to the comptroller, who'd been with the bank since it first opened. She filed a sexual discrimination lawsuit against him and won. The bank's board of directors fired him the next day. But, the damage was done for the rest of us women who already had lost our jobs."

Mike shook his head and fixed his eyes on Dana. "It's hard to believe in this day and age that a male bank president could get away with firing a series of women for that length of time with no one at the executive level paying attention."

"I went to see an attorney. He said if I challenged the firing in court and won, the judge would award me my job back — nothing more. I couldn't imagine working for that man again. So, I was out of work for a few months and then took an offer from three local businessmen. They wanted me to continue doing their allotments, as I'd been doing for them at First Citizens. So we set up a small business and I did the allotments for their three companies for about nine years. We did very well. I made them a lot of money, while my salary barely increased. One of my clients said I should stop making all that money for them; I should buy the company and make all that money for myself. They had never incorporated the company,

314

filed as a Limited Liability Company, or filed *any* sort of legal paperwork. So basically, I told them I'd give them each $250K if they'd sign over the operation to me and walk away. If they refused, I told them I'd take the business away, regardless. They weren't happy, but they signed. Within two years I'd paid off my loan and we were doing well."

Mike leaned forward in his chair and shook his head. "That's quite a story, and a bold move to stand up to those three gents! I'm going to be very careful around you in the future. I'll come to work one day and find out you have my job!"

Dana smiled. "It sounds simple now, but I remember a lot of sleepless nights, stomach acid, and gnashing of teeth. A retired Marine Corps attorney provided me free help, and he was with me during the crucial meeting with the three men. I honestly couldn't have done it without him. I gave him a small piece of the ownership when I took over the company."

"Was that Call Me Bill?" Mike asked.

"No, that company was called Military Services Incorporated — better known as MSI. A few months after I'd paid off the loan, I was having lunch with Jim Fugitte. I'm sure you've heard of Jim. He and I started Call Me Bill. But what you don't know about Jim is he was the bank president and my boss at First Citizens when I worked on the allotments. He started the incentive pay plan. He was the president prior to the one who fired me."

"I see — the plot thickens," Mike said.

"Yes. Anyway, Jim Fugitte and I were having lunch one day, and he suggested he and I combine our allotment companies, and then start a new phone bill pay company. I decided he was right — phone bill pay was the way of the future. That company became Call Me Bill. And after a brief period, phone bill pay turned into online bill pay, and then NETZEE came courting, and you know the rest of the story."

"That's quite a tale, Dana! I can assure you my story is not nearly as interesting," Mike said, still shaking his head. "I have a feeling there are a lot of details in there you didn't mention too — a lot of hardship and struggles. No wonder you're so tough, and so knowledgeable about lots of different areas. You've had to learn. You've had lots of people take advantage of your knowledge and your work ethic. I'm guessing that small part of your history is why you're extremely careful about the payments being done correctly. But just think, if you hadn't been fired from that first job at the bank, you might not be where you are today. Have you considered that?"

Dana looked down at her lap and nodded her head slowly. "I have — many times. It helps to take away the sting of being fired, which I still feel sometimes. Even when you've been unjustly fired and you know you did nothing wrong, it still makes you feel as if you're not good enough, and people treat you like you're a pariah. It's hard to explain." She felt that way now, simply talking about it.

Mike looked at Dana, but was silent. He slowly reached across the table and laid his hand on hers. "You're *not* that person. You're one of the hardest working, most competent people I've ever met. And you have the capacity for so much more. That's how you need to think of yourself."

Dana felt an electric spark shoot up her arm when Mike placed his hand on hers. The surprise of his touch nearly caused her to jerk back her hand. She could feel her cheeks burning again.

Just then, two waiters in white shirts and black slacks appeared at their table, each carrying a large tray. "Chicken Alfredo for the lady and a medium-rare filet with baked potato for the gentleman. I'll be back to refill your tea, ma'am. Can I get you another gin and tonic, sir?"

"Sure, that'd be great." After the waiters left the table, Mike picked up his glass. "Here's to getting to know each other, and to what looks like a fantastic dinner!"

"It does," Dana said. "I don't think I've ever had a bad meal here. I thought you deserved a good dinner after all the trouble you went through to get our servers fixed today. You just don't know what a relief it is to get those things up and running again."

Mike laughed. "You were going to stop thanking me, remember?"

"I do, sorry. Now, tell me how you got your start in the banking world."

Mike took a bite of his steak and thought about it. "As I said, my story is not nearly as interesting as yours."

"Let me be the judge of that," Dana said. "Were you born in Atlanta?"

"No, I was born in the small town of Paragould, Arkansas, a town of around ten thousand people. I'm sure you've never heard of it. Most people haven't. But Paragould was a very interesting town to grow up in during those days. It was a town of entrepreneurs. It also was a town full of guys who came back from World War Two and started up small businesses, so I grew up in a town full of business people."

"Wow, sounds like a great place to be from," Dana said.

Mike took another bite of his steak and washed it down with his gin and tonic. "When I was a kid, my dad told me I had three choices; I could be a doctor, a lawyer, or a banker. I didn't think I'd ever make it through biology class, so being a doctor was out. I didn't know enough about what a lawyer did for a living. So, I figured I'd be a banker. I got my first paycheck in banking at age 13 by washing windows and mowing grass at a local bank. At age 16, I moved inside the bank and got my first real banking paycheck. My mother was happy about that because now I was working in the air conditioning."

Dana laughed. "You really have been in banking your entire life!"

"That's true, I have." Mike took another bite and then set down his fork and knife. "I have a degree in Banking and Finance from Louisiana State University. My first job after graduating was with First Tennessee Bank in Memphis. I was a credit guy. That became my area of expertise, and I stayed in the credit world for most of my banking career. After my initial stint in credit, I moved to the international side for a while. From Memphis, I went to Little Rock and back to the credit side as a lender to big companies. From Little Rock I went to the First City Bank of New Orleans, Louisiana, and mainly did specialty lending to oil companies. I became president of the company, and then went back to Tennessee, but this time to Johnson City, where I ran 19 banks for them. At this point I was getting a little tired of banking, so I learned some consulting skills from a mentor of mine and joined the consulting world. That was a lot more fun," he added with a grin.

"I'm sure it was after all those jobs in banking. With consulting, you get to pick the clients and sometimes they even take your advice!"

"That's right! And I was lucky enough to have some good clients. I did a lot of what I called operations management consulting. I traveled to off-sites — you know, meetings with the executives away from the office to talk about changing their organizational structures and doing process improvement-type things. We'd also play a little golf and have some real nice working dinners. I thoroughly enjoyed my time consulting."

Dana rolled her eyes and laughed. "I'm sure you did! And you actually got paid for this too?"

"I actually did," Mike said, grinning. "This led to starting the company I sold to NETZEE, which was called Dyad. When I was working as a consultant, I was around entrepreneurs constantly. I met a director who said we needed to start a business that automates as many of a bank's functions that are technically possible. So our idea was to manufacture a kiosk of sorts, which could replace people in a branch and do everything you could do at a bank — manage your accounts, make deposits, get cash, take mortgage and other loan applications, set up lines of credit, etc. We were doing quite well, especially with a bank out of Spain. That business was what my partner and I sold to NETZEE, incidentally, on the same day you sold Call Me Bill to NETZEE."

"I remember that." Dana's face softened. "3 September 1999 was a good day for NETZEE."

"My business partner at Dyad was Alan Wingart, now the CEO of NETZEE. Were you aware of that?"

Dana's eyebrows raised. "No, but that might explain why you became the Chief Operations Officer — they trust you."

"Yes, we've worked together for a long time — about 15 years. I have great respect for Alan. He has been my mentor for many years and I've learned a lot from him. Unfortunately, he's a big-picture thinker. I'm not sure he's much of an operator. Even more unfortunate, it doesn't appear Bill Harper is much of an operator either. I think the world of both men, but NETZEE is suffering from not having experienced operations managers at the helm."

Dana nodded her head. "Yes, but you're one. As the Chief Operations

Officer, I'm sure you're passing on to them all the issues NETZEE's operating entities are having, and you're advising them on the decisions they need to make to address these issues."

"You'd think they would consider my advice, wouldn't you? But they used the money raised from November's IPO to acquire additional companies, and there was no money left for operating capital or improvements. I'm sure they never intended to operate NETZEE for this long, but to package it and sell it at a profit during the hyper-growth period we just went through. Unfortunately, the tech market has been in decline recently, and it's increasingly resembling a free-fall."

Dana put down her fork and took a drink of her tea. The candidness of Mike's words surprised her. "Are there any prospective buyers?"

Mike shook his head. "Not right now. It'll be hard to get a buyer when most of NETZEE's operating entities are hurting. There are only a couple entities generating revenue, and not enough to make up for the revenue losses of the others."

"I'd like out," Dana said abruptly. She'd been wanting to say this for several months, but didn't have the nerve. She felt she could let down her guard tonight. "I'm tired of not being able to operate properly, and I'm tired of begging for things and waiting for the ax to drop. What is the chance they'd let me out of my contract?"

"No chance at all." Mike said without hesitation. "Besides, I don't want you to leave. I need you. During our weekly teleconferences, you're never shy about telling me all the problems going on in the company. The others are more timid. You've passed on information that turned out to be quite helpful. Why would you want to leave all that fun?"

Dana groaned, but was thrilled to know she'd been able to help him. She certainly didn't envy him his position at NETZEE. "The way NETZEE is being operated could hurt my reputation with my customers. I don't want to be associated with a badly managed company. I'm sure you can understand that."

Mike shrugged his shoulders. "I understand, Dana. Hell, I want out too for the same reasons! I used to provide consulting advice to troubled companies like this. But no one at NETZEE is taking my advice. I'm learning a lot, though. I'm learning what *not* to do, and what doesn't work."

Dana looked down at her plate. She certainly enjoyed working with Mike, and he was the only part she'd miss if she left NETZEE. "Any chance of buying back the part I sold to NETZEE?"

"I'm sure the answer to that is no as well. NETZEE is a publicly held company. And there's still hope they'll get an offer for the entire thing." Mike picked up his fork and began eating again.

Dana decided to do the same, and to drop the idea of leaving. She could tell the issue was off the table. And why would they let her leave, anyway? The contract she signed committed her to nearly another year. "Then I guess we'll have to keep plugging away, as you said, and hope for a quick sale to a company that has a lot of extra capital on its hands. How's the steak, by the way?"

"It's delicious. Good thing I don't mind it cold because I was doing more talking than eating. I might have to find a reason to come to Elizabethtown more often."

"I hope it's not because of more broken-down servers!" Dana pushed aside her empty plate and placed her drink in front of her. "But I'm always happy to bring you here to eat, and there are several more good places in the local area."

"Thank you. I'll be happy to come back for any reason. This is a pleasant break from Atlanta. Even the airport in Louisville is an easy in and out. Now, how about we change the subject and not talk about work for a while? Do you have kids, Dana?"

"That was quite a change in subject!" Dana was taken aback. They hadn't talked about personal things before. "Yes, I have two — a boy and a girl. Ryan is 18 and graduated from high school this year. He just started his first year of college. Liz is 15 and a sophomore in high school. How about you, any kids?"

"Yep, I've got three; two boys and a girl, in that order. Michael is the oldest. He was born in 1979. Barrett was born in 1980, and my daughter, Shelby, was born in 1985. Their mother and I divorced quite a while ago, but we all get along fine. Shelby is the only one still at home."

"I'm divorced too, but it's recent." Dana wasn't sure why she divulged that now, but she wanted Mike to know and felt relieved to get it out in the open.

"Are you doing OK? It's a big adjustment, I know."

"I'm doing OK. I was the one who wanted the divorce, but as you said, it's still a big change and has been hard on everyone. We'd been together about 25 years, but we just grew apart."

"Sounds like my story," Mike said in a sympathetic voice. "All I can tell you is it does get easier. Just like other tough things that happen in life, time heals the wounds."

Dana nodded her head slowly and stared down at the table. Suddenly, she was uncomfortable looking directly into Mike's eyes. She liked him a lot, but felt self-conscious discussing something so personal with him. "I probably need to get home soon. Tomorrow is a workday and you never know when the boss is going to call," she said with a smile. "Are you stopping at the office in the morning before your flight?"

"No, my flight is at 7AM. I'm trying to make a 9AM meeting in Atlanta. But listen, if you need to get home, you go on and leave. I'll get the check," Mike said, leaning to one side and pulling his wallet from his pants pocket.

"OK, and thank you for dinner. I know I'm not supposed to thank you anymore for the Herculean effort you went through for us today, so I will just say I very much appreciate getting our servers in good working order again." Dana reached around and grabbed her coat and purse.

Mike laughed as he pushed back his chair and stood up. "I'm glad that all worked out. Be careful going home. We'll talk again on Friday — teleconference day."

"That's right — Friday. Enjoy the rest of the evening, Mike."

"Thanks. You too."

Dana carried her coat to the restaurant's foyer and put it on before going outside. She could have stayed all night and talked to Mike Bowers. But she'd told Liz she'd be home half an hour ago. It was hard to pull herself away. She was so busy working all the time, she rarely took time out to enjoy herself — even if technically this was a work dinner. She bounded down the restaurant steps with renewed vigor and quickly located her car. On the way home, she decided to try her new cell phone to call Marie.

"Dana! It's so good to hear your voice! I can hear you so well," Marie said. "Are you ringing from your new cell phone?"

"Yes, I love this thing! I'd resisted for a while, but I do feel better having one now. If the kids need anything, it's much easier to reach me."

"You sound in a particularly cheery mood," Marie said in a suspicious tone. "Have you done something evil? Why are you so cheery? Were you able to get yourself evicted from NETZEE?"

Dana laughed. "I wish, but no. I just finished having dinner with Mike Bowers, my boss at NETZEE. I told you a little about him last week when we talked. He flew up for the day with a crew from Birmingham to get my servers back up. They'd been down for two days — can you imagine? Mike is staying the night, so we had dinner this evening."

"What specifically do you like about this man? Describe him to me."

Dana took a deep breath. She thought for a moment. "From the time I first heard him speak, I thought what an engaging man — so vibrant and full of energy, yet also compassionate and fun to be around. I just felt an instant connection to him. Over the past couple months, I've gotten to know him better from our weekly teleconferences and all our other phone calls. It's like we share a kinship or something. He loves banking as much as I do, and we can talk for hours about this stuff."

"Hmm, sounds like I need to meet him." Marie said. "Is this turning into more than a working relationship?"

"No, I just really enjoy talking to him." Dana could feel her heartbeat quicken — the same way it used to feel when she told a lie to her parents and was about to get caught. "He's just really nice. I like working for him, that's all."

There was silence on the other end of the phone. Finally, Marie cleared her throat. "Then I suppose there's no need to tell you it's generally *not* a brilliant idea to fancy your boss, or to get involved with *anyone* right now since it's so soon after your divorce."

"I know that, Marie. We just enjoy each other's company. There's no more to it than that."

"Just looking out for you, Luv. How are the kids?"

"They're doing fine. They seem to be adjusting well — better than I thought. As you know, they were pretty close to their dad. They live with me most of the time."

"I'm thrilled to hear they're adjusting well. Kids are resilient. They bounce back quickly."

"I'm almost home, Marie, so I'll let you go. I just wanted to say hi and also test my cell phone from the car."

"Ta-ta, Darling! Hugs to the kiddies."

Dana heard the click as Marie hung up her phone. She thought about Marie's warning. She was right, of course. It never was a good idea to get involved with your boss. Nor was it ever a good idea to get too friendly. She thought about Mike Bowers. It may be too late for caution.

35

February 2001

Loretta appeared in the doorway of her office. "Dana, Mr. Bowers is on the phone for you, line one."

"Oh, thank you, Loretta!" Dana's chest and throat tightened, and her heart raced. She took a deep breath and worked to calm herself. This is ridiculous. We talk all the time, she told herself, picking up the phone. "Good morning, Mike! How's everything in Atlanta?"

"Morning, Dana." Mike's voice was absent the jovial-sounding tone Dana was used to hearing. "I'm afraid things are not good in Atlanta."

"Really? What's going on?" She was half afraid to ask because she didn't want to hear any bad news today. She'd been unusually cheerful lately, despite all the struggles at work and the challenges of her recent divorce.

Mike let out an audible sigh. "As you are well aware, NETZEE has been losing money nearly from the time it started operating. But lately, we've been hemorrhaging money. NETZEE burned through nearly $62 million in cash in a little over a year. Right now we're facing Nasdaq delisting and are in survival mode. It has been hard to make payroll for a while now, but we've managed to do so." He hesitated. "However, in two weeks, I'm afraid we won't be able to make payroll."

"What? Are you serious?"

"I wish I weren't." Mike's tone was low and solemn.

"Oh my God!" Dana's voice wavered. "What's going to happen?"

"That's why I'm calling you this morning, and I'll be calling several of the other company heads today too. I've been told to let you know how desperate the situation is now, and to tell you NETZEE is planning to sell your companies."

Stunned into silence, Dana stood up at her desk and stared blankly out the window. Not making payroll in two weeks was simply incomprehensible. What about her employees? What would they do? She had a fleeting thought he might be joking with her, but quickly dismissed the idea. Mike didn't seem the type to pull such a joke.

"Are you still there, Dana?"

"Yes, I'm here." She could barely swallow.

"I can't tell you how sorry I am to call you up out of the blue and ruin your day like this, but Alan directed me to let each of you know as soon as possible. And unfortunately, it has become my job to unwind NETZEE, sell off the companies, and wrap up this whole thing."

"Are they going to sell *all* the companies?" Dana asked.

"Not immediately. Right now, they asked me to find buyers for three of them. They're keeping the bill pay company in Portland, Oregon, and selling yours. I'm not sure why they made that decision, except they seem to think the company in Portland is doing a little better right now. Since both companies do essentially the same thing, anyone who wants to transfer from Elizabethtown to Portland is welcome to do so. I have the authority to make that offer to your employees."

Dana didn't know what to say, although she doubted any of her employees would want to relocate to Portland, Oregon. They all were from the local area, and most had lived in Elizabethtown or nearby their entire lives. She couldn't think at that detailed level right now, anyway. She backed up and sat down in her chair. "I'm still in shock, Mike. I knew the situation was getting dire, but I supposed I believed they'd find a buyer and we'd move on. It never occurred to me you'd call up one day and say, 'Oh, by the way, NETZEE is going to sell your company.' I thought there would be more warning, more signs we were moving in that direction."

"I did too, Dana. But you hear the rumors, too. It's no secret the Nasdaq is about to delist us. I'm sure you've heard the saying, 'A dot-com's life span is measured by its burn rate' — the rate it spends burning through its capital. All the signs were there, but no one wanted to acknowledge them. NETZEE's owners know how to do acquisitions. They don't know how to be operations managers. And my recommendations went only so far. They tried to get the companies they acquired to buy in by letting them continue to run themselves. But the companies never learned to work together, and they didn't have the capital they needed, making it tough for them to operate. Then, of course, the market turned south almost as soon as NETZEE got up and running, which made it nearly impossible to find a buyer in time. All those things came together to create the perfect storm, which is where we are today."

Dana was hardly listening. She knew all that. She was thinking of her employees. Some of them had been with her since her early days, doing military allotments at First Citizens Bank. Over the last three or four years, she'd hired some of her lifelong friends as employees. It was a similar story regarding her customers — some she'd had since her early days at MSI. What would happen to them as they transferred operations to the Portland company? And what would her employees and customers think of *her* now? Would they blame her for this? Dana's mind was leaping ahead to what she could do to fix the problem. She tried to think clearly. "Will all our customers transfer to the bill pay company in Portland?"

"Yes, that's the plan right now — hopefully a seamless transfer. Regarding your employees, we'll offer severance packages and continued health insurance for one year, if they stay and assist with the transfer to Portland. If they leave early because they have another job lined up, they'll forfeit the severance pay and health insurance, which they shouldn't need anyway if they have another job."

"We just got moved into this new building, Mike. What a waste! We could've stayed in the old building had we known this was going to happen." Dana's stomach felt sick.

"I know. They could've made better decisions, that's for sure. It took little foresight to predict this turn of events."

Mike continued to talk, but Dana wasn't listening. Instead, she was staring out the window with myriad thoughts churning through her mind. She didn't want her company dismantled! She'd worked too hard to get it where it was today, and all that was needed was a little capital and better decision-making — nothing she hadn't been able to manage before. If they had allowed her to make the decisions, they certainly wouldn't be in the position of not making payroll right now! But why couldn't she have her company back? NETZEE didn't want it. They'd been trying to find a buyer for months. Why couldn't *she* be the buyer? Except, the thought of not working with Mike made her feel empty inside.

"Dana, are you still there?" Mike's voice resounded through the phone.

"Mike, I want my company back. I think you and I should buy it."

Mike was silent for several long moments, then cleared his throat. "What?"

"I think you and I should buy back my old company from NETZEE," Dana repeated, slowly and clearly.

"I wasn't sure I'd heard you correctly. I can understand you wanting to buy back your former company, but I don't see where I'd have a role in that."

"I do," Dana said adamantly. "We've been working together for nearly two years now, and I think you agree we work well together. Both of us have a long history of banking experience and a particular understanding of community financial institutions. We see eye-to-eye on things that are wrong, and we agree on why they went wrong. I like to do product design and sales, and you prefer management, strategy, and operations — not to mention you're good at the finance and logistics side of running a company."

"You're right about all those things, but NETZEE is a publicly traded company, Dana, and for now anyway, still listed on the Nasdaq. I'm a company officer and it would not be legal or ethical for me to break off a piece of a public company and try to buy it."

Dana was not deterred. She'd been wanting her company back for a long time so she could make the decisions again. The thought of having Mike work with her was even more enticing. "I could talk to Alan or Bill about buying back my former customers at Call Me Bill. Just off the top of my head, I think that's all I'd want back. That would be the easiest thing to do as well. I don't think I'd want any of the new customers we've brought in since we became NETZEE because they'd have ties to the rest of NETZEE's financial operations and then we might have all the same issues crop up. I think it'd be best if we made a clean break, and bought back only the customers who would have no further ties to NETZEE."

"You do remember your company is losing money right now, don't you?"

"Of course I remember! But I also know I can turn it around and grow it bigger than it was before," Dana said emphatically.

Mike let out a hardy laugh. "I have no doubt you'll do exactly that! One thing I learned about you almost instantly, Dana Smolenski, is when you set your mind on something, there's no getting you off it. You take that bull by the horns and shake it for all it's worth!"

Dana hesitated. She wasn't sure if he was making fun of her or paying her a compliment. "Mike, I honestly believe if we bought back my old clients from Call Me Bill, and picked up where I left off, with me doing sales and product design, and you managing operations, we could turn it around in less than a year."

Mike was silent.

After a moment, Dana decided his silence was a sign he was at least considering her proposal, so she continued with her rationale. "If NETZEE is going down the tubes, what would you be doing then, anyway? It sounds like after a few more months, you're going to be out of a job — unless you're considering trying to buy back your former company too."

"No, I hadn't even thought about it. But now that you brought it up, I can tell you emphatically I don't need to think about it. I have no desire to buy back my old company."

"Good," Dana said, feeling more confident by the minute. "But I *do* want mine back, and I know you'd make a great business partner, Mike. Tonight, I'll put together a short proposal laying out the specific clients I'd want to buy back and at what price, and some other specifics about the deal. I'll

328

run it by you in the morning. I won't mention your name anywhere. As you said, there could be ethical or legal issues involving you in the sale of a public company when you're still the COO. If you think the proposal is OK, I'll give Alan a call tomorrow and see if I can meet with him. Does that sound like a viable way forward?" Dana was afraid to hear his response.

But Mike simply chuckled. "You're like a bulldozer, Dana, and I mean that in a good way. Sure, it sounds like a reasonable way to proceed. Are you thinking of bringing anyone else into the partnership?"

Dana's heart jumped into her throat. She was thrilled he didn't say no! "I'm not thinking that far ahead, but it's something we could consider if we feel we need the capital or want to spread the risk. Guess it'll depend on what price we can negotiate and how much you and I want to invest."

"Right, I agree. There's much to consider. Well, Dana, I look forward to seeing what you put together tonight. I feel like I should thank you for thinking of me and offering to partner with you on this. When I called you 20 minutes ago to tell you the bad news that NETZEE was planning to sell your company, it never would have occurred to me in a hundred years we'd end up discussing a partnership to buy back your former company! But hell, I have to admit it sounds exciting! I might get to try out those restaurants in Elizabethtown sooner than I thought," he added, laughing. "Maybe I shouldn't have admitted I liked the airport in Louisville. I could end up spending more time there than I ever expected."

Dana could not believe what she was hearing! She was ecstatic at the notion she and Mike could be business partners soon. She couldn't think of anyone she'd rather have as a partner than Mike Bowers when starting up a new company. With their diverse skills, they made a perfect team. Equally important, he seemed to respect her opinion as much as she respected his. "I certainly hope it works out and you'll be trying out those restaurants, because I know we'd make a great partnership, Mike. I certainly want to try, and I'm happy you're willing to give it a shot too. I'll forward that proposal to you in the morning and let me know what you think, OK?"

"OK, Dana, we'll try it and see how far we get with this idea of yours. Have a good evening and we'll speak again in the morning."

"You too," Dana said, as she hung up the phone. She took a deep breath and grinned from ear to ear. What a turn of events! The phone call had gone from hopeless to hopeful in 20 minutes. She pulled out her laptop and began typing. All the negotiating with NETZEE would be her responsibility because Mike couldn't get involved at all in the sale. That shouldn't be too much of an issue, though. After the negotiations to obtain ownership of MSI from her three old bosses, any subsequent negotiations should be a piece of cake. This one shouldn't be anywhere near as contentious. She sorted through her current list of customers and added the ones she wanted into a new database. Typing the discussion points for her phone call with Alan tomorrow took only 30 minutes. The entire plan seemed so straight-forward to Dana, it was as if she'd been planning it in her mind for years. In fact, it seemed the most natural thing in the world — she and Mike as business partners.

* * *

The morning couldn't have come soon enough for Dana. It must have been 2:00 AM before she finally drifted off to sleep. But she didn't feel tired. She was excited to be up and getting started with the day. Alan Wingart's calendar was full until 10:30 AM, so she scheduled her call to him then. Since NETZEE was planning to sell her company soon, Dana imagined Alan would be thrilled to hear he might have a buyer already.

She dressed quickly, fixed a cup of coffee, and quietly headed out the door. Liz was still asleep, but she'd soon be up and getting ready for school. The traffic from Dana's house to the office in Elizabethtown was typically light this time of morning, and she arrived in 20 minutes. She made the coffee, grabbed a muffin, and settled into her desk. Her plan was to call Mike before too many people arrived at the office, making it hard for them to talk at both her end and his. She picked up the phone and dialed Mike's number.

"Good morning, Dana! I didn't think you came into the office so early. Should I expect to see you this early when we're working together?"

"I wouldn't hold my breath," Dana admitted with a sarcastic laugh. "I had a lot to do this morning, which is the only reason I'm calling so early. And I remember you told me you like to get into the office bright and early, so I took a chance and called. I figured it'd be easier to talk before everyone else shows up."

"You're right. I just finished reading the proposal you emailed last night. For a first cut at the issues, I'd say you captured things pretty well. I do have a couple additions. Do you want to start the discussion and I'll chime in?"

"Sure," Dana said. "I discovered last night I'd been thinking about this more than I realized. It didn't take me long to throw together some bullets for discussion, which I figured would help us decide what kind of offer to make NETZEE too. I'm hoping your insights and close relationship with Alan will help us make an informed offer."

Mike cleared his throat. "I can shed some light on that issue already. Alan called me last night after you and I spoke. He wanted to know how things went yesterday. I figured it was best to be upfront with him. So I told him you were planning to call him today because you might be interested in buying back part of your company. I have to say, his mild reaction surprised me. He said it didn't matter to him if he sold your company or combined the business with NETZEE's bill pay company in Portland. So if you had any thoughts about us getting a fire sale price tag, it doesn't sound like one's coming."

"Wow! I certainly didn't expect *that* would be his response." Dana threw down her pen. "I don't understand why NETZEE wouldn't be highly motivated to sell — and to sell quickly. Their expenses far exceed revenue at this point. I would think the sooner they sell my company, the better for their bottom line — at least for a while. Do you have any idea why Alan would have this reaction?"

331

"No, I really don't. I thought about this a lot last night, and like you, I would've expected them to jump on an offer and be ready to close quickly. Maybe they're still holding out hope for an offer for the whole thing. And maybe they believe joining your company's business with the Portland bill pay company makes a potential sale more attractive. But I'm guessing here, because I really have no idea."

"The idea that NETZEE wouldn't be motivated to sell never crossed my mind. I suppose all I can do is call Alan as planned and see what he says."

"That's right, keep with your plan. When you're done talking, I'll be curious to hear how he reacted. I can tell from your voice you're discouraged by this turn of events, but try not to feel that way yet. You're a determined and persistent woman, Dana. I'd be surprised if you don't somehow get your way," Mike said, with a chuckle.

"Thanks for the vote of confidence." He was right; it was too early in the game to get discouraged. "I'll call you when it's over." Dana hung up the phone, opened her briefcase, and pulled out her papers from last night. She spread them over her desk and began studying them. Then she started making notes, writing her talking points all over the pages. She had two hours until her phone call with Alan. That wasn't much time to put together a thorough and more convincing argument than she'd drafted last night. But everything she wanted for herself and for Mike hung on this phone call. She simply had to convince Alan it was the best thing for everyone, or her professional and personal future would not move in the direction she so desperately desired.

36

1 May 2001

Dana set her signature to the last of the many documents and slowly placed her pen back in the cup on the center of the table. She folded her hands in front of her and took a deep breath. Then, she looked up from the table and squarely into the eyes of NETZEE's attorney. "Thank you, Jason, for putting together a smooth closing this morning. No issues and no surprises — just the way I like it."

Jason Bartel smiled broadly and clasped his hand over Dana's. "You're most welcome, Dana, and congratulations! I have to say, I'm going to miss you around here. You were always a breath of fresh air and you made our meetings a little more entertaining," he added, with a glimmer in his eye. "I wish you and iPay the best of luck." He stood up and gathered his papers into his arms. "Call me if you need anything."

"I will and thank you again."

Jason Bartel left the conference room, closing the door behind him. Dana sat there, savoring the moment the company she and Jim Fugitte sold to NETZEE — a mere 18 months ago — became hers again. Yet, she couldn't help thinking the moment was bittersweet, and that robbed her of the euphoria she'd long expected would envelop her today. Long ago, she'd discovered all business transactions — including today's — created consequences she seemed unable to forecast. Was it because she was so practical and so logical she was incapable of foreseeing the disappointment, hurt, and even anger, of some of her employees who her decisions negatively affected? She stared out the large windows to the crowded streets below. In Atlanta, her problems seemed far away. But tomorrow she'd be back in Elizabethtown, having to face them again.

There was a knock at the door and when Dana looked up, she could see Mike Bowers' face through the rectangular glass. Smiling, she stood up and motioned for him to come in.

Mike opened the door and closed it gently behind him. His face broke into a wide grin. "Jason told me you're done already! Congratulations! I know it's an enormous relief to get this day behind you and move forward. I really wish I could have helped you more with all the details, Dana. Yet it looks like against all odds, everything worked out in the end."

Dana rolled her eyes, but was still smiling too. "You're right about that — I'm thrilled this day is here and the signing is complete. What a relief! And I'm definitely ready to get out of here and go have a relaxing lunch somewhere."

"Me too! We might even need to have a celebratory drink! Since it's such a beautiful day outside, which seems wholly appropriate for today's closing, I thought we'd walk to one of my favorite lunch spots. It's only a ten-minute stroll from here."

"Sounds great!" Dana gathered her paperwork, placed it in her bag, and they departed NETZEE's office. They rode the elevator to the busy first floor lobby and exited the building. Outside in the sunshine, Dana felt a sense of renewal. She breathed in the fresh early Summer air, looked over at Mike, and smiled. Whatever disappointments she'd experienced during preparations for the purchase of her former customer base and business, in no way did it deter her from being ecstatic about her new partnership with Mike Bowers. They would build iPay from the ground up. As with Call Me Bill, they'd come up with another memorable name — 'iPay.' She knew Mike felt bad about not being able to get involved in any of the hard negotiations. Nor could he help much with the prep work, which would enable operations to continue smoothly on day one of iPay's existence. But it was unavoidable. He had to steer clear of any conflict of interest — even a perceived one. Otherwise, they had everything to lose.

Mike opened the door to the restaurant and ushered in Dana ahead of him. He walked over to the maitre d', whispered something, and she led them to a table with a lovely view directly over a small garden. Mike pulled out her chair, and she sat down facing the window. He took a seat next to her, also facing the window. "This is perfect, thank you," he said to the maitre d'.

"Can I get you a drink before your server arrives?" she asked.

Mike looked over at Dana, then up at the maitre d'. "Yes, we'd like two glasses of champagne, please. Seems we have something to celebrate!"

"Great! I'll bring those right over. And congratulations!" she added, with a smile.

"Thank you." Mike reached over and grabbed Dana's hand. "We really do need to celebrate this victory, and we need to think of it as a victory because you had to win several minor battles to make today happen. I'm proud of you, Dana. Since you first surprised me during that phone call nearly three months ago declaring you and I should buy your company, you've had to single-handedly fight an uphill battle with Alan Wingart over every small thing. I still have no idea why he and Bill Harper were not more motivated to sell your company and why they had to play hardball."

Dana was nearly stunned to silence as Mike held her hand. Her pulse raced and she found it difficult to look him in the eyes. "I . . . I agree. I don't know why they had to make it so hard, except they probably knew how much I wanted it back. But as much money as NETZEE is losing every month, you'd think they'd have snapped up our one million dollar offer." She didn't want him to let go of her hand, but she was afraid he could feel her trembling.

The maitre d' appeared, carrying two glasses of champagne. Mike gave Dana's hand a gentle squeeze and let it go. "Champagne for two," she said, as she placed the glasses in front of Mike and Dana.

"Thank you," Mike said, as she left the table. He picked up his glass and looked at Dana. "OK business partner, how about a toast to iPay and to our new working partnership?"

"Absolutely." Dana reached for her glass.

Mike held up his glass. "Here's to the birth of iPay and the birth of S&B Holdings, better known as Smolenski and Bowers. May a successful partnership between you and me enable iPay to grow into a wildly successful company!"

Dana reached out and clinked glasses with Mike. "Cheers to S&B Holdings!" She grinned broadly and took a sip of the champagne. "I can hardly believe this day is here and the company now belongs to us, or as you noted, to S&B Holdings."

"I knew you'd make it happen. I feel like I've been sitting on the sidelines, silently hemming and hawing, and watching you do all the heavy lifting, which you did well, I might add."

"Thank you," Dana said. "I have to admit, I was hoping to get it for less than a million. But I won't complain about paying a third of the price NETZEE paid Jim and me to buy back essentially the same 150 customers we sold them less than two years ago."

"No, I'd say we didn't get too bad of a deal. It helped that the dot-com bust put a heavy damper on prices. I told Alan he should be thrilled to get any sort of offer in this environment. But I think you were correct — they knew you wanted it back and that's why they didn't feel any pressure to negotiate." Mike looked down at the table and shook his head. "Although, I really don't like that they're keeping the float, nor do I like a few other things they did near the end that made the terms riskier than we'd like them when starting a new company. However, I've been reminding myself that sometimes you have to take the bad with the good, so we'll let that go and instead focus on the future."

"I know what you mean. I didn't like some things that happened at the end either. That being said, I wanted back those 150 customers who had no other business ties to NETZEE. I figured with your operating and management experience, we can make up for anything we might have given up. As I said before, I'm convinced we'll be cash flowing in a year." She sounded more convincing than she felt at the moment.

A server appeared at their table and they placed their order. After she left, Mike relaxed back into his seat and placed his hands on the table. "I have some other good news for you."

Dana tilted her head and raised her eyebrows. "You do?"

"I found an apartment in Elizabethtown. I'm planning to be up there Monday through Friday. I figured I can't help you run things when I'm in Atlanta all the time."

Dana's eyes widened and she blinked several times. She couldn't believe her ears! Yet his news surprised her too, since he'd never once mentioned moving to Elizabethtown. "That would be great! But what about your daughter? I thought she lived with you most of the time."

"Shelby can live with her mom during the week. I'll fly home on weekends and she can stay with me then. I've already talked to her and to her mom. It's not a problem."

Dana grinned ear-to-ear. "That will be great! It'll help a lot having you there. And I agree, I can't see how you can learn the bill pay business without being there most of the time. I'm also a firm believer two heads are better than one, so I'm really looking forward to having a partner with large company experience. It'll be nice to get your thoughts and recommendations on things."

"I hope you still feel that way in six months," Mike said, with a grin. He lifted his gaze to the two servers carrying trays of food to their table. After they left, Mike scooted his chair closer to the table, placed the napkin in his lap, and picked up his knife and fork. "I still remember the day we first met. It was in your old office. I was expecting a simple meet and greet, and you were sitting in that big chair of yours at your desk, armed with a yellow legal pad full of things you wanted from me — and expected to get!"

Dana sat back in her chair and laughed out loud. "What? I did? I don't remember that. Did you give me what I wanted?" Her eyes narrowed.

"I doubt it! I don't recall NETZEE *ever* having enough capital to give you everything you wanted."

"Well, I believe in taking a company's revenue and ploughing it back into the company to grow it. I know you operated Dyad that way too."

"I did," Mike said. "Anyway, the point of my telling you that little story is

337

to let you know how impressed I was with you the very first day we met. As I've watched you operate over the past 18 months, I'm even more impressed with your performance. You know a lot about many varied things. You routinely passed on useful information to the rest of us during our weekly teleconferences. You helped me do my job better. So now I can say with complete assurance, I know you will be on top of all the many details we'll need to address for iPay. I'm sure you have a list of things you want already, right? Do you have a list going now on your yellow legal pad?" Mike was still grinning and looking squarely at Dana, waiting for an answer.

"Of course I do!" she admitted, laughing out loud. "I added to it on the plane this morning. If you really want to know, I *always* have a 'to do' list going. But in all seriousness, since I've already been running the company for NETZEE during the past 18 months, I know the problem areas and where we need to invest money, so really I was just prioritizing things."

"Of course you were!" Mike shook his head and laughed. "I would be disappointed if you said you didn't have a list of things you want, prioritized by date and cost."

Dana put down her silverware and gave Mike a mischievous grin. "As long as we're telling stories about first impressions, I'm going to tell mine about you."

"Oh no, I'm not sure I want to hear any more." Mike chuckled and put down his fork too.

"Do you remember the initial meeting NETZEE held in Birmingham, right after all six companies were acquired, and they brought us together to tell us the plan? I remember sitting at the conference room table listening to one boring speech after another. I was having a hard time staying focused. Then you got up to talk. You were the only one who seemed prepared. You talked about your background and being a consultant for banks, doing strategic planning, organization design, and process improvement. You were energetic, engaging, impressive, and intriguing. Suddenly, I was paying attention!" Dana laughed. "I really liked you from that very first meeting. I felt an instant connection. We have a lot in common, and our business relationship just grew from that first meeting."

"Thank you. I'm relieved to learn someone was awake and listening to me. But seriously, I admit I liked you from the start and felt an instant connection as well. Later, maybe more than a business connection, but I was aware you had just gone through a divorce. There was the problem of you working for me too."

Dana listened to Mike talk and heard the same words come out of his mouth that had spun around in her head for months. She'd liked him a great deal too, but didn't want to acknowledge it, even to herself. It was too terrifying at this point in her life. Her eyes dropped to the table. She sighed and shook her head. "I feel the same way, but didn't want to say anything and jeopardize our business relationship, which is *really* important to me."

He reached over and placed his hand on hers. "I don't want anything to jeopardize our business relationship either. We're just getting started on a fantastic business opportunity. Soon I'll be in Elizabethtown most of the time and we'll have a lot more time together. We'll just see where things go, but the future is looking bright indeed!" Dana thought Mike looked happier than she'd seen him in a long time. "There will be a lot of opportunities to be together. I was looking at a list of all the conferences and trade shows on the schedule for the rest of the year. We'll have to build a good-sized travel budget for the two of us."

"I think so too. Trade shows make for long, tiring days, but are necessary evils. I hope you'll soon feel comfortable letting me take on more of the work and responsibility. You've been calling the shots for a long time now. Are you going to be OK with me disagreeing occasionally?"

"Of course I will," Dana said. "I'm looking forward to sharing the responsibility. There are several areas of the business I'd love to have nothing to do with, such as the logistics and finances. I know you like those areas, so if I don't have to get involved on a daily basis, it'll give me more time to focus on product design. I never expected you'd be iPay's chairman on paper only. Now that S&B Holdings owns iPay, I want decisions to be 50-50."

"Good." Mike nodded his head. "I definitely want to get involved at that level, but I'm going to have quite a learning curve the first few months.

339

Because of that, I'm planning to sit back and watch things for a while."

Dana thought that was a sensible approach. "You'll pick up things quickly, Mike. With only eight employees to start, you'll be able to get a handle on things in no time. I'm glad we're able to stay in the same building and not have to move somewhere else. That makes things easier, and we'll have room to expand when we need it." Dana picked up her knife and fork again and continued to eat. She felt better focusing on the positive things. Maybe if she could expand the business quickly, she could hire back a few of the employees she had to let go.

"Yeah, I agree," Mike said, nodding his head. "Being able to stay in your current building is a big plus. I hated to see everyone move again, not to mention moving all that equipment, when it seems like you just got settled in there." He finished his lunch and pushed back his plate. "One aspect I'll be able to take over and manage right away, if you're OK with it, is dealing with our two new shareholders in iPay. I don't know how much they'll need managed, but I've got a lot of experience in that area."

"Do you mean the two banks? If so, that's a great idea. I'm happy to let you deal with them. Thank goodness we could bring them in on the deal. I think we'd have been fine without the extra capital — not that extra capital isn't always a good thing — but I do believe since we're in the middle of this dot-com bust, we're desperately going to need their financial creditability to reassure customers iPay will not be just another failed company."

"I completely agree. I was pretty worried about our ability to generate many new customers in this troubled era. However, I think if we can say iPay has two national banks as shareholders, we have a much better chance of securing customers."

"I agree."

"What time is your flight?" Mike asked.

Dana glanced at her watch. "3 PM. I'll need to leave for the airport as soon as we're done here."

"No problem, I'll take you."

Dana smiled. "That would be great, thank you." She noticed Mike was still looking at her, and she was feeling uncomfortable. "Is something wrong?"

Mike took a breath and then frowned. "Not with me, but I was going to ask you the same thing. I know you're happy about this morning's closing, but you look like something is bothering you. Anything I can help with, or you want to discuss?"

Dana looked out the window and shook her head.

"I can tell you're upset about something, what is it?" Mike asked, in a gentler tone.

Dana sighed and continued to stare out the window. "Nothing really; nothing you can help with, anyway. I feel bad about having to let go so many employees. I tried to look at our situation objectively and figure how many people we can afford when we won't be making a profit for a while, and I figured we can afford only eight. Some employees we no longer need or can afford are my lifelong friends, and a couple of them are pretty mad. I tried to explain the situation, but it didn't make a difference. They're angry and no longer speaking to me, and I feel terrible about them losing their jobs."

"I'm sure you do," Mike said sympathetically. "That's a hard call, but one every manager has to make at some point. Whether to hire friends to work for you is a tough decision by itself. On one hand, you know they're going to be loyal employees and you'll be able to trust them. On the other hand, it's harder when you have to let them go. It can destroy friendships, that's for sure. But I have a feeling your friends will come around, eventually."

"I hope so, because I miss them. We tried to soften the blow by making sure they received a good severance package, transition assistance, and another year of health insurance. I have to say, NETZEE was surprisingly generous about the severance package."

"I thought they did pretty well with that aspect too." Just then, the server brought the check to the table. "I insist on paying for our congratulatory lunch," Mike said, handing the server his credit card. "I may be broke soon, so I need to pay now while I still can."

Dana smiled. "I certainly hope not!" After the server left, Dana leaned over and pulled her calendar out of her bag. "Since you'll be in the office during the week now, can we plan to sit down Monday morning and talk

341

about the way forward? I want to run over the issues I know we'll face right away, discuss the employees' responsibilities, and was hoping to get your ideas on a few other items. I'm thinking mid-week we'll be ready for our first meeting with the employees. You've met everyone already, but it would be good to introduce you formally as iPay's chairman."

"We need to do all those things. I'm completely at your disposal, so anytime Monday works for me. Let's say 10 AM?" Mike pushed back his chair and reached for his sport jacket. "And now, I need to get you to the airport, young lady."

"Yes, you do. Thanks again for taking me, and thanks for lunch too." Dana put away her calendar and picked up her bag.

They exited the restaurant, walked back to the office, and Mike retrieved his car. During the ride to the airport, Dana gazed out the window as the sights of Atlanta whirled by. "I won't miss having to fly to Atlanta all the time. I thought we had a lot of traffic in Louisville."

"Yeah, it's pretty bad here." Mike glanced over at her. "Being in Elizabethtown during the week will be a pleasant change. Maybe a couple times a week, we can get together for dinner? It'd give us a chance to throw around ideas in a more relaxed environment. I can come up with some good ones after a gin and tonic," he said with a grin.

"Sure, that'd be great!" Almost nothing made her as happy as spending time with her new business partner. "But you know, as soon as you move to Kentucky, you'll have to become a bourbon drinker. You can't drink gin and tonics in the birthplace of bourbon."

"I suppose you're right. I think I can handle that."

They merged into the departure lanes at Hartsfield-Jackson Airport and Mike steered the car to the drop off area. He got out of the car, walked around to Dana's side, and helped her out of the car. He leaned over and gave her a quick hug, then kissed her lightly on the cheek. "See you Monday, Partner."

Before Dana had time to react or search his face for clues of what just happened, Mike was back in the car and preparing to depart. She slowly turned and walked into the airport terminal, but this time when she walked away, she was grinning ear-to-ear. Today had been one of the best days she could remember in many years, professionally and now personally. Dana felt transformed when she was with Mike, and the issues she faced every day seemed trivial when considered with the whole of her life now. The seed of a personal relationship between them had been planted; she could feel it in her entire being. It needed only time and togetherness to grow. She was fairly sure she could make that happen, because she wanted it more than nearly anything else in the world.

37

November 2001

Dana slowly swiveled her chair to face the wall of windows in her office and then rocked lazily, watching the robins peck the bare ground for worms. It was a sunless morning and the clouds sat low on the horizon, making the sky appear blended with the landscape. Mike would arrive soon. They'd planned to meet prior to iPay's six-month status meeting at 9AM. Dana found it difficult to believe it had been six whole months since that day in Atlanta when she signed the documents to buy back 150 customers from NETZEE to start iPay. Where did those months go? Did time go by faster when you were happier? It must work that way. Clearly time flew when you were busier, and they certainly were busy at iPay.

Dana heard the lilting cadence of Mike's voice echo down the hallway and smiled to herself. She couldn't help it. Her days were immeasurably better since they began spending the weekdays together. She brought that happiness home in the evenings and it carried over to the weekends as well. Even the kids had noticed, although they believed it was because their mom got back her company. Dana hadn't broached the development of her and Mike's personal relationship with them. It was too soon. She wanted to be sure their relationship was durable before she brought Mike home to meet her family. But soon, she figured; it would be soon.

"Good morning, Sunshine!" Mike was standing in the doorway of her office. He held a cup of coffee in one hand and a folder in the other.

"Hey there!" Dana spun around in her chair to face him. "Thanks again for dinner last night. I really enjoyed it."

"I had a great time too. It was a pleasant break from all the work you're piling on me." He flashed her a devious look. "You ready to discuss a few issues before our nine o'clock? We've discussed most of them already, but I didn't want to spend all of last night talking business."

"Sure, I've got time now." Dana grabbed her yellow legal pad and placed it on the desk in front of her.

"Great." Mike pulled up a chair and settled into it. "As I mentioned last night, I've spent the last few months sitting back and observing, trying to understand what you do well, how you operate, what you don't like doing, those sorts of things. I wanted to observe your long-time employees too and learn what they do well."

"That was a smart thing to do," Dana said. "Obviously you wouldn't know much about the way we work on a day-to-day basis."

"The other thing I've been doing is trying to figure out where I fit in. These last few months have been tough for me. I'm learning how to dance here. I want to make sure I can bring something to the table that'll make a difference."

Dana sat up in her chair and frowned. "You *do* bring something to iPay that makes a difference! You've already provided valuable guidance in many areas. I know it has been hard on you, sitting back and watching all my long-time employees do what they've been doing for years, only now at a different company. I know you've been trying to figure out where you fit in. But believe me, I need you and you *are* making a difference."

Mike leaned back in his chair and chuckled. "I know I've passed along some information that has helped here and there. I'm certainly having a good time building this company with you too, Dana; that's not the issue. The issue for me is how to take some of the load off you and allow you to focus on the areas that are your forte. You're in your element when you're using your creativity to design and sell products. What continually amazes me is your ability to see the dots before anyone else can and connect those dots in a way that tells the customer what they want even before they know

345

they need it. That's true talent, and you've got that. I don't have it. No one else who works here right now has it either — just you. So that's where you need to spend your time and energy. On the other hand, you want nothing to do with strategy, logistics, and finance."

Dana had been hanging onto his every word. She'd never thought of herself the way Mike just described her. But he was right; she hated spending time on the business side of owning a company. What she liked best was designing, creating, and selling her product, and she really didn't want to bother with any of the rest. "Yes, you're right."

"Good, because that's where my experience lies," Mike said. "I've spent nearly all my working life in management, strategic planning, and operations. When I was a consultant, those were my areas of expertise. That's where I think I can help grow iPay and also take a load off you."

Dana nodded her head. "That would be wonderful, and I'm more than happy to turn all that over to you."

Mike leaned forward in his chair. "You've been successful with your companies, but I don't believe you've gotten a company beyond $2 million in revenue. I think I can help get iPay over that $2 million threshold."

"I'm confident you can too. I don't know whether I'd just not held onto a company long enough to get beyond $2 million, or I was too focused on the product and didn't have enough time for sales, or what. But you're right about that $2 million number."

"So, those are the areas where I feel I can contribute the most," Mike said. "I can help with sales too. I know that's an area where you bring a lot to the table because you can explain iPay's products better than anyone else. But I've been studying your method and delivery, and I feel I'm ready to take some of that load off you too."

"I'm more than happy to share the sales load!" Dana relaxed back into her chair and grinned. "I've watched you, and you're a pretty good salesman yourself."

Mike cocked his head sideways. "I did a good job selling myself to you, don't you think?"

"You certainly did!" Dana laughed as she rocked back and forth in her chair. "Yes, I admit you did. Which reminds me, I was thinking it might be time to have you over for dinner and meet my family. What do you think?"

A flicker of amusement crossed Mike's face. "You mean I've passed the test so far? You think I'm ready to meet the family?"

"I'm more concerned whether my family is ready to meet you."

"I can't answer that question, but I'm ready when you are. The bottom line is I'm here to stay. Six months ago I decided I liked you well enough to find a place in Elizabethtown to live during the week. That should indicate how I feel about you and my commitment here."

Dana could feel the blood rush to her face and chest. "I feel the same way about you, Mike. I can't tell you how happy I am we're working together to build iPay. I think we make terrific partners because you and I could sit and talk forever about the business."

"And we do — all day long and most evenings!"

"I know, you'd think we had nothing else to talk about!" Dana rolled her eyes. "Maybe after we return from our trade show next weekend, I'll ask my mom and grandmother over for dinner, and my friend Marie too, and you can meet them along with Ryan and Liz."

"That sounds great. I'd love it." Mike leaned over and glanced at his notes. "Speaking of the trade show, I thought that'd be a good time for me to get up to speed on my marketing and sales pitch, and take some pressure off you."

"Absolutely, whenever you feel ready," Dana said. "By the way, we were right six months ago when we figured we'd need to tell potential customers we're two-thirds owned by national banks. I've had several people ask what we're doing differently to make sure we won't be merely another collapsed company. After I tell them iPay's two major shareholders are First Interstate Bank of Billings and Arkansas National Bank of Bentonville, they're satisfied. I'd say that's giving us instant credibility and strategic advantage."

"Yeah, I don't know if that was foresight on our part or just plain luck." Mike interlaced his fingers behind his neck and leaned back in his chair. "I've found both banks easy to work with too. They're small town banks, friendly managers, and not a lot of layers to go through to get a decision."

"That's good to hear," Dana said. "I've not worked with them much since you offered to manage their relationship with iPay. But I've heard from customers regarding how helpful those banks have been in explaining how they do the money transfers. Sometimes when I'm giving my sales pitch, the customer thinks we do bill payments by mailing checks, like most other bill pay companies. I have to explain we transfer actual money. Often it's better if the bank explains how they perform the transfer. Makes the customer feel more secure."

Mike raised his eyebrows. "I would think the customer would feel better about it costing less to send actual money instead of a check and therefore saving *them* money. Obviously, it's riskier for us because you can't get back the money if you do something wrong, but that would be our problem, not the customer's."

Dana's smile disappeared. "And everyone wonders why I'm such a stickler, constantly checking transactions to be sure they're correct. It's because I got badly burned by that jerk who fired me because our new data system caused so many errors. That's *never* going to happen to me again."

"Hey, it's OK," Mike said, in a gentle voice. "I figured out a while ago that's probably why you check and re-check to make sure there are no errors. That guy was an asshole who didn't know the first thing about being a manager. The only justice that occurred was someone finally sued him, and then he was fired. I'm just sorry it was too late to do you any good. But that's all behind you now. We're moving up in the world of bill pay!"

"You're right." Dana's voice was apologetic. "I still get really mad every time I think about it — even though it has been years now. You'd think I'd forget about it, but it was one of those defining moments in my life I'll never fully get over."

"You need to let it go, Dana. It was completely unjustified and you've proven repeatedly you're a talented and successful businesswoman."

"Thank you, Mike." Dana looked down at her lap and shrugged. "I'm trying to let it go, but you know how stubborn I am." She looked up at him and smiled.

Mike laughed. "You certainly can be a stickler when you get your mind on something — and that's OK. You've worked hard for everything you have, and feel your reputation is at stake, so you want things done right. That's a good way to be. By the way, I had a call from an old friend yesterday and he told me back in mid-May NETZEE filed with the SEC to restate and reflect their one for eight reverse stock split. So, as it turns out, it was a good thing we got out when we did. I can see a total collapse of NETZEE soon."

"Geez!" Dana frowned. "That would have occurred just a couple weeks after our closing."

"Right."

"That's pretty scary. I'm so glad when NETZEE bought MSI, we agreed to a cash sale and not shares in NETZEE, as happened with most of NETZEE's other acquisitions. Otherwise, we'd be holding shares right now that would be essentially worthless."

"No kidding! I wouldn't want to be holding NETZEE stock."

"No, that story makes me feel even more fortunate about the way things turned out for us with iPay," Dana said. "Actually, I'm satisfied with the way things are going already. I predicted we'd be cash flowing about a year after start-up, and I think we're going to be close to hitting that mark. The handful of people we hired two months ago are doing well, and I estimate in another couple months we'll need to hire two or three more."

Mike looked down at the papers in his folder and nodded his head. "If we make the changes we just discussed regarding managing iPay, we should be profitable by the end of our first year. That would be a good time to rent additional space too."

"Yes, it would." Dana nodded her head. "I'm happy to let you take a turn at negotiating for more square footage."

"I've already done a little research and made a couple calls," Mike said. "There's room in this building for us to expand over the next few years if we keep growing. Apparently, there's no shortage of vacant office space in Elizabethtown right now. The dot-com bust might have something to do with that. Anyway, it's good news for us."

Loretta popped her head around the office doorway. "Dana, Mike, everyone is ready in the conference room."

"Good, and thanks for the heads-up, Loretta," Mike said. "We'll be there shortly."

After Loretta left, Dana picked up her yellow pad and pen, and scooted to the edge of her seat. "Are you ready?"

"Whenever you are, my dear."

Dana led the way out of the office and down the hallway, smiling to herself, knowing Mike was behind her. They agreed on the important decisions; but she knew they would long ago. From the time they first worked together at NETZEE, she sensed he would make a terrific business partner. And what a comfort it was to have someone at her side who she trusted and could share the load with as a business partner and a companion. After all her years struggling alone in the banking world, Dana now had a true partner.

38

June 2002

Dana could hear Mike's voice through the wall of their adjacent offices, and from the sounds, he was having a lively conversation. She settled back in her chair and a smile eased across her face. Staring at their adjoining wall, she rocked back and forth, content to listen to the intonation of his voice. Life had been going so well lately. She tried not to dwell on it, not wanting to tempt fate. But over the past year, she came to believe she finally understood what it meant to have a soulmate on Earth. For the first time, she regarded this man as a part of her being. She would not feel complete if they weren't together.

"Hey, what are you thinking about? You look like you're worlds away."

Dana blinked, suddenly realizing Mike was no longer in his office, but was standing in her doorway. "Sorry! I was thinking about something and just zoned out."

"Yeah, I could see that. Got a minute?"

"Sure, come on in."

He grabbed a chair and pulled it up to the side of Dana's desk. "You won't believe the call I just got."

"Yeah?"

"From an attorney representing some company on Wall Street. Wondering if we're interested in selling iPay!"

Dana's eyebrows knitted together. "Seriously?"

351

"I'm serious!"

Dana hesitated. "How did he hear about us?"

Mike shook his head. "I didn't ask. Friend of a friend, or business associate, I suppose."

"What did you tell him?"

Mike lifted his arms and shrugged. "I told him we weren't planning on selling anytime soon, but if we changed our minds we'd let him know, and thanks for the inquiry. I didn't know what else to say."

Dana was still peering at Mike. "I don't know what to say either!"

Mike reclined in his chair, his fingers interlaced over his chest. "I'd say this is a good indicator iPay's reputation is getting out there. I know our business certainly is picking up. By the way, we have the computer guys coming today to run the wires in the new offices. They'll be hooking up all the new equipment tomorrow and things should be ready for the new folks to move in on Wednesday."

"Good, because we need to get them trained and working."

"I know. Things are really busy. I hope the additional 6,000 square feet of space will be enough," Mike added.

"Yeah, me too. Are you free for dinner tonight? I thought we could talk about our trip next week to Las Vegas without all the interruptions here."

"Sure, I'm free every night. You're the one with commitments, Sweetheart!" Mike smiled at Dana and then stood up. "I'll see you later then."

* * *

Mike held open the heavy wooden door to the restaurant on the outskirts of Elizabethtown, and Dana walked in ahead of him. He waved to the maitre d' as they wove their way through the tables toward the back corner, to what had become 'their' table. "I hope you're not getting tired of coming here so often," he said, "but I love the food and the quiet atmosphere. I hate trying to talk in a place that's so noisy I have to yell to hear my own words."

"I know what you mean. This is my favorite place too, so no problem." Dana hung her purse on the back of her chair and settled in. She watched as Mike took his seat, and once again considered how lucky she was to have this intelligent, personable, humorous, and handsome man sit across the table from her.

As the waitress approached, Mike looked up at her and smiled. "Good evening, Sarah! It's nice to see you here tonight. I think I can safely say Dana will have an iced tea. I'll take a martini straight up with three olives."

"Good evening, Mr. Bowers," she said with a broad smile. "I'll have those drinks right over to you."

Mike looked back at Dana and then reached across and cradled her hands in his. "I've been to Las Vegas numerous times, but I've never looked forward to it so much as this time!"

Dana smiled and squeezed his hands. "That's exactly how I feel, but I'm not much on Las Vegas, anyway. I like to see the shows, but I'm not a gambler."

Mike pursed his lips and nodded his head slowly. "I can see that about you. You're too practical. You wouldn't squander your hard-earned money on gambling."

Dana laughed out loud. "You're right! I'm way too practical. What about you? Do you like to gamble? I'll bet you do."

"Why do you say that?" Mike asked, with a mischievous expression.

"You took a big gamble agreeing to partner with me and iPay when you hadn't had time to give it much thought — unlike me, I'd given it a lot of thought."

Mike nodded his head and peered at Dana. "I don't mind taking a leap when it appears promising. And you're right; I do like to gamble, but mainly I play the tables. I don't do slot machines. But I don't plan to do any gambling next week. I expect we'll be pretty darn busy the entire time we're there."

"I agree. The last time we did a trade show in Las Vegas, I remember working 12 to 14-hour days. We were exhausted by the time we got home."

The waitress brought the drinks to the table and then took their dinner orders. As soon as she left, Dana reached across the table and took the pick of olives from Mike's martini. "I knew I should've ordered extra olives," Mike said, feigning a disappointed look.

"The best part of your martini! Well, I left you the part you like."

"Yes, I suppose it's a good thing for me you don't like alcohol." He picked up his drink and held it up. "Cheers!"

Dana laughed and picked up her iced tea to clink her glass with Mike's.

"Actually, we are celebrating something," Mike said. "The past couple weeks, Roberta and I have been going through all the numbers, and I'm happy to say iPay is cash flowing now for the first time."

Dana clasped her hands together. "I knew we had to be close. That's great news!"

"Yes, it is. You called it months ago. You predicted it would take about a year and you were off by one month."

"That's always a big milestone," Dana said. "We doubled in size our first year of operating, with no signs of slowing down. I don't think there's much more we could ask of a new company."

Mike leaned back in his chair and stretched out his legs. "I agree. iPay has had solid growth over the past 13 months. I have to say I'm really enjoying myself now too. I've learned a lot about the way you and the others operate, and I feel I've been able to help by taking care of the day-to-day management of iPay." He took a deep breath and sighed. "Most important, I'm really enjoying our working together. We've done more traveling together during the past year and gotten to know each other pretty well. We make a great team, both in and out of the office. Maybe the only downside for me is I've had to switch to drinking bourbon since I'm officially a Kentuckian. But I will admit, it has been growing on me lately and I'm now enjoying a bourbon nightcap most evenings."

"What?" Dana raised her eyebrows and laughed. "Mike Bowers has become a bourbon drinker?"

"Yes, ma'am, I have! But don't worry, I'll still have a martini occasionally because I wouldn't want to deprive you of your olives."

"That's very thoughtful of you!" Dana sat back in her chair and gazed at Mike. "I suppose if that's the only downside — you had to start drinking Bourbon — things are going pretty well for you, Mike Bowers."

"I can't complain too much, my dear. I did get you in the deal too."

"What? You didn't know you were getting a 'two-fer'? That reminds me, I talked to Bill at the First Interstate Bank in Billings today. A couple days ago he talked to our other investment partner at Arkansas National Bank. He said they couldn't be happier about iPay's performance. They really like working with us and are more convinced than ever they made a wise decision to be our investment partners. He knew they relayed this message to us at our one-year status meeting, but he wanted me to know how happy they are to be part of iPay."

"That's great, Dana! I'm really enjoying working with both of them as well. We owe it all to your good relationship with them when they were your customers at NETZEE. If you hadn't had such an excellent reputation with them, we'd never have convinced them to take on the risk of being our investment partners when we started iPay. They told me they trust you to not make mistakes with their money. They watch iPay's error rate closely."

"Yes, they do, and it helps immensely that ours is probably the lowest in the field."

Mike leaned one elbow on the table and stared out the window. "I'm also learning a lot working with them. They provide executive management to iPay that's been uniquely helpful for me. Managing a bill pay company differs significantly from what I did before, and they've helped me get a handle on the nuances. Now that the first year is under my belt, I'm feeling a lot more comfortable."

"I don't think we could safely grow much faster. We're busy all day long and hiring as fast as we can accommodate the new folks. That's all good, but a little stressful too." Dana looked up to see the wait staff bringing their dinners to the table. She leaned back as they placed the plates in front of them.

After they left, Mike leaned across the table and reached for Dana's hand.

"How about we not talk about work anymore tonight and pretend we're a normal couple out for a relaxing dinner."

Dana scrunched up her face. "We can try to pretend we're a normal couple, but I don't know how that's going to work out . . . But honestly, life is good and I'm pretty content these days."

"Me too, Dana," Mike said. "I'm pretty content too."

39

Summer 2003

Dana glanced out the front window of her home for the umpteenth time during the past 30 minutes. She sighed and plopped down on the couch, dropping her gaze from the street to the petunias and impatiens in her flower bed just below the window. The red and purple blooms swaying lazily in the warm breeze made her reminisce how this time of year was relaxing for most people. Kids were out of school, people were on vacation, and the heat and humidity slowed down a person whether they wanted to or not. But she felt anything but relaxed. She hadn't had time to come to terms with things before she sensed the need to return to the office. Of course no one said anything, but she could feel it. The few times she allowed herself to think about losing her mother, it felt like someone had their foot on her heart, pressing down until she could no longer breathe. She'd been unable to discuss it with anyone but Grandma, who had her own demons. Dana sat quietly on the couch, fixated on the flowers weaving back and forth.

Marie was uncharacteristically late. Dana had spoken to her at the funeral, of course. But last night Marie called, insisting they were going to spend some quality time together today, when the kids were with Joey. Another 10 minutes passed before her new silver-blue Audi turned into the driveway and came to a stop behind Dana's car.

Dana blinked hard several times, trying to shake off her fog. Gathering what strength she could muster, she lifted herself off the couch and padded over to the kitchen door, opening it as Marie was walking up the side of Dana's car. She wore slim-style Levis, high-heeled black pumps, and a silver-colored silk shirt. Dana looked down at her own shorts and t-shirt and sighed.

"So sorry, Darling! I'm aware I'm late, but I simply had to stop and get some ice cream to make the day a bit cheerier." Marie was through the door with her large grocery bag and tiny designer purse before Dana could say hello. She opened the freezer door, shoved in the ice cream, then spun around and gave Dana a good looking-over. "Goodness! You look awful! Are you not sleeping?"

Dana shrugged. "I wish I had half your energy, because I feel like I could sleep all the time. I still can't believe she's gone." Her eyes filled with tears and she looked away.

"I know, Darling. It's awful. I miss Mummy too. And I can't help thinking of her every time I see a sweet. She was always baking me something lovely." Marie put her arms around Dana and gave her a long hug. "Your mum is someone you never get over — ever. You'll think of her daily for the rest of your life. Our mums are such a part of our world that everything reminds you of them. But I try to remember only the happy and fun times I had with my mum, the memories that make me laugh. Then when I think of her, I'm smiling and it puts me in a cheery mood. It'll take a while, but you'll get there too."

"I know," Dana said. "I just need another 10 years to get used to the idea I won't ever see her again. That's the thought that's so hard to comprehend."

"Your mum loved ice cream more than anything, so why don't we get a couple bowls and have an ice cream toast to her."

"She'd like that."

Marie retrieved the ice cream from the freezer and filled up the two bowls. Dana sat at the kitchen table and watched; her brain was still fuzzy. "Here you go, Darling," Marie said, "Let's dedicate the first spoonful to your mum."

Dana picked up the spoonful of the Rocky Road ice cream and tapped

Marie's spoon. "We love you, Mom. I miss you so much already, but I'm glad you're not suffering anymore, and I hope they have ice cream in heaven."

"That's the spirit! Well done! Honestly, Mummy wouldn't want you to be sad. So let's get your mind on something cheerier, if only for a bit. How's that cute fiancee of yours?"

Dana looked down at her ice cream. Her face softened to a grin.

Marie leaned back in her chair and laughed. "That certainly put a smile on your face!"

"I can't help it. Thinking of Mike and our future together is the one thing that makes me feel less anxious and more grounded." Dana took a deep breath and immediately felt her insides relax. "He's the bright spot in my life right now, that's for sure. We're talking about getting married in the Fall down in Seaside, Florida, with all the kids there to help us celebrate."

"That sounds perfect, and I suspect the weather should be lovely that time of year as well." Marie finished her ice cream and put her bowl in the sink. "How are things at iPay? Are you still thrilled about working together, or is it hard to work all day and play all night with the same human?"

Dana shook her head. "It's not hard at all when you believe you're soulmates. We both say all the time how much we love it. We have such a great work rapport, and he has taken most of the responsibility off my shoulders for the day-to-day management of iPay, which I could not be happier about. He does all the hiring and takes care of major personnel decisions. As you know, I had a habit of hiring people I knew, which worked out fine until we became a bigger company. Mike's philosophy is to branch out and search for the best people we can find. We're now doing Statewide searches, and if we keep growing, we'll expand to nationwide. We've hired some tremendous people lately, so obviously his method works."

"I might have to pop over and check out the new talent!" Marie said, winking at Dana.

Dana glared at her. "Don't you dare! All I need is some love-sick puppy in our office — and even worse when the inevitable heartbreak occurs."

Marie curled up her lip. "Don't get your knickers in a twist!"

"The other thing that has been especially fun for us to do together is travel to all the trade shows," Dana added. "They're a lot of work and make for some long days, but we've had a great time taking those trips together. They helped us get to know each other better. Plus, we discovered the two of us make a pretty good sales team."

"That much is obvious since iPay has grown leaps and bounds since you two started the company, hardly two years ago if I remember correctly. That's an excellent indicator you were right back then about you two making excellent business partners."

"I knew immediately there was an unusual connection between us," Dana said. "You know how on rare occasion you feel an instant spark with someone? It was like that. And the more we talked and got to know each other, the more sure I was about us making excellent partners. I think his strengths are my weak areas and vice versa, so in the office we complement each other well. The other thing we have is deep respect for each other. I'm convinced you've got to have respect to have a good relationship, whether it's business or personal."

"I agree with you whole-heartedly. Respect for each other is as important as love. How are the kids adjusting to the idea of you being married again?"

Dana leaned on the kitchen table, cradling her chin in her hands. "They seem OK with it. Mike says his kids are fine too. We've taken the attitude that they're all adults and should want their parents to be happy. If not, then too bad, because we're going to be together regardless of how they feel. Hopefully, they're all focusing on their own lives now, anyway."

"That's a sensible attitude, but I'm pleased they all are fine with you two being married. Relationships are hard enough without family causing problems." Marie sat back in her chair and crossed her long legs. "The last time I talked to Ryan, he said he might fancy working at iPay when he finishes university. Is that still his plan?"

Dana laughed. "Yes, and I'd love to have him working sales if he'd ever stop having so much fun and get finished! I think he'd make a great sales rep, and with iPay growing so fast, we could use him now."

"I know you'd love having him work there with you and Mike. He does have the proper personality to make an excellent sales rep!" Marie cocked her head. "By the by, whatever happened to NETZEE?"

"I thought I told you they went under! In December of last year, they liquidated all their assets and dissolved the company. I'm so glad Jim Fugitte and I made a cash deal with NETZEE when we sold MSI."

"How awful." Marie frowned. "What about iPay? Have you gotten any more offers?"

Dana rolled her eyes. "It's crazy! We owned iPay 13 months before we turned a profit, and it was about this same timeframe when we got our first offer. We sort of laughed it off, and then less than a year later we got another inquiry, and we just got a third one. Mike and I just shake our heads. As iPay's market share gets larger, so do the offers, but we're nowhere near ready to sell. We're having fun growing the company, and there's a lot more we want to do before we'd ever consider selling. Besides, what would I do with myself all day? I'd just find a way to start another company."

"Yes, you would. You have a fire under your bum, and I can't see you slowing down one bit for many, many years."

Dana laughed. "I don't see me slowing down either. But right now, there's no chance of that happening. We're growing at a pace that's almost faster than we can manage. We've had to double the square footage of our office twice already. It's a good thing all the office space next to us is open and we've been able to lease it easily."

"Goodness, I didn't realize business was booming that much! Are your customers still primarily community financial institutions in Kentucky?"

"No, that's the thing," Dana said. "Most of our new customers are not in Kentucky. We're spreading out all over the country. We have thousands of transactions occurring daily and we've developed a reputation for not making errors. That has become our niche and a critical piece in our marketing strategy — no errors."

Marie reached over and touched Dana's hand. "No one would understand that better than you."

Dana sighed and shook her head slowly. "Yes, I learned that lesson in spades." She glanced at Marie. "When I think back to those days, I never could have imagined how much my life would change, what all I've been through since then . . ."

"I know, Darling. You've been through a lot of change — mostly good, but some of it tough." Marie's eyes softened. "You've changed too. I don't know if you realize it."

Dana screwed up her face. "I have?"

"Oh, absolutely! You used to be such a pushover! Sorry, Darling, but you were." Marie leaned forward and looked Dana squarely in the face. "Remember that young chap who worked with you as an intern for Jim Fugitte, and you did all the work and he took most of the credit?"

"Of course I remember because you never let me forget it."

"That's because I despised watching it," Marie said. "Example number two: those three chaps you worked for at MSI. You did all the work, and they took all the money. Example number three . . ."

"OK, enough!" Dana stood up and spun around toward the sink. "You're right. But I learned my lesson too."

"You did, and that's my point." Marie stood up and went over to Dana. "You've learned to stand up for yourself, and I hope it's because you understand how truly good you are at what you do, and not because you believe you're lucky or for some other ridiculous reason. You're talented and creative and one of the hardest working people I know — male or female. Every single thing you've gotten in this male-dominated industry, you deserve."

"Thank you for saying that, Marie. Mike tells me the same thing." Dana stood at the sink, her gaze fixed out the window. "I'm getting more used to hearing it, and I believe it on a surface level. But after decades of thinking one way, it's hard to change your opinion. That applies to so many things though, doesn't it?" She fell silent, then dropped her head and stared into the sink. "But I'm working on it. I'm sure it goes back to the incident of being fired by that short-sighted, stupid man. He took away my self-respect, and it's a continual battle to convince myself I'm deserving of some success. I'm trying, but it's a slow process. It's incomprehensible how one person can have such a negative effect on you that will linger for decades and affect so many other aspects of your life. It's unfair, and you know how I hate unfairness."

Marie put her arm around Dana and stared into the sink as well. "I keep trying to convince you the world is not fair, hoping to keep you from disappointment. But you continue to believe you can make it so — and good on you! All that past heartache, yet you remain an idealist."

"I know, how naïve is that?"

"The problem is you're just too nice. Now, it's such a lovely day, let's sit out back." Marie hooked her arm through Dana's and headed for the patio door. "Things will look brighter after being outdoors for a bit. And while we're out there, I shall tell you all about the new fellow in my life!"

Dana turned her head to look at Marie. "What? What new fellow? Lord, that poor guy! Never mind, I don't want to know. I get to know them, and then you dump them and they're calling me, all heart-broken. I can't take it anymore."

Marie laughed heartily as she held open the door. "You never know. I might decide to keep one someday."

"I guess crazier things have happened," Dana said, as she considered how she and Mike came to know each other. "You just never know what life's going to bring you!"

40

August 2006

The sun peeked through the slats of her bedroom shutters as Dana awoke. She glanced at the clock on her nightstand and confirmed it was too early to get up, so she rolled over in the other direction and watched her husband of nearly three years sleep. She observed the rhythm of his chest as it rose and fell, and monitored his shallow, barely discernible breathing. It was palliative to Dana's deportment this morning. Today was going to be a celebratory, eventful, but taxing day, and having Mike by her side relieved her former burden of bearing the stress alone. She took a deep breath and sighed. There were many reasons to be grateful and content with life these days.

Mike stirred and slowly rolled over and opened his eyes. "Well, good morning, Sunshine! There must be something special going on today for you to be awake before me."

Dana leaned over and kissed him. "Something special? I can't recall anything off the top of my head."

"Wait, I remember now," Mike's voice teased. "I think this is the day we get two new partners. Yes, I'm sure of it. Today's the day!"

"Oh, right!" Dana laughed, but her eyes lingered on his face. "I was just thinking how happy I am to have you to share all these milestones. Things mean so much more when you can celebrate with someone who's as happy as you because they also worked hard for it. It's just icing on the cake when you love that person too."

"It sure is." Mike wrapped his arms around Dana and pulled her close. "We have much to celebrate today and can look forward to an exciting future with our two new partners. Although I'll miss working with our banks in Billings and Arkansas. They were superb partners for the past five years and perfect for what we needed at the time."

"I'm going to miss them too. The fact that they were long-time customers first makes it harder to let go, and now they're our friends and colleagues." Dana hesitated and sighed. "But I agree, it was time to bring in two new partners who can better help us now."

"It's definitely time! And it's also probably time for us to get up and head to the office. When is Dave Lockwood showing up?"

"Ten o'clock," Dana said. "I'm really excited to finally introduce you to him and to show him around the new office too. I'm not sure I'd ever have gotten this far without all the help he gave me. He's an amazing man to take a chance on me like he did when there was no assurance he'd ever get anything in return. He's just a nice guy who wanted to fix an injustice, he used to say."

"He definitely did that. If not for him, you and I probably would have never met either. Maybe I need to thank him too!"

"You're right; I doubt we'd ever have met. I don't want to think about it! But yeah, probably time to get ready and head into the office. It's going to be a crazy, busy day."

* * *

As Mike rounded the corner and turned into the expansive parking lot, Dana looked up at the new two-story white concrete and stone structure. Never in her wildest dreams did she imagine she'd own a company that required this amount of space to house its employees and equipment. As Mike pulled into the designated parking spot, Dana looked at the sign in front of their car — 'Chairman.' She looked over at the sign in front of her parking spot next to Mike's — 'CEO.' The rapid success of iPay still astounded her. She glanced over at Mike and found him gazing at her.

"You're deep in thought about something, Darlin'." He reached over and laid his hand on her leg. "Everything OK?"

"Yes, everything is fine . . . no, it's great! I just keep thinking about how we got to today. Sometimes I want to pinch myself and make sure it's real." She placed her hand on top of Mike's and squeezed it gently. "The best part is being married to you. I'm thankful for that every day."

Mike leaned closer. "I agree; the success of our company is a wonderful thing, but it wouldn't have the same meaning — or be nearly as much fun — without you."

Dana reached down and picked up her bag. "Guess we better get inside. I'm sure someone is looking for us by now."

They exited the car and went into the new building, stopping in the kitchen to get a cup of coffee before heading to their respective offices. Dana placed her large black tote on top of her desk and sank down in her over-sized leather chair. She sipped her coffee and stared out the window, wanting just a few quiet moments before the chaos began. The sprinklers were on — an attempt to counter the heat and humidity already taking their toll on the newly planted shrubs and annuals. Yet the building and landscape presented a crisp, orderly appearance — the image Dana wanted her company to reflect when representatives from the two new investment companies approached the building this afternoon.

She finished her coffee and glanced at the clock. There was a little time before Dave Lockwood would arrive. Pulling her folders out of her tote, she spent the next hour studying charts and making phone calls.

At exactly ten o'clock, Loretta knocked on Dana's partially opened door. "Dave Lockwood is here for your ten o'clock meeting, Dana." She ushered him in and then gave him a big smile as she turned to leave. "It's great to see you again, Colonel!"

"Always a pleasure, Loretta." Dave Lockwood turned sharply toward Dana and stretched out his hand. "Top of the morning to you, Dana!"

Dana's face broke into a wide grin as she stood up from behind her desk and gave the colonel a hearty handshake. "Good morning, Colonel! It's great to see you again! Have a seat over there and I'll join you," she added, waving her hand toward the table in the corner.

"Thank you," he said, turning around and grabbing a chair.

"How have you been? Are you keeping busy in retirement?"

"I'm fantastic, Dana, and yes, I'm certainly busy. It's like they say; you're so busy after you retire, you wonder how you ever had time to work."

"I'm happy to hear you say that," Dana said. "Some people don't know what to do with themselves after they retire, and then they get bored and depressed. But I remember you love to fish, and you had plans to retire to your cabin and spend a lot of your time fishing and hunting."

"That's exactly what I'm doing, and I want you to know my retirement has been enhanced significantly by the nice percentage of profit you gave me from MSI." Dave sat up in his chair. "By the way, I didn't mean to show up on such a busy day. Loretta just told me you're signing the papers this afternoon to bring in two new investors."

"No, it's fine. Everything is ready for the signing, and I've blocked out the rest of the morning for you." Dana pulled out a chair close to Dave's and sat down. "Mike is anxious to meet you too."

"I'm looking forward to meeting him as well. I understand he also grew up in the banking world."

"That's right. He tells people he was a credit guy, mostly did lending of various sorts. When he got tired of being in banking, he did some consulting, but still in the areas of management and credit. So yes, he's like me — been in the banking world his entire career."

"Made it easy for you two to get together," Dave said. "I'm sure you find a lot to talk about."

Dana laughed. "That's certainly true! Maybe too much to talk about, and then we never seem to stop working, even at home."

"I suppose that can be the downside to working with your spouse. But that's a pretty minor downside compared to all the plusses." Dave sat back in his chair and stretched out his legs. "How did you two meet?"

Dana looked down at her lap and laughed. "The story is somewhat convoluted! About two years after you helped me get control of MSI, I joined up with an old boss and friend, and we combined our two bill pay companies, which he ran, while I started up a phone and internet bill pay company named Call Me Bill."

Dave raised his eyebrows. "Wow, that didn't take long."

"No, and it grew really fast too. After about two more years, we got an offer on Call Me Bill. You might remember the crazy dot-com era. We weren't going to sell, but the company who made us the offer wouldn't take no for an answer, so finally we agreed. The company was called NETZEE, and Mike was their Chief Operations Officer."

"Boy, a lot has happened since I last saw you. But obviously you're not at NETZEE now. What happened? Did you two decide to leave NETZEE and go out on your own?"

Dana shook her head. "Not exactly. As Mike says, NETZEE was profitable for about half a second, then they started burning through their cash like crazy, and before long they were about to go bust — just poor management, that's all. They were trying to sell off parts of the company in order to survive, so I asked Mike if he wanted to go in with me to buy back essentially what I'd sold to NETZEE two years earlier. He agreed, we bought it back, and now here we are, five years later."

"Unbelievable!" Dave said, rocking back and forth in his chair and chuckling. "That's really an incredible story! I couldn't be happier for you, Dana. All your hard work and brains paid off, and you came out on top. And obviously you're doing well with this latest venture," he added, raising his hands and looking around.

"We are, we're growing like crazy and can hardly keep up with it. We started with three thousand square feet of space and kept doubling it until there was no more space in our building to lease. Then we had people scattered all over town, at which point Mike said we needed to build our own office building." Dana smiled and shrugged her shoulders. "So, here we are!"

"I hear a strange voice!" Mike stood in the doorway, a grin spread across his face. "Is this the famous Dave Lockwood?"

"Yes, it is!" Dave stood up and went over to shake Mike's hand. "But I don't know about the famous part."

"You're certainly famous around here! Dana sings your praises often." Mike pulled out a chair across from Dave and sat down. "It's good to put a face to the stories."

"I was just telling Dave how you and I met," Dana said.

"Did she tell you it was her idea to start up this current endeavor that has been snowballing since we opened the doors?"

"I would have expected no less," Dave said.

"He had a lot to do with it too," Dana said, her thumb pointed toward Mike. "It's a partnership for sure. But he lets me be the operator, which I love, and he does the day-to-day management."

"Things worked out better that way," Mike said to the colonel. "It would be a crime to waste this woman's talent by having her pay bills and order supplies."

"You're right about that," Dave said, nodding his head. "You're bringing in two new investors, I hear. Is this to enable more growth?"

"In a nutshell, yes," Mike said. "We had two banks we'd worked with since the beginning of iPay, and they'd been customers of Dana's for years before that. They were terrific partners; we did very well with them. But we got to a point where we needed to do a restructuring and we needed to recapitalize. Basically, we needed to trade up and get two banks with more experience. We interviewed six investment companies and took bids, and in the end, we sold their ownership percentages to Bane Capital and Spectrum Equity. We're signing the papers this afternoon."

"I'm assuming these are investment banks as opposed to commercial banks?" Dave asked. "They have no banking retail business?"

"Right, they're investment banks only. The big plus for us is they have the experience to provide executive management to iPay. They'll own two-thirds of the company, just like the previous two banks, and have seats on the board and a voice. But Dana and I will continue to manage the company. Essentially, it's the same arrangement as before, except the two new banks are better aligned with our current needs."

"I see," Dave said. "Have you had offers to buy iPay yet?"

Dana and Mike looked at each other and laughed. "All the time, it seems," Dana said. "And we're surprised every time we get one."

"Any plans to sell?"

Mike shook his head and chuckled. "Are you kidding? And miss all this fun? But seriously, we just completed this new 18,000 square foot building and want to enjoy it for a while. We have some more things we want to accomplish too, before we talk about selling. And of course, we haven't had a good enough offer yet either. So I think selling is a way off."

"Good," the colonel said. "Then I'll know where to find you the next time I come to town."

"Speaking of coming to town, what brings you to Elizabethtown?" Dana asked.

"Just visiting friends for some fishing and golf. I had a free morning and wanted to make sure this time I stopped by to see how things were going with you, Dana, and I'm glad I did. From our very first meeting, I had a feeling you'd take your company and make it highly successful. Now I see you've been able to do that a couple times already. All the work and angst you went through to take MSI from those three gents was worth it, wouldn't you say?" The colonel tilted his head and gave Dana a discerning smile.

"You have no idea!" Dana said. "I think about that often. Actually, I think about my good fortune to have met you in the first place; and second, I think about all the business and legal strategies you taught me and how they've helped me later in my career too. That's why Mike said you're famous around here. I never would be where I am today without all the help you gave me."

The colonel rested back in his seat and laced his fingers over his chest. "Nothing made me happier than seeing you get what you deserved. I hate to see people being taken advantage of, and you certainly were." The colonel looked squarely at Dana and his voice turned serious. "There was only one thing I was afraid might happen. You're someone who believes if a person works hard enough, the world will treat him or her fairly. But the world isn't always fair, and some things don't go the way we want or the way they should. But if you give up at the first — or even the second — threat of failure, you'll get comfortable taking the easy way out. Once you've obligated yourself to something, see it through no matter how hard it gets. That's the only way to have peace with yourself and prevent beating yourself up later."

"You're absolutely right," Dana said. "I hate it when things aren't fair, and I'm continually trying to make them so. And I probably would've given up and walked away when my one boss got mad and refused to sign the agreement to sell me MSI. Because when he stormed out of the room, I absolutely thought all was lost. If you hadn't told me to sit there and wait patiently because he might calm down and come back, I'd have left the room for sure. Then — just as you predicted — he came back and signed. The company became mine, and the rest is history. What a day that was! I'll never forget it."

Dave Lockwood looked down at the floor, an amiable smile spread across his face.

Dana smiled too. "As I said, I learned a lot of strategies like that from you, and I continue to practice what you taught me."

Dave looked up at Dana. "You're a deserving person, Dana. I'm thrilled it worked out. Sometimes it doesn't."

"I'm thrilled it worked out too," Mike said. "Otherwise, Dana and I agree we most likely never would have met had she not gained control of MSI, and then hooked up with Jim Fugitte to create Call Me Bill, which my company wanted in the worst way. Which means I need to thank you as well for helping Dana, because I benefited significantly from it too — I got a fantastic wife and partner!"

"That you did!" Dave nodded his head.

"Now, how about a tour of our new place, Dave? If Dana doesn't mind, I thought I'd tag along and give you some highlights."

"Absolutely, if you have the time," Dave said. "Since you managed the building process, it'd be good to have you along."

Mike stood up and ushered out Dave ahead of him. When he got to the door, Mike stood back and waited for Dana. "After you, Darlin'! By the way, you're looking particularly lovely today," he added in a voice only Dana could hear.

Dana laughed to herself as she passed in front of him. Mike had a way of making her feel exceptional, at work and at home. He lifted her spirits, brought stillness to her mind, and an order to her world she hadn't known. He had become an intrinsic and indispensable partner, and compared to everything else she'd worked for in life, this had become her most valued asset.

41

1 June 2010

"Let's have everyone line up on the front steps," Dana yelled. "Taller folks can line up in the back and off to the sides, if you all don't fit on the steps, but let's try to get everyone in, please." She turned around to Loretta and smiled. "I want you in the picture too, so go line up. This won't take long. I just want a couple pictures to have as a reminder of everyone." She brushed her hair away from her eyes, but the warm Summer breeze blew it over her face again. Sweat was running down the middle of her back.

After another five minutes of shifting and queueing, Mike took the half-dozen pictures Dana instructed, and the group edged their way back into the building. One by one, Dana watched as they slowly shuffled through the front door, some silent, some chatting amicably. Each individual brought back a memory of how they came to work at iPay. Today was certain to be a historic and unforgettable day, but she hadn't expected to become so emotional about saying goodbye to her employees. The thought of giving up the building she and Mike had designed and constructed only a few years ago also created that unpleasant pressure in her chest, that sense of loss. She took a deep breath and tried to relax. Even the most rewarding experiences in life could harbor some downside or black cloud, something that brought the entire experience back into perspective.

Loretta touched Dana's shoulder. "The reporter is here, Dana."

"Oh right; thank you, Loretta. Can you let Mike know I'll be there in a minute?" Dana squeezed through the line of employees still making their way back to their offices. She hurried into the restroom to freshen up and to comb her wind-blown hair. Standing in front of the mirror, she gazed at her reflection and remembered a similar experience in 1986, before that infamous meeting with her new boss, who soon would fire her for 'incompetence.' How Dana wished he could see her now and know how successful she'd been with all the companies she'd founded. Her gaze fixed on her mirrored face as she washed her hands and blotted the perspiration from her forehead. There were delicate lines around her eyes now that curved upward and were visible when she smiled. That wasn't so bad, she decided. She'd had a life full of enough joyful times to create permanent laugh lines around her eyes. Grandma had them too, Dana remembered. Her stomach felt a sudden emptiness. Grandma would have relished this day for Dana.

She finished combing her brown shoulder-length hair and bangs. At least her hair was something that hadn't changed. Same cut, same look. She dropped her brush into her bag and exited the restroom. Nostalgia could be a dangerous thing on a day like today. It was good Marie was stopping by later to help them celebrate. Marie wouldn't stand for any ruminating. Dana looked up to see Mike heading down the hallway towards her.

"Hey gorgeous, I was looking for you! The reporter is waiting in the conference room." He had a bottle of water in his hand and a satisfied grin covered his face.

"On my way," Dana said in an upbeat tone. She hurried down the hallway and entered the conference room, followed by Mike. "I hope you've not been waiting long," she said to the woman sitting at the large, rectangular table. "I'm Dana Bowers and this is my husband, Mike."

The woman stood up and leaned across the table to shake hands with Dana, and then with Mike. "Hello! I'm thrilled to meet you both. I'm Beth McPherson."

Mike pulled out a chair across the table from the reporter and motioned Dana to sit down. He took the chair next to hers and settled back, crossing one ankle over his other knee. "We had a few pictures to take care of outside," he said to the reporter, with a grin.

"Of course! It's a big day for iPay." Beth McPherson opened her notebook and picked up her pen. "Would you mind if I taped our interview? Helps me remember details and quotes I might want to use."

"Sure, no problem," Mike said.

"Great!" She pushed a button on her recording device. "I know this is a busy and exciting day for you both, so I'll get started. Last night I did some reading online about iPay. It's surprising how much information there is on the internet. From my research, I understand iPay is the largest independent online bill pay provider in the US." Beth picked up her notebook and started reading from it. "iPay has partnerships with over 50 providers of information processing and online banking solutions. It supports over 1.2 million subscribers, and 3,600 — about 40% — of the nation's community financial institutions and half the nation's credit unions. Is this accurate?"

"38% is the actual figure," Mike said, with a laugh. "We like to round up to 'nearly 40%,' but yes, that's accurate."

"We started out in 2001 with eight employees, and today we have 250," Dana said. "We're proud of what we've been able to accomplish in a few short years."

Beth McPherson nodded her head. "Yes, nine years is not long in the lifespan of a company. I understand the city of Elizabethtown is quite happy and proud of your accomplishments too, and even the mayor of Louisville, Jerry Abramson, has added iPay to an elite list of highly successful, fast-growing companies he calls the High Impact Portfolio."

"Yes," Dana said. "That was a huge deal for us."

Mike glanced over at Dana and nodded his head. "Yes, it was."

"What do you think makes iPay stand out from other online bill pay companies and made you successful so quickly?"

Dana shifted forward in her seat and rested her arms on the table. "We decided we were going to be true experts in online bill payments, and I think that personal commitment to provide the best solution and the very best service we could to our niche customers — the community financial

375

institutions — is what sets us apart. Our customers know we'll do whatever it takes to get their money to the right place on time."

"That's right," Mike said. "The other thing that's different about us is we move actual money, which most people don't know. There are only five companies on the planet that do what we do — move real money and not checks. We process hundreds of thousands of these transactions daily, and over the entire time we've had iPay, we've lost somewhere around $28,000. When you consider the vast amounts of money we move every day, and for all those years, that's pretty incredible." Mike reached over and grabbed the arm of Dana's chair. "And that accomplishment is due primarily to Dana. She spent many nights personally calling financial institutions to make sure they processed the transactions correctly and on time. She had a 'no errors' mentality at her other companies too and she brought that mentality to iPay."

"Those are impressive numbers," Beth McPherson said.

"Those kinds of numbers are very attractive to a potential customer too," Mike added, "which is the primary reason iPay stands out from its competitors." He looked over at Dana and placed his hand on her shoulder. "iPay differs from competitors because they don't have this lady as their chief product developer. Of course, I'm married to her and might be a little biased, but my wife is incredibly gifted in understanding the problem and coming up with the technical solution. Equally unusual is her perseverance and tremendous capacity for work. She never gives up until she's satisfied with the solution. In a nutshell, *she's* the main reason iPay has been so successful."

Dana could feel the blood rushing to her cheeks. "We both contributed to iPay's success. I love working on product design and sales, and Mike enjoys managing the company. We have a great partnership that works well for us both."

"It sounds like a partnership made in heaven," Beth McPherson said. "So why sell now? You must have had offers before. What made you decide this was the right time and Jack Henry was the right buyer?"

Mike leaned forward in his chair. "We had an investment banker out of

Chicago help us figure out what to do. The key piece of advice he gave us was if someone offers you more money than you can make in five or six years, it's time to sell."

Beth McPherson glanced up at Mike. "I read that Jack Henry and Associates are paying $300 million for iPay. Is that correct?"

"Yes, it is," Mike said.

"Then congratulations again. It must be an unbelievably exciting day for you! I can't imagine how you must be feeling," Beth said. Her eyebrows raised and her head cocked sideways. "How are you feeling?"

"Unbelievably excited — just as you said!" Mike laughed.

Dana nodded her head in agreement. "We feel truly blessed. I'm not sure all this has sunk in yet. But we'll miss our employees, and we're also going to miss working with the board members from our two investment banks — Bane Capital and Spectrum Equity. We were lucky because they were superb partners, and it was clear from our first meeting they wanted the best for iPay."

"They certainly did," Mike said. "It was the first time we were exposed to such diversely talented board members, and through their coaching, iPay became a real powerhouse. Three were local, but the others were from Atlanta, Chicago, New Jersey, Pittsburgh, and Tulsa. All of them were easy to work with, and we had lots of laughs over the years. Every decision the board made was unanimous. Not a lot of companies can say that."

"I suspect not." Beth said.

Mike sat up in his chair. "And particularly noteworthy, when you consider the talent in this group of folks, Dana was the one who engineered the sale of iPay and drove the entire process — including the sales price. The board deferred completely to her. That's what I call respect."

Beth peered at Dana. "Yes, I agree." She picked up her pen and looked back at Mike. "What will you do now? Is retirement on the horizon?"

Mike laughed and then glanced at Dana. "I was thinking it would be nice to kick back and take some time off, but I'm pretty sure my wife has other ideas."

Dana hesitated. "We have this small company in Billings, Montana that helps financial institutions with federal compliance issues. It's not losing money, but it's not making any either. Now that I have time, I'd like to focus on getting it up to its real potential. The need for this kind of company came out of the banking reforms following the 2008 near-collapse of the banking industry. Congress created a set of regulations all financial institutions have to comply with, and our company, called Digital Compliance, helps financial institutions meet these standards. There aren't many companies providing this type of service right now, so I believe there's huge potential."

"The problem is this is unfamiliar territory for us, and a whole new skill set to learn," Mike said. "It requires in-depth understanding of the problem, figuring out what technologies are required, designing and creating the products, finding customers, and then implementing the solution. Basically, we'll be starting from scratch."

Dana smiled sheepishly. "It'll be a lot of work until we get it built up enough to relinquish control to an experienced manager. But I feel we have too much invested in this company to allow it to languish. And the need for someone to provide this service is obvious."

"In other words, we won't be retiring anytime soon," Mike added, flashing a disappointed look at the reporter.

"Mike will be doing what he likes to do," Dana countered. "He'll be working to secure investor funding and then getting the board up to speed. He'll be taking over the day-to-day management, like he did with iPay, and we'll probably end up moving the company from Montana to Elizabethtown."

"You'll keep working in this same building?" Beth asked.

Mike shook his head. "No, this building and all iPay employees will belong to Jack Henry after today. We'll probably lease the same office space on Ring Road we used for iPay before we built this building in 2006. Funny story, I walked through our former building last week and right away it was clear no one had occupied it since iPay was in it four years ago. There are still things hanging on the walls that pertain to iPay, like calendars and notes. I couldn't believe it!"

"That is hard to believe," Beth said, "but sad too. I hope that's not an indicator of declining business in Elizabethtown."

"That was my thought too," Dana said. "Anyway, Mike has been telling me I need to slow down and take time to celebrate the small victories before I run head-long to the next problem. So with that in mind, we do plan to take a vacation before we tackle Digital Compliance."

"Excuse me," Loretta said, while knocking on the conference room door. "Dana and Mike, the closing papers from Jack Henry are coming across the fax now. You said to let you know."

"Great!" Mike said. "Thanks, Loretta. We'll be there in just a few minutes." He turned around to the reporter. "Sounds like perfect timing because I think you were about done with your questions, correct?"

"Yes, that was my last one," Beth said, reaching forward and hitting the button on her recording machine. She looked up at Mike and Dana. "Thank you very much for the interview. It was a real pleasure to meet you both. Congratulations again, and I wish you the best of luck with your next endeavor."

"You're welcome," Mike said, as he stood up and reached across the table to shake the reporter's hand.

"Yes, you're most welcome," Dana added, also shaking her hand. "Thank you for the good wishes too."

Beth McPherson gathered her bag and papers and left the conference room in front of Dana and Mike. Dana looked up at Mike and grinned. "Are you ready to sign the papers and make this deal official?"

"As ready as I've ever been!" Mike said, with a sly grin.

Dana felt his hand on the small of her back as he guided her down the hallway. She couldn't remember anything feeling so inherently right.

Epilogue

Dana Bowers, along with her husband, Mike Bowers, grew iPay to become the largest independent electronic bill pay provider in the United States.

The June 2010 sale of iPay to Jack Henry and Associates for $300 million was the largest sale of a private company in the history of Kentucky.

In 2009, Dana Bowers was awarded an Entrepreneur of the Year Regional Award from Ernst and Young. They selected her from a field of over 1,700 nominees of the best entrepreneurs in the United States.

In 2011, Dana Bowers became the first woman to be inducted into the Kentucky Entrepreneur Hall of Fame.

In 2012, Dana and Mike moved Digital Compliance from Billings, Montana to Elizabethtown, Kentucky. Under their direction, and later the same board members from Bane Capital, Digital Compliance grew and was renamed as Venminder. As of mid-2021, Venminder had 150 employees and an annual revenue of nearly $20 million. iPay (now owned by Jack Henry and Associates) and Venminder together provide employment to nearly 450 people in Elizabethtown, Kentucky.

Dana's son, Ryan, is now the Director of Sales for Venminder.

SB Holding Corporation — the company Dana and Mike established to co-found iPay before they married — still exists. It supports many charitable organizations, with particular emphasis on education and health care.

After initially keeping their relationship a secret for fear their parents would disapprove, on 25 May 2013, Dana's daughter, Liz, married Mike's son, Barrett. They now have two children.

Mike and Dana Bowers continue to work together — and to be happily married. They live in Elizabethtown, Kentucky.

* * *

About the Author

Janice M. Graham is a retired US Naval Officer and also had her own consulting company. She is a magna cum laude graduate of the University of Kentucky (BA), the Naval Postgraduate School (MA), and The George Washington University (PhD). Dr. Graham has published numerous articles on national security, issues concerning the military, and the study of innovation and organization transformation. She is a contributing author and the editor of *Countering Biological Terrorism in the US: An Understanding of Issues and Status* (Dobbs Ferry, NY: Oceana Publications, 1999). This is her first work of fiction based on a true story.

Made in the USA
Monee, IL
31 July 2021